THE PAPER MUSEUM OF CASSIANO DAL POZZO

SERIES B ~ PART SIX

FLORA: THE *ERBARIO MINIATO* AND OTHER DRAWINGS

THE PAPER MUSEUM OF CASSIANO DAL POZZO

A CATALOGUE RAISONNÉ

Drawings and Prints
in the Royal Library at Windsor Castle,
the British Museum, the Institut de France
and other Collections

General Editors
Arthur MacGregor and Jennifer Montagu

Editor, Series A ~ Antiquities and Architecture
Amanda Claridge

Managing Editor
Kate Owen

Project Co-ordinator
Rea Alexandratos

Patrons and Sponsors
Accademia dei Lincei
Académie des Inscriptions et Belles-Lettres
British Academy
Getty Grant Program
Monument Trust
Olivetti
Royal Collection Trust
Warburg Institute

SERIES B ~ NATURAL HISTORY

PART SIX

FLORA
THE *ERBARIO MINIATO* AND OTHER DRAWINGS

VOLUME ONE

Fabio Garbari and Lucia Tongiorgi Tomasi

Volume editors

Brent Elliott and Martin Clayton

The Royal Collection
in association with
Harvey Miller Publishers

First published 2007 by
Royal Collection Enterprises Ltd,
St James's Palace, London SW1A 1BQ

www.royalcollection.org.uk

This catalogue has been published with the financial assistance and the support of the Fondazione Cassa di Risparmio di Alessandria

FONDAZIONE
CASSA DI RISPARMIO DI ALESSANDRIA

ISBN 978-1-905375-20-2 (Volume 1)
978-1-905375-21-9 (Volume 2)
978-1-905375-18-9 (Set)

British Library Cataloguing in Publication Data
A catalogue record for this book is available from the British Library.

Composition by Libanus Press, Marlborough, Wiltshire
Monochrome and colour origination by Grafikon, Belgium
Printed and bound in Belgium by Grafikon

Distributed by Brepols Publishers, London/Turnhout; www.brepols.net

CONTENTS

VOLUME ONE

THE CATALOGUE RAISONNÉ

SERIES A
ANTIQUITIES & ARCHITECTURE

I
Ancient Mosaics and Wallpaintings
Helen Whitehouse, 2001

II
Early Christian and Medieval Antiquities
(2 volumes)
John Osborne and Amanda Claridge, 1996, 1998

III
Sarcophagi and other Reliefs
(3 volumes)

IV
Statues and Busts

V
The *Antichità Diverse* Album

VI
Classical Manuscript Illustrations

VII
Ancient Inscriptions
William Stenhouse, 2002

VIII
Vases, Lamps and other Objects
(2 volumes)

IX
Ancient Roman Topography and Architecture
(3 volumes)
Ian Campbell, 2004

X
Renaissance and Later Architecture
and Ornament
(2 volumes)

SERIES B
NATURAL HISTORY

I
Citrus Fruit
David Freedberg and Enrico Baldini, 1997

II
Fungi
(3 volumes)
David Pegler and David Freedberg, 2006

III
Fossil Woods
Andrew C. Scott and David Freedberg, 2000

IV
Birds
(2 volumes)

V and IX
Fauna and Natural Curiosities

VI
Flora: the *Erbario Miniato*
(2 volumes)
Fabio Garbari and
Lucia Tongiorgi Tomasi, 2007

VII
Flora: *Syntaxis Plantaria*
(5 volumes)

VIII
Flora: the Aztec Herbal

PRINTS
Three volumes

ACKNOWLEDGEMENTS

The authors would like to thank the following for their assistance during the research and preparation of this work for publication: Lucia Amadei, Keeper of the *Herbarium Horti Pisani*; Giuseppe Pistolesi, Curator at the Botanic Garden of the University of Pisa; Federica del Carratore and Antonio Borzatti von Löwenstern of the Livorno Natural History Museum; Marco Maovaz, Curator of the Botanic Garden of the University of Perugia; Prudence Leith-Ross for assistance with the English common names; David Pegler for contributing the entries on the mycological drawings (**33–51**); Antonio Graniti and Ian Rolfe for their comments on **280**; and Enrico Baldini for his advice on **287**. Special thanks are owed to Lisa Chien, who translated the authors' original text.

These volumes have been many years in the making, and the editors are particularly grateful to past and present staff of the Royal Library and of the Dal Pozzo Project, especially Henrietta McBurney and Jean Cozens; to the staff of the Royal Horticultural Society Lindley Library; to the staffs of the libraries of the Linnean Society, and the Natural History Museum: Stefan Dressler, Jennifer Edmonds and Julian Shaw; and to Ingrid Skoglund of the Göteborg University Library.

Editorial note

The project to catalogue the Paper Museum of Cassiano dal Pozzo is now twenty years old, and the current format of the volumes may have evolved from what was envisaged when the authors began to undertake their researches in 1998. To harmonize this volume with earlier catalogues in the series, the much longer text prepared by the authors has had to be edited to a more concise form than they had anticipated. From the catalogue entries have been omitted: descriptions of the style and quality of each drawing, a general discussion of which may be found on pp. 30–2; some mentions of contemporary and earlier depictions of the same plants; and some information about the folklore and medicinal uses of the plants, particularly post-seventeenth century. The authors have nonetheless agreed that, despite their divergence of opinion about the editorial policy, publication of such an important document of early modern science should proceed.

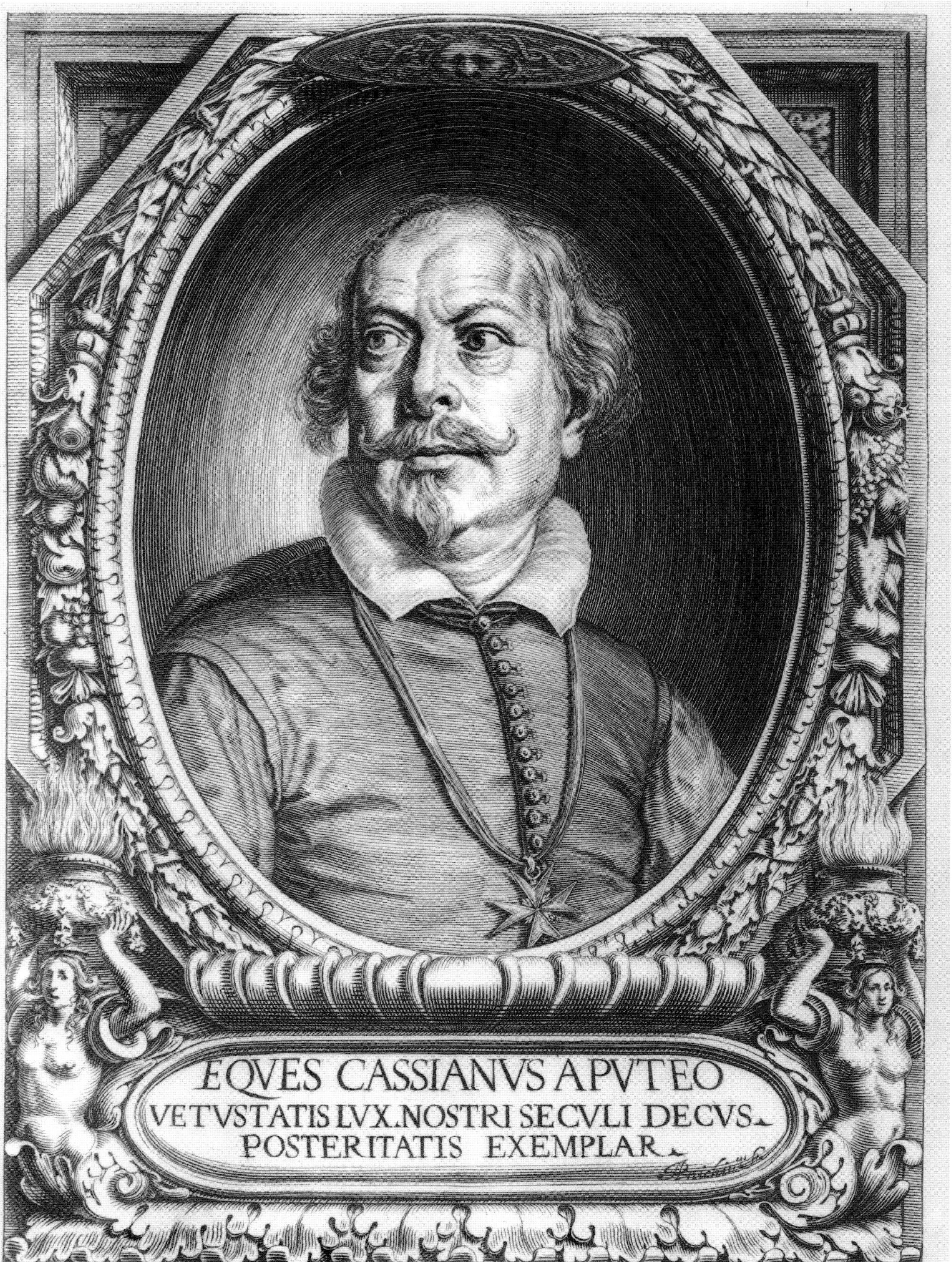

Fig. 1. Pietro Anichini, *Cassiano dal Pozzo*. Engraving. Frontispiece to Carlo Dati's funerary oration, 1664

THE PAPER MUSEUM OF CASSIANO DAL POZZO*

Francis Haskell and Henrietta McBurney

CASSIANO DAL POZZO is celebrated today as one of the most important art patrons in seventeenth-century Italy [Fig. 1]. He commissioned more than forty paintings by Nicolas Poussin and owned many others by some of the finest artists of the day. A friend of Galileo and a correspondent of Peiresc, Cassiano was closely concerned with developments in the political and intellectual life of his time. Yet contemporary scholars admired him above all for his learning in the fields of antiquities and natural history and for the extraordinarily ambitious project that grew out of these interests, a project that he described as his *Museo Cartaceo*, or 'Paper Museum'.

Born in Turin in 1588, Cassiano went as a young boy to Pisa, where he was placed in the care of his father's cousin, the Archbishop of Pisa, and received his university education in law. It was here in Tuscany that his interests in the worlds of art and science were nurtured, partly through his cousin's connections at the Medici court, and partly in the intellectual circles centred on the University of Pisa and its Botanic Gardens. In 1612, after briefly pursuing a legal career in Siena, he moved to Rome, where he was to remain for the rest of his life.

In 1622 Cassiano was elected to the first scientific society in Europe, the Accademia dei Lincei, in which he was to play a very active role. Soon afterwards, he entered the service of Francesco Barberini (1597–1679), who became a cardinal in 1623, the year of his uncle Maffeo's election as Pope Urban VIII. In 1625–6 Cassiano accompanied the Cardinal on diplomatic missions to Paris and Madrid, in which cities he enriched his understanding of painting and developed a particular interest in the works of Leonardo da Vinci and the young Velázquez. On his return to Rome, Cassiano, together with his younger brother Carlo Antonio (1606–89), began to build up a collection of paintings, books, medals and drawings. After the death of Prince Federico Cesi (1585–1630), founder of the Accademia dei Lincei, he acquired a large number of Cesi's books and scientific instruments.

Cassiano also conceived the ambitious project of employing artists – many of them young and unknown, but some of great distinction – to make copies for him of all surviving traces of Roman civilization, from household items to manuscripts, sculpture and mosaics. This 'Paper Museum' was then classified thematically in order to build up as complete a record as possible of ancient religion, customs, dress, architecture, theatrical spectacles, and so on. Equally interested in the natural world as in antiquities, Cassiano

* For a full version of this Introduction, with footnotes and references, see A.I, pp. 9–26.

commissioned a similarly large number of drawings of geological specimens, citrus fruit, fungi, plants, fish and birds. In collaboration with such scholars as Giovanni Battista Ferrari and Federico Cesi, these natural history drawings were also classified, and in such a way that they anticipated modern systems of taxonomy.

Although largely unpublished, the Paper Museum was widely used in the seventeenth century as an instrument of study and research; scholars and dilettanti from all over Europe visited Cassiano in Rome, or wrote to him asking for information, and in return sent him reports of strange natural occurrences and local antiquarian investigations.

When Cassiano died in 1657, the Paper Museum passed to his younger brother Carlo Antonio, who not only added to the collection but also rearranged parts of it. On the latter's death in 1689, the collection passed to his son Gabriele (1642–95) and on Gabriele's death to his eleven-year-old son Cosimo Antonio (1684–1740). It was during Cosimo's nominal custodianship that the family collections began to be dispersed, mainly to pay off debts. The library, which included the Paper Museum, was the first to go: in 1703 it was sold for the sum of 4,000 *scudi* to Giovanni Francesco Albani, Pope Clement XI (reg. 1700–21), from whom, in 1714, it passed to his nephew, Alessandro Albani (1692–1779), for the same sum. The Paper Museum thus joined the important collection of drawings and prints already belonging to the Albani family. Under Albani ownership, large parts of the dal Pozzo collection were reorganized and some were amalgamated into other sequences of drawings in the family's possession. In 1762 the greater part of (by then Cardinal) Albani's collection of drawings and prints (about 200 folio volumes) was purchased for 14,000 *scudi* by King George III, through the agency of the architect James Adam. It was brought to London in 1763 and incorporated into George III's extensive library in Buckingham House. By the time an inventory of the collection was drawn up early in the nineteenth century (Inventory A: see p. 8), many of the dal Pozzo volumes had been reordered and re-bound. In some cases the drawings had been lifted from their original mount sheets, remounted on eighteenth-century paper and given wash borders.

Towards the end of the eighteenth century, two volumes containing drawings of classical antiquities were separated from the main body of the material; these, known as the Franks albums – after the last collector through whose hands they passed – are now in the British Museum. Another offshoot from the main collection is a group of six volumes of drawings now in Sir John Soane's Museum. These were separated from the Albani collection by the Adam brothers before it reached the library of George III, and were bought by Soane at the Adams's sale in 1818. The eight volumes of botanical and mycological drawings in the Institut de France, Paris, did not form part of the Albani sale to George III, and remained in Rome until their requisition by the French in 1798.

In 1823, when most of George III's library was given to the nation by his son, George IV, and transferred to the British Museum, a number of dal Pozzo volumes of prints (and at least one volume of the drawings) were further separated from the main corpus; these were rediscovered in the British Library in the 1980s. However, the main body of the Paper Museum was retained in the Royal Collection and since 1834 has been housed (with the rest of the Royal Library) in Windsor Castle. Just after the First World War, a large part of the natural history material (probably fifteen volumes) was dispersed from the Royal Library at the behest of the then Royal Librarian, Sir John Fortescue. The contents of these volumes, many of which were in the possession of the London art dealer Jacob Mendelson just before the Second World War, are now scattered among private and public collections in Europe and America. A number of these drawings have been returned to the Royal Collection since the 1970s, either through gift or purchase. Other drawings from the Paper Museum have appeared in salerooms: in September 1987 a group of 107 natural history drawings was sold at Sotheby's, New York, and in 1990 another collection of 500 drawings after the antique, previously owned by the Stirling-Maxwell family, was sold at Phillips, London. Since then, other drawings have gradually come to light.

The decision to produce the present catalogue has its own history. The Paper Museum remained in relative obscurity after it left Italy in the mid-eighteenth century until the late nineteenth century, when scholars began once more to consult Cassiano's drawings. It is to two German archaeologists – Friedrich Matz (1843–74), one of the founders of the great published corpus of Roman sarcophagus reliefs, and Adolf Michaelis (1835–1910) – that credit is due for the 'modern' revival of interest in the Paper Museum. Their work, and that of the British scholar, Thomas Ashby (1874–1931), provided the inspiration for the study by Cornelius Vermeule, who, in two major articles in the 1960s, catalogued the drawings of sarcophagi and reliefs in the Royal Library and the British Museum. In the same period Sheila Somers Rinehart embarked on a comprehensive study of the Paper Museum, and in the 1970s Jean Goldman attempted a general artistic assessment of the drawings. The decision finally to produce a fully illustrated catalogue raisonné of the entire Paper Museum was made in the mid-1980s, when research brought international scholars to Windsor to inspect the visual counterparts of the documentary evidence for Cassiano's *Museo Cartaceo*.

However, it soon became clear that it would be impossible to adopt for this body of drawings the same principles as those used in the volumes devoted to the drawings of Leonardo, Holbein, Canaletto and other great masters belonging to Her Majesty The Queen. Despite Cassiano's well-informed love of art and the fact that he had access to distinguished artists, including Pietro Testa, Pietro da Cortona and others of real stature, it is clear that it was the documentary and not the artistic aspect of the enterprise that was important to him. The drawings in the present publication, therefore, are catalogued not by artist, but by subject matter. Viewed from this perspective the drawings readily divide into two categories: those concerned with Antiquities and Architecture (which we have called 'Series A') and those dealing with Natural History ('Series B'). The former group encompasses about 4,000 drawings and the latter almost 2,800. The aim of this catalogue raisonné is to reconstruct in some measure the intellectual and artistic achievements embodied in Cassiano's Paper Museum.

Francis Haskell, Joint General Editor of the catalogue raisonné since its inception, died in January 2000.

CHRONOLOGY

Events in the dal Pozzo household	Year	Contemporary events	Publications
Cassiano dal Pozzo born in Turin	1588		Smet, *Inscriptionum*
Moves to Pisa	1598		
Made knight of the Order of St Stephen	1599		
	1603	Cesi founds Accademia dei Lincei	Gruter, *Corpus*
Birth of Carlo Antonio dal Pozzo	1606		
Cassiano graduates from Pisa University; Carlo Antonio dal Pozzo, Archbishop of Pisa, dies	1607		
Cassiano appointed judge in Siena	1608		
	1610	Galileo moves to Pisa	
Leaves Tuscany	1611	Galileo elected to Accademia dei Lincei	
Arrives in Rome	1612		
	1613		Besler, *Hortus Eystettensis* Pignoria, *De Servis*
	1614	Cesi records Palestrina mosaic	
	1616	Galileo censured	
Cassiano's father (Antonio dal Pozzo) dies	1619		
Carlo Antonio arrives in Rome	1620		
Cassiano elected to Accademia dei Lincei	1622	Francesco Barberini elected to Accademia dei Lincei	Olina, *Uccelliera*
Appointed to the household of Francesco Barberini	1623	Maffeo Barberini elected Pope Urban VIII	Galileo, *Il Saggiatore*
	1624	Poussin arrives in Rome	
Travels to France: meets Peiresc	1625		
Travels to Spain; elected to Accademia della Crusca of Florence	1626		
Carlo Antonio marries Teodora Costa; brothers move to Via dei Chiavari	1626–7		
	1628		Faber, *Animalia Messicana*
	1629	Faber dies	
	1630	Cesi dies	Petau, *Ad Iuliani opera* Stelluti, *Persio tradotto*
	1631		Campanella, *Atheismus*
	1632		Galileo, *Dialogo*
Cassiano buys Cesi's collection	1633	Galileo is condemned	Ferrari, *De florum cultura*
	1634–5		Bosio, *Roma Sotterranea*
Poussin begins planning *Seven Sacraments* for Cassiano	1635–6		
	c. 1635–6		*Galleria Giustiniana*
	1637	Peiresc dies	Stelluti, *Trattato del legno fossile minerale* Junius, *De pictura veterum*
	1638		Montano, *Raccolta tempij*
Carlo Antonio nominated *Capitano di Fanteria*	1642		
	1644	Urban VIII dies; Giovanni Battista Pamphili elected Pope Innocent X	
	1645	Francesco Barberini in exile in Paris	

Events in the dal Pozzo household	Year	Contemporary events	Publications
	1646		Ferrari, *Hesperides*
	1648	Francesco Barberini returns to Rome	
	1650	Pietro Testa dies	
Cassiano's last documented commission from Poussin: *Pyramus and Thisbe*	1651–2		Hernández, *Rerum medicarum Novae Hispaniae Thesaurus*
	1655	Fabio Chigi elected Pope Alexander VII	Suarès, *Praenestes antiquae*
Carlo Antonio serves as *Conservatore* of Rome	1656–78		Pignoria, *De Servis* (2nd edn)
Cassiano dies; Poussin's *Annunciation* executed, probably for his memorial. Carlo Antonio takes over the knighthood in the Order of St Stephen	1657		
	1657–69		Agostini, *Le gemme antiche figurate*
	1662	Gude visits Rome	
	1664–5	Skippon visits Rome	Bellori, *Nota delli Musei* Dati, *Delle lodi*
	1665	Poussin dies	
	1668		Falconieri, *Inscriptiones athleticae*
	1670–94	Bellori holds post of papal antiquary	
	1679		Spon, *Miscellanea*
	1680		Fabretti, *De Aquis*
	1682		Reinesius, *Syntagma*
Carlo Antonio serves as *Console Capitolino*	1684		
	1687		Mabillon, *Iter Italicum*
Carlo Antonio dies	1689		
	1690–9		Ciampini, *Vetera monimenta*
Gabriele dal Pozzo dies	1695		
	1699		Fabretti, *Inscriptionum*
	1700	Giovanni Francesco Albani elected Pope Clement XI	
Paper Museum sold to Pope Clement XI [Albani] by Cosimo Antonio dal Pozzo	1703		
Paper Museum passes to Cardinal Alessandro Albani	1714		
	1719–24		Montfaucon, *L'Antiquité expliquée*
	1721	Michelangelo dei Conti elected Pope Innocent XIII	
	1731		Doni, *Inscriptiones antiquae* Gudius, *Antiquae inscriptiones*
Cosimo Antonio dal Pozzo dies	1740		
	1743	Winckelmann becomes librarian to Cardinal Albani	
Paper Museum bought by George III	1762		

SUMMARY OF KNOWN DAL POZZO DRAWINGS

Series A: Antiquities and Architecture

I. WINDSOR CASTLE: Royal Library	**Folios**	**RL**	**Ashpitel 1862**	**Heaton-Smith***	**Michaelis 1882**	**Robert ASR**
Bassi Relievi Antichi 1	95	8145–8255	A40	155	I, II	I
Bassi Relievi Antichi 2	66	8256–8322	A41	156	–	II
Bassi Relievi Antichi 3	70	8323–8400	A42	157	III	III
Bassi Relievi Antichi 4	79	8401–8483	A43	158	IV	IV
Bassi Relievi Antichi 5	69	8484–8551	A44	159	V	V
Bassi Relievi Antichi 6	69	8552–8628	A45	160	VI	VI
Bassi Relievi Antichi 7	69	8629–8701	A46	161	VII	VII
Bassi Relievi Antichi 8	79	8702–8783	A47	162	VIII	VIII
Buste e Statue Antichi 9	77	8784–8860	A48	163	IX	–
Bassi Relievi Antichi [*10*]	120	7994–8113	A52	153	X	–
Bassi Relievi Antichi (*portfolio IXa*)	30	8114–8144†	A53	154	IXa	IXa
Mosaici Antichi I	96	8928–9035	A50	165	XI	–
Mosaici Antichi II	103	9036–9221	A51	166	XII	–
Antichità Diverse	108	10189–10297	A9	184	XVIII	XVIII
Architec(tura) *Civil*(e)	150	10354–10504	A12	186	XV	–
Ancient Roman Architecture	50	10780–10846	A17	190	–	–
Buildings and Architectural Ornaments	12	10741–45, 10750–56	A16	189	–	–
Disegni di varie Antichità. Nettuno	220	11120–11521	A31	196	XIII	–
Terence	23	26645–26667	–	–	XXI	–
Il Vergilio nel Vaticano I	52	26668–26719	–	–	XXII	–
Il Vergilio nel Vaticano II	53	26720–26773	–	–	XXIII	–
Ancient mosaics and paintings (loose folios)	34	19201–19234	pf. 5	–	pf. 5	–
Architectural drawings (loose folios)	32	19243–19287	pf. 5	–	pf. 5	–
Bas-reliefs (loose folios)	2	11880–11881	–	–	–	–

* number assigned by Evelyn Heaton-Smith, who worked in the Royal Library between 1905 and 1916, under Sir John Fortescue
† dispersed; four identified in Franks I (see British Museum); another catalogued as A.I.132

II. BRITISH MUSEUM	**Folios**	**Drawing no.**	**Michaelis 1882**
Franks I	172	1–202	I
Franks II	134	203–523	II
'New' drawings	87	–	–

III. BRITISH LIBRARY	**Folios**	**Shelf mark**
Plans of Fortified Places	28	118.e.18

IV. SIR JOHN SOANE'S MUSEUM	**Folios**	**Vol. no.**	**Ashby 1904**	**Fairbairn 1998**
Montano I: *Archiiettu*(ra) *del Montani*	138	125	–	840–1027
Montano II: *Montan I*	97	124	–	1028–1191
Montano III: *Tempj del Montani*	98	123	–	1192–1392
Codex Coner: *Architect*(ura) *Civilis Andrea Coneri Antiquita Monume*(nta) *Rome*		165	115	1–165
Architect(ura) *Civile Frammenti*	88	119	–	488–533
Vasari Album: *Gio. Vasari*	207	132	–	534–839

V. DISPERSED	**Folios**	**Phillips 1990 lot nos**
Ex-Stirling-Maxwell I – *Sculpture*	124	219–298
Ex-Stirling-Maxwell II – *Architecture*	101	299–374

SUMMARY OF KNOWN DAL POZZO DRAWINGS

Series B: Natural History

I. WINDSOR CASTLE: Royal Library	**Folios**	**RL**
Natural History: Birds I	44	dispersed
Natural History: Birds II	49	dispersed
Natural History: Birds III	54	dispersed
Natural History: Birds IV	44	dispersed
Natural History: Fossils V	45	25480–25535
Natural History: Fishes VI	61	dispersed
Natural History: Fruits VII	53	dispersed
Natural History: Plants VIII	74	dispersed
Natural History: Plants IX	67	dispersed
Natural History: Plants X	56	dispersed
Natural History: Plants XI	56	dispersed
Natural History: Plants XII	55	dispersed
Natural History: Plants XIII	58	dispersed
Natural History: Fossils XIV	62	25536–25591
Natural History: Fossils XV	48	25592–25639
Natural History: Fossils XVI	57	25640–25696
Natural History: Fossils XVII	38	25697–25734
Natural History: Conc et Plant	29	dispersed
Natural History of Birds	92	27599–27690
Erbario Miniato	214	27691–27901
The Aztec herbal	41	27902–27938
A volume of drawings of animals	25	dispersed
A volume of drawings of plants or corals	16	dispersed

II. PARIS: Institut de France	**Folios**	**MS nos**
Fungorum genera et species I	216	968
Fungorum genera et species II	206	969
Fungorum genera et species III	177	970
Plantae et flores I	129	974
Plantae et flores II	108	975
Plantae et flores III	193	976
Plantae et flores IV	193	977
Plantae et flores V	178	978

III. DISPERSED MATERIAL, previously at Windsor (see I. above)

Located, as of 2005:

Accademia dei Lincei	Fondo A, 40bis/1–4
Courtauld Institute Galleries	Witt collection: 3218, 3745, 3865
Ex-Herbert Boone	Sotheby's NY 1988, lot nos: 125–182. 99 drawings
Fitzwilliam Museum	PD.(42–43)-1956
Rijksmuseum, Amsterdam	1966:87
Victoria and Albert Museum	Circ.13-1925, E.(731–5)-1949/E.(2776–7)-1962
Other collections	98 drawings

INVENTORY A*

References to volumes containing dal Pozzo drawings

Antiquities and Architecture

[p. 3] Terence, illustrated with Figures. 23 D°

[p. 3] Il Vergilio nel Vaticano 2 Vols. V1, 52 pages. V2, 54 D°

[p. 4] Ancient Roman Architecture 50 pages. Fol.

[p. 4] Buildings & Architectural Ornaments. 43 [in pencil *42*] D° Fol.

[p. 4] Antichita Diversi. 173 Drawings. Fol.

[p. 4] Mosaici Antichi. 2V. Fol.: V1–96 pages. V2–102 D°

[p. 4] Bassi Relievi Antichi. 9 Vols Fol. V1–95 pages. V2–67 D°. V3–70 D°. V4–79 D°. V5–67. V6–70. V7–69. V8–78. V9–120 D°

[p. 4] Busti & Statue Antichi. 76 pages

[p. 4] Disegni di varie Antichita. 220 pages. Fol.

[p. 4] Architectu: Civile & Milit: (containing a medley of Plans in different parts of Italy & elsewhere & entire Buildings) 147 pages

[pp. 164–7] Six Portfolios of Architecture

[p. 166] N° 5

1. 18 large coloured Drawings of the Mosaic Pavement at Palestrina, with 2 Copies of the same engraved in 1721. The Abbé Barthelmy says that the 'Commandeur Pozzo fit copier en grand la Mosaique, mais par parties detachées, conservant dans les desseins les couleurs des differentes objets qu'elle representent, les Dessins etoient retracées en dix-huit morceaux, dont Suares, Evêque de Vaisons donna une description succincte dans son histoire imprimée a Rome en 1655'.

[p. 167] 2. 2 Prints of separate parts of the same Pavements

3. 7 coloured Drawings of Mosaic

4. 43 Drawings of ancient Buildings in Rome

These are partly prepared for binding

Natural History

[p. 3] Drawings of Birds. 4 Vols Fol. V1, 44 pages. V2, 49 D°. V3, 54 D°. V4, 44 D°

[p. 3] D° of Fruits. 1 Vol Fol. 53 pages

[p. 3] D° of Fishes. 1 Vol Fol. 61 D°

[p. 3] D° of Plants. 6 Vols Fol. V1–74. V2–67. V3–56. V4–57 [in pencil *40 only;* p. 141: *56*]. V5–53 [p. 141: *55*]. V6–58.

[p. 3] D° of Fossils. 5 Vols Fol. V1–45. V2–62 [in pencil *including*] 12 of Index. V3–48. V4–57. V5–38 & 3 of Index.

[p. 3] Sixteen Drawings of Plants. Fol. [p. 143: A Volume (sixteen pages) containing drawings of Corals?]

[p. 3] Twenty five Plates of Drawings in Water colours of Quadrupeds. Fol. [p. 143: A Volume containing twenty-five pages of Drawings of Animals]

[p. 4] Conc: & Plant. Fol. 16 Shells & 13 Plants [p. 142: Twenty-nine Drawings (sixteen of shells & 13 of flowers). let.[d] 'Natural History. Conc: et Plant.']

[p. 4] Drawings of Birds. Fol. 92. Drawings [p. 143: A Volume (92 pages) cont: Drawings of Birds. Small Fol. let.[d] 'Natural History of Birds']

[p. 4] Erbario Miniato. 209 Drawings, with an Index [p. 142: A volume (214 pages) containing Drawings of various Plants. let.[d] 'Erbario Miniato']

[p. 4] Libellus de Medicinalibus Indorum herbis a Martino, Collegii Sanctae Crucis. Compostus: cum 37 figuris coloratis. MS. [p. 142: libellus … 41 pages. small fol.]

* Inventory A is a manuscript inventory preserved in the Royal Library dating from *c.* 1810–16, drawn up by, or under the direction of, Frederick Augusta Barnard, Royal Librarian from 1774 to 1830. Many of the volumes are listed twice (first on pp. 3–4, then on pp. 141–67). On p. 141 is a list of seventeen of the Natural History volumes, numbered I–XVII as detailed on the previous page here. The earlier (and usually more detailed) entries in Inventory A are transcribed above, with variations in the later entry noted where significant.

SERIES B: NATURAL HISTORY

General introduction to the drawings

David Freedberg

THE IMPORTANCE of Cassiano's drawings of natural history cannot be overestimated. Largely commissioned by a group of Galileo's closest friends and supporters, they provide the visual evidence for crucial developments in the modern study of palaeontology, mycology, botany and zoology. Among them may be found some of the earliest illustrations ever produced with the aid of a microscope. Together they constitute one of the most ambitious attempts ever to classify the natural world through the use of visual description. Ultimately that attempt would fail, as the very men who commissioned these drawings came to realize. But before they arrived at the conclusion that visual description in itself was not entirely adequate to reveal the mysteries of nature – and was even of limited use in analysing them – they provided the world with one of the most beautiful and comprehensive records of how the natural world looked at any period in history.

Made at the same time as Galileo's pioneering investigations into astronomy, mathematics and physics, these drawings and the documents associated with them have remained unknown to the vast majority of historians of science, and have been omitted from almost every treatment of the scientific revolution of the seventeenth century. But while there were certainly precedents for encyclopaedic collections of drawings of nature – commissioned by men such as Conrad Gesner and Ulisse Aldrovandi – none could match this one in terms of size, comprehensiveness or accuracy. No one before had paid quite such meticulous attention to local flora, fauna or geology, or to the ever-increasing variety of species that were daily being reported and imported from the Americas. And none had been even remotely as rigorous in excluding the fabulous and the fantastic that until then had so bedevilled the study of nature. For while there is no shortage of anomalous specimens in Cassiano's collection of drawings, each one of them reproduced something that had actually been seen and studied. Every specimen, in other words, actually occurred in nature, unlike the fantastic monsters, prodigies and wonders that populated the pages of Gesner, Aldrovandi and so many other sixteenth-century natural historians. This was no longer a world in which the chief motor for explanation was either historical or the force of similitude (generally anthropomorphic): it was a world in which nothing could be taken as given unless it had been recorded and analysed by direct observation. It is not surprising that the first systematic use of both the telescope and the microscope should have emerged from the same group of people who were responsible for the drawings commissioned in the present series, and who themselves went into the field to make detailed notes on everything they saw.

But who were these people? At first, they were the young men who had gathered round

Federico Cesi, Prince of Acquasparta (1585–1630), when he founded the Accademia dei Lincei ('Academy of the Lynx-like', with reference to the fabled acuity of that animal's vision) in 1603, at the age of eighteen [Fig. 2]. Its first members were Cesi's lifelong friend, Francesco Stelluti (1577–1653), the obsessive and itinerant Dutchman, Johannes Heckius (Heck, van Heeck, 1576–*c.* 1620), and the more obscure Anastasio de Filiis (1577–1608). Seven years later, in 1610, they invited the aged Giovanni Battista della Porta (?1535–1615) to join them: he was perhaps the most famous Italian student of nature, science and magic in the age before Galileo. In the following year the Lincei invited Galileo Galilei (1564–1642) himself to join them, and he willingly accepted. This was the year in which Galileo made his famous demonstration of the capabilities of his telescope on the Janiculum in Rome, and was received in triumph and celebration by the Jesuits. Later the same year, three talented Germans, Johannes Schreck (1576–1630), Johannes Faber (1574–1629) and Theophilus Müller (1576–1618), were invited to join the group.

Fabio Colonna (1566–1640), the distinguished botanist from Naples, became a member in 1612, but it would be six more years before two key figures in the active core of the group, Virginio Cesarini (1595–1624) and Giovanni Ciampoli (1590–1643), were added to their number. By then Heckius had gone mad, and Galileo had encountered the first serious opposition to his Copernican ideas. In 1622 Francesco Barberini, whose uncle would soon be elected pope, joined them, and in the same year Cassiano dal Pozzo himself was elected a Linceo. These were the chief players in the story, and they will feature time and again in the volumes in this series. They were the ones who went into the field to collect botanical, zoological and geological specimens, who supported Galileo and edited the *Saggiatore* in the years in which he was discouraged by the threat of excommunication, and who put together the bulk of the drawings in the present corpus. And it was they who realized the prime importance of making visual records (or commissioning such records) of everything they saw and encountered.

Cassiano became a prime mover in all this. He commissioned beautiful drawings of birds and citrus fruit, and he had the facsimile made of an old Aztec herbal (the so-called *Codex Badianus*) when he visited the Escorial in 1626. But – most importantly of all in the present context – it was he who in 1633 bought the contents of the great library formed by Cesi, thus preserving for posterity the visual heritage of the Lincean researches. The library contained not only books and instruments, but also the drawings of natural specimens that Cesi had commissioned from the earliest days of the academy onwards. But since we know that Cassiano continued to add to this inheritance, and that he himself commissioned natural history drawings in order to aid his own researches and to make them available to others, the following questions arise: which of the surviving drawings come from Cesi's collection, and which were commissioned and collected by Cassiano himself? And who made them? These are difficult questions to answer, although there is a considerable amount of internal and external evidence to help us along the way.

At the time of writing, the surviving natural history drawings that have been identified from Cassiano's Paper Museum number more than 2,500. They are chiefly to be found in the Royal

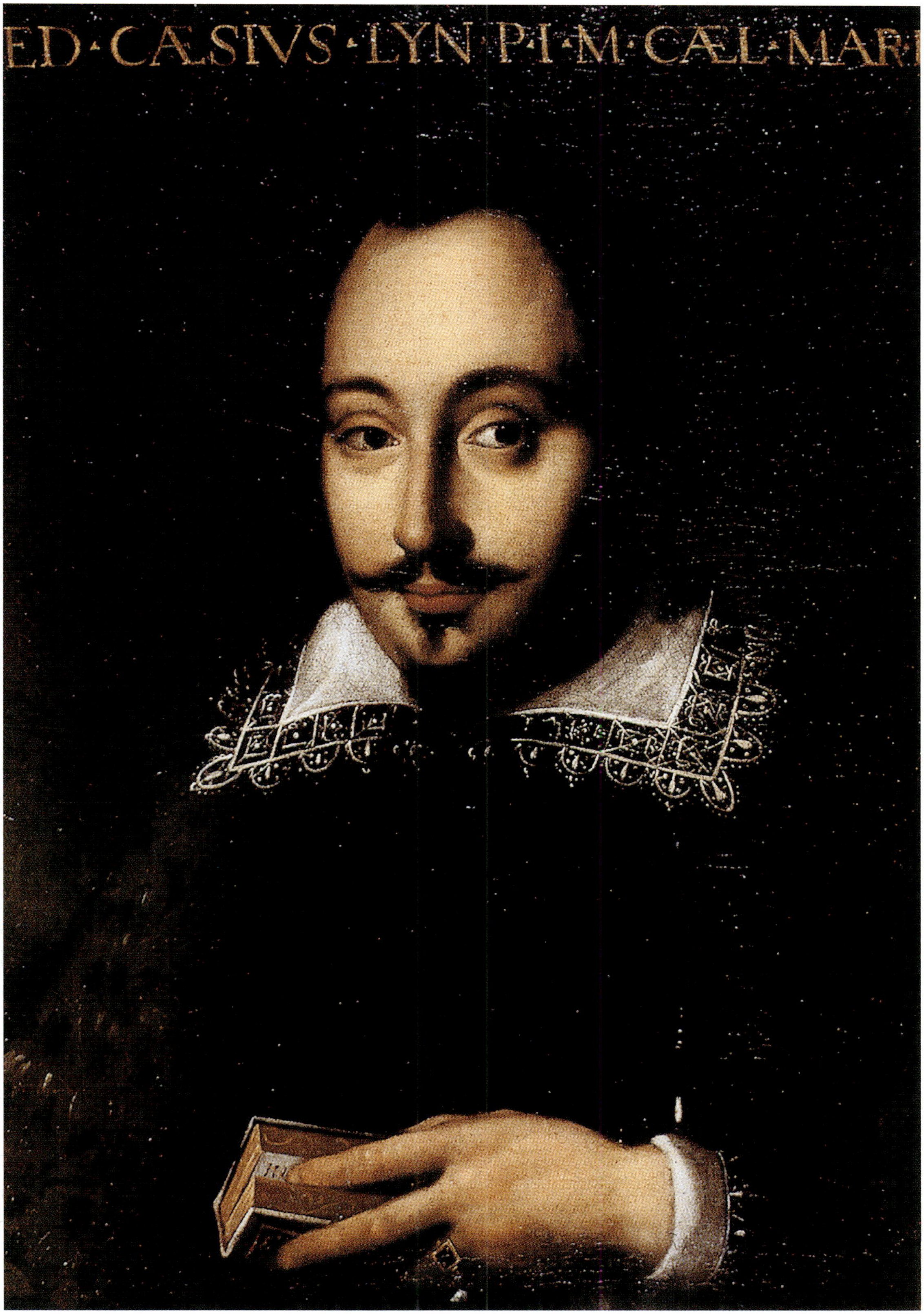

Fig. 2. Pietro Fachetti, *Federico Cesi*. Oil on canvas. Rome, Accademia Nazionale dei Lincei

Library at Windsor Castle and the Institut de France in Paris, but also in a number of other public and private collections. Since this is material that has not generally been known, and since it represents only a portion of what we know that Cesi and Cassiano commissioned and collected, it is very likely that more will come to light, even as the volumes in this catalogue raisonné appear.

The surviving drawings are preserved in a variety of bindings and as loose sheets, and the numbers may be broken down as follows. In Windsor there are a total of 253 folios (with almost 350 drawings) of fossil and mineral specimens bound into five volumes entitled *Natural History: Fossils* [Fig. 3]. The so-called *Erbario Miniato*, catalogued here, has 211 folios of drawings of plants and mushrooms, while that entitled *Libellus de medicinalibus Indorum herbis* (also known as the Mexican or Aztec herbal) has 41 folios showing Mexican plants with their Aztec names. The album entitled *Natural History of Birds* has ninety-two folios of ornithological drawings. In Paris, the volumes described as *Plantae et flores*, numbered I–V (MSS 974–978 in the Institut de France), contain more than 800 folios of botanical specimens and the occasional drawing of insects and other animals (in MS 978). Although entitled *Plantae et flores* on their spines, these are presumably the volumes of the so-called *Syntaxis Plantaria* often referred to in the Lincean documents. The volumes labelled *Fungorum genera et species*, numbered I–III (MSS 968–970 in the Institut de France), have 584 folios of fungi.

In addition, some 480 loose sheets – showing mammals, birds, fish, crustacea, corals and sponges, citrus fruit, plants and mushrooms – have been located so far. These were once bound into now dismembered volumes. The spine of the *Erbario* carries the number VI, suggesting that it was part of a larger series of volumes, and it is probable that there were at least two other albums *en suite*. Even from these figures the enormous scale and ambition of the corpus is apparent.

The catalogue raisonné broadly follows the chief divisions suggested by the material: (i) citrus fruit (published as Part B.I); (ii) the three volumes of mycological drawings in Paris and other loose mycological material at Windsor (B.II); (iii) fossil woods and other geological specimens (B.III); (iv) birds; (v) mammals, fish and other fauna; (vi) the *Erbario Miniato* and other flora (published here as Part B.VI); (vii) the five volumes of the *Syntaxis Plantaria* in Paris; (viii) the Aztec herbal; and (ix) minerals and curiosities (see p. vi for a complete list of proposed volumes in the catalogue raisonné). Some subdivision is inevitable, according to the quantity of drawings concerned and to whatever may be discovered about their original or early organization.

The *Erbario Miniato* and the Aztec herbal in Windsor are in vellum bindings which date at least from the time that they were in the Albani collection, and which very probably are the bindings made for Cassiano; both have green wash fore-edges. The drawings in the *Erbario Miniato* are still on their original folios; those in the Aztec herbal are inlaid. The volumes entitled *Natural History: Fossils* and *Natural History of Birds* are in calf bindings made some time after the drawings they contain entered the Royal Collection in 1762; here the drawings are laid down. The volumes in the Institut de France are in eighteenth-century boards with leather spines, perhaps also made at the time that they belonged to the Albani family. On the basis of internal evidence it would seem that the drawings in the Albani volumes reflect their

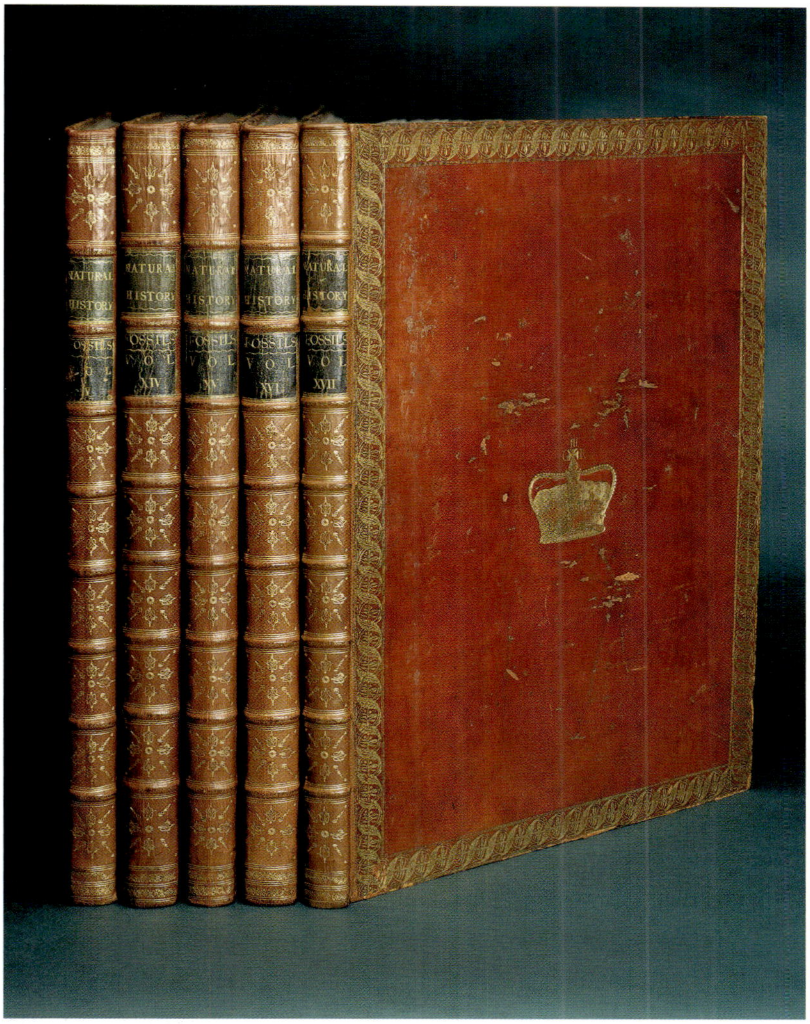

Fig. 3. The five volumes of *Natural History: Fossils* in George III bindings. Windsor, Royal Library

earlier seventeenth-century ordering much more closely than the sometimes haphazard ordering in the volumes re-bound in the Royal Library in the late eighteenth century.

Many of the drawings carry inscriptions and numbers. These are in a variety of hands, and refer to many different things – the name of a specimen, the date of its discovery or its reproduction, and its possible occurrence in other sources, and so on. A large number of the fossil, fungus and plant drawings feature inscriptions in Cesi's own hand. Especially in the case of the fossil drawings, these are often erased or cut off; fortunately, Cassiano had them copied by a scribe who reproduced these now truncated inscriptions elsewhere on the same sheet. This same scribal hand appears in the extensive indexes now bound into the plant and fungus manuscripts in the Institut de France and in the plant and fossil volumes in Windsor. To what extent these indexes reflect the original ordering of the folios to which they refer (whether in Cassiano or Cesi's collection) has yet to be clarified.

A similar uncertainty applies to the surviving indications of numbering, usually arabic numerals applied in brown ink in a small seventeenth-century hand, but occasionally in roman numerals or letters, either upper or lower case. The extent to which these 'Pozzo' numbers reflect the organization of the images in existing or planned treatises, such as those on birds and citrus fruit (and perhaps others yet to be discovered), remains uncertain in most cases. The only group of natural history drawings bearing 'Pozzo' numbers to have come down to us essentially in its original order is the *Erbario Miniato* volume, the subject of much of the present catalogue (**1–211**). The numbering system here follows the order in which the plants are discussed in a standard botanical reference work, Mattioli's commentary on Dioscorides' *De Materia Medica* (*I Discorsi di M. Pietro Andrea Matthioli . . . nelli sei libri di Pedacio Dioscoride Anazarbeo della Materia Medicinale*, Venice 1568). This ordering would, however, have been suggested by Cesi's inscriptions on the drawings, which usually cite the relevant page numbers in Mattioli's work, and thus may not be representative of the general approach to numbering in the Paper Museum. Some of the 'Pozzo' numbers in the *Erbario Miniato* are also found on other, unrelated, botanical sheets in Cassiano's collection (*426*, *523*, *562*, *563*, *598*, *599*, *603*, *604*: present catalogue numbers **281–286**), suggesting that the *Erbario*'s numbering was self-contained and not part of a larger scheme. In the case of the drawings of geological specimens, a single number could be assigned to several specimens on a sheet, indicating that a different system of numbering was being used. One set of 'Pozzo' numbers among the antiquities drawings refers to an inventory of a group of drawings acquired by Cassiano's brother, Carlo Antonio dal Pozzo (see A.I, pp. 37–8), and further research has to be done on the extent to which Carlo Antonio continued to expand and organize the collection of natural history drawings. Given the lacunose state of our knowledge about the original ordering and binding of the majority of the dal Pozzo drawings, no overall conclusions may yet be reached.

The method of mounting drawings most commonly used by Cassiano was by inlay. A window a few millimetres smaller than the drawing sheet was cut out of the mount sheet, and the drawing pasted on it, with an overlap of about 5mm. The overlap was burnished at the back so that the sheet lies completely flat, and the drawing was often framed within double lines drawn in ink on the mount sheet. Because most of the drawings in the natural history series were at the time of their entry into the Royal Collection lifted from their seventeenth-century mount, trimmed and relaid, with wash borders added, evidence of the original mounting method has disappeared. It is likewise possible that drawings from Cesi's collection were cut down when they were in the collection of Cassiano, his brother, or his heirs. Thus, with the passage of time, much valuable evidence has been cut off or erased, and we must look for other evidence for the original ordering and provenance of the drawings.

Sometimes the situation is very clear. For example, on the basis of their inscriptions, the occasional date and a wide variety of external evidence, it can be established that the drawings in the Institut de France were commissioned by Cesi. The drawings of fungi are the *Icones Fungorum* which he and his friends repeatedly discussed from the very beginning of their association. The botanical drawings in both the so-called *Syntaxis Plantaria* in Paris and the Windsor *Erbario Miniato* also carry Cesi's inscriptions and can be related in many ways to the Lincean researches in the field. In the *Erbario Miniato* there are constant references to the corresponding specimen in 'my Mattioli', Cesi's own copy of the 1568 edition of the work of the great botanist. The simple but proud inscriptions referring to the use of the microscope, chiefly in the Paris volumes, find parallels in Cesi's letters to his Lincean friends and in the occasional passage in their great compendium of American flora and fauna, the *Rerum medicarum Novae Hispaniae thesaurus, seu, plantarum, animalium, mineralium Mexicanorum historia*, which was published in its complete form only in 1649–51. We shall return to this work, the so-called *Tesoro Messicano*, later.

Then there are the drawings that relate to other, chiefly Lincean publications. Those drawings now bound into Volumes XIV–XVII of the *Natural History: Fossils*, for example, were also commissioned by Cesi himself. A few were reproduced as etchings in the small *Trattato del legno fossile minerale* published by Stelluti in 1637, and the group as a whole is repeatedly referred to there, as well as in Cesi and Stelluti's correspondence and other papers still preserved in the Vatican Library, in the library of the Accademia dei Lincei in Rome, and in that of the École de Médecine in Montpellier.

If the fossil and fungus drawings, and most of the flower drawings, have a Cesian provenance, many others were commissioned by Cassiano himself. As already noted, the volume in Windsor entitled the *Libellus de medicinalibus Indorum herbis* is the facsimile that Cassiano had made of the Aztec herbal, the *Codex Badianus*. The original manuscript had been compiled more than seventy years earlier, in 1552, by a converted Nahuatl Indian for the son of Philip II's viceroy, Antonio de Mendoza. It probably inspired Philip to send his personal physician, Francisco Hernández, to Central America to explore its botany and zoology. Hernández, subsequently known as the *Protomedicus* of the Indies, spent more than six years there, from 1571 to 1577, gathering all kinds of information and many drawings about these matters. He brought this material back with him and deposited it in the Escorial, where it was seen by Cassiano in 1626.

Several further groups of drawings, now largely disbound from the volumes that once contained them, actually exceed the Cesian ones in terms of finish and refinement, and can only have been commissioned by Cassiano. Firstly, there are the drawings that he had commissioned in preparation for his own entry presentation to the academy, the *Uccelliera* of 1622. These are by the same meticulous and attractive hand as other bird drawings ordered by Cassiano in connection with the small unpublished ornithological treatises he wrote himself and which may still be found among his papers. Indeed ornithology seems to have been his particular area of interest and competence. Then come the fine drawings of citrus fruit, commissioned by Cassiano in preparation for the illustrations of a book that appeared in 1646, Giovanni Battista Ferrari's *Hesperides sive de malorum aureorum cultura*. Of all the drawings in Cassiano's Paper Museum, this was the largest group ever to be published.

In their almost complete suppression of any acknowledgement of his role in their production, both the *Uccelliera* and the *Hesperides* are typical of the natural history works published with the help of Cassiano. For although we know from his papers that he played a key role in their preparation and in the preliminary research for them, they were actually written by friends of his, in these instances the lawyer Giovanni Pietro Olina and the Jesuit professor of Hebrew and Rhetoric, Giovanni Battista Ferrari, respectively, and Cassiano's name is scarcely mentioned in their pages. Both books name Vincenzo Leonardi as the author of the drawings on which their illustrations were based. Furthermore, one of the bird drawings has his signature on its verso, and it is reasonably clear that it is by the same hand as the best of the citrus drawings, documented as being by him. On stylistic grounds, there is much to be said for the view that many of the finest animal drawings in the corpus are also by Leonardi. Unfortunately, his is the only name we have discovered so far which can definitely be associated with any drawing or group of drawings in the Natural History series.

A number of other possible candidates may be excluded. While we know that Heckius, Stelluti and Colonna all made drawings of natural history and other specimens, their hands appear not to be found among the drawings from Cassiano's Paper Museum. In the course of his travels, Heckius made a large number of rather crude drawings, now preserved in his manuscripts in Rome, Florence, Montpellier and elsewhere, but these are very different from anything in this series. So too is the occasional surviving drawing attributable to Stelluti, while for Colonna we have only references to drawings that he made. Other Lincei, especially Faber, Schreck and Cesarini, also made use of drawings in their researches, but we have almost no evidence (except rarely in the *Tesoro Messicano*) of what they may have commissioned or drawn themselves. Whatever the case, however, there can be no doubt of the importance that all these men attached to the graphic recording of everything they saw.

But why, specifically, were these drawings made? It was not just to have a visual record and proof of their manifold researches, or to make clear the errors and shortcomings of the ancient authorities, from Aristotle to Theophrastus, Pliny to Dioscorides. It was to help them in the complex taxonomic tasks in which they were engaged. How much better to have a clear drawing than to describe something in words (always potentially ambiguous), or to have a multiplicity of different names for what might be the same thing. With the aid of drawings, people might at least attempt to ensure that one name was given to one thing, not one name to many things or many names to one. If they could not send a specimen to their correspondents, or ask for one to be sent, they could at least circulate a drawing with a name attached to it.

The other reason for the production of these drawings was that they should serve as a means of assisting in the distinctions between species, of ensuring that a particular specimen was not assigned to the wrong species, or that it did not partake of more than one species. Nothing obsessed Cesi and the early Lincei more than those phenomena that seemed to straddle the borderlines between classes, such as the fossil woods, or what they called species of ambiguous or doubtful nature. Indeed, if we turn to Cesi's vast attempt to classify all of the plant world, the *Tabulae Phytosophicae* appended to the *Tesoro Messicano* of 1628, or to his even more ambitious attempt to put all of nature in order, the outline plan still preserved in Naples (Biblioteca Nazionale) and entitled the *Speculum Rationis*, we find one overriding concern. This was the problem of how to deal with species that were of a middle nature, as Cesi put it, intermediate between one species and another or partaking of the character of two or more species.

The problem of anomaly was evidently closely allied to this, and so in the *Tabulae Phytosophicae* we find a section on plants that were of a *mezza* or *mezzana natura* (the terms often used by Cesi and his correspondents), and in the *Speculum Rationis*, a division headed *De mediis naturis in universo*. Here would be included species of a doubtful or ambiguous nature, *de ancipiti natura, seu de ancipiti specie, seu ambiguis*. And the next division was that entitled *De plantis imperfectis*, in which Cesi planned to discuss those plants with a defect or distinctive characteristic – *defectu vel nota peculiari* – or that were otherwise anomalous. One of Cesi's great breakthroughs was his realization that the problem of the ambiguous case would only be resolved by close attention to the reproductive systems of plants. In this respect he was one of Linnaeus's most important predecessors.

Very swiftly, Cesi and his friends realized that in order to discover the truth in such matters, they would have to penetrate the mysteries of reproduction, and to this end they studied ferns and fungi of every description, anatomized the marine turtle and the bee, and began to make use of the microscope. There are several puzzling drawings of eggs and foetuses, and the earliest illustrations ever made of botanical specimens with the aid of a microscope. These last appear in the volumes of plant drawings in the Institut de France where the newly perfected instrument (a rudimentary example had been used previously by Giovanni Battista della Porta) was used to scrutinize the sori and sporophytes on the underside of ferns. It would be several years before the first *printed* illustrations made with the aid of the microscope appeared. These were the anatomy of the bee prepared by Cesi, Stelluti and Colonna in honour of the papal jubilee in 1625, and the enlargements of the seed-pod and seeds of the 'Chinese rose' (*Hibiscus mutabilis* L.) in Ferrari's *De florum cultura* of 1633.

While it is clear that most of the drawings in this corpus were made for the purposes of research and taxonomy, it is just as clear that many were intended for eventual publication. Above all, this emerges in the case of the citrus drawings, published in Ferrari's *Hesperides*, for which Cassiano himself undertook a considerable portion of the preliminary research and organized much of the necessary funding. In the case of the fossil drawings, only a few were eventually selected for reproduction in Stelluti's strangely evasive work on fossil woods of 1637, the *Trattato del legno fossile minerale*. One of the beautiful series of ornithological drawings was used in the *Uccelliera* of 1622, and others (as we may judge from the treatises written by Cassiano himself and preserved in the library of the Accademia Nazionale dei Lincei in Rome) may well have been intended for further, never-realized publications in this domain. The same probably applies to the animal and flower drawings. Cesi may have intended to publish at least part of his great series of fungus drawings but this project, like so many others of his, never saw the light of day.

The one project to which this does not apply was the *Rerum medicarum thesaurus novae Hispaniae, sive plantarum animalium mineralium Mexicanorum historia*. This was the great compendium of material on American plants and animals that first appeared in incomplete form in 1628 but was eventually published in full as late as 1649–51, long after Cesi had died and the academy was effectively defunct. Its many illustrations bear no direct relation to the drawings in the present corpus, but its story is instructive. Cesi had been preparing this work ever since he had heard of the Neapolitan doctor Nardo Antonio Recchi's summary of the massive collection of notes and illustrations gathered in Mexico by Hernández, and neglected ever since. In 1610 Cesi had proposed to publish Recchi's manuscript (which he had bought from Recchi's heirs), accompanied by a commentary by his fellow Lincei. When Galileo made his epochal visit to Rome in 1611 he paid a special visit to Cesi's palace in the Via Maschera d'Oro to look at illustrations of more than 500 Mexican plants (presumably those in Recchi's manuscripts), and when asked his opinion confessed that neither he nor anyone else could identify them correctly.

By the end of the decade Cesi had prepared more than 800 woodcuts for the proposed work, several of which he then annotated himself, and finally, in 1628, a first edition, funded by Cardinal Francesco Barberini, appeared. This contained Schreck's edition of the botanical material, Faber's expansive commentary on Mexican animals, a set of important annotations by Fabio Colonna, and the first thirteen tables of Cesi's own vast attempt to classify all of the botanical world, the *Tabulae Phytosophicae*. Then Cesi died, and had it not been for the devoted and patient efforts of Cassiano and Stelluti, no further material would ever have appeared. But for years they kept the project alive, bringing it up to date, and seeking new sponsors for a revised and expanded version. Thus it was that the definitive edition of the *Tesoro Messicano* appeared in 1651 (though several copies also carry the dates of 1648 and 1649), long after the death of Cesi and of almost all his original *confrères*. This time the book was not subsidized by the now-exiled Barberini, but rather by the Spanish ambassador, Alfonso de las Torres, who had been involved in the project by Cassiano. It contained the parts already printed in 1628 with new front- and end-matter, as well as seven of Cesi's *Tabulae*, which the latter had apparently left incomplete and which were now edited and completed by Stelluti. It also included Hernández's *Liber Unicus* on Mexican animals (including birds, fishes and insects) and minerals. This Cassiano had had copied at the time of his visit to Madrid in 1626.

But the woodcuts in the *Tesoro Messicano* are rudimentary and lacking in detail compared to the bulk of the surviving drawings in the Paper Museum. Presumably they were based on the now-lost illustrations that Hernández himself had made in South America, or on Recchi's copies of them. But while Cesi realized the importance of publishing Recchi's material as evidence of a world unknown to the ancient authorities, he knew that it was possible to have much better illustrations made, with closer indications of colour, texture and detail, both inner and outer, than had ever come from the Americas. He and his fellow Lincei made it their business to find draughtsmen – and then engravers – who could convey with precision and detail both the things they had examined with their own eyes and the remarkable specimens seen by reliable eyes abroad.

This is why these drawings are so important. They, more than anything else, provide the visual evidence for the Lincean researches into natural history. Aside from Ferrari's *Hesperides*, also published after Cesi's death and written by someone who was not a Linceo himself, the published material offers only the palest shadow of the quality of their researches in this domain. The illustrations in works such as the *Trattato del legno fossile minerale* and the *Tesoro Messicano* have nothing like the precision and analytic intensity of the drawings. They testify to the fact that they were based on direct observation of a persistence that the printed illustrations hardly ever suggest. The drawings show the same specimen from one side and from another, in sections and in segments; they focus on parts of plants or animals or minerals, from the snout of a porcupine to the seed-pods of plants, from the sulphuric florets and pyritic growths on fossil woods to the interiors of shells and the details of leaves and grasses, from the legs and beaks of flamingos to their wings and feathers. They carry inscriptions about colours or actually show them; sometimes they record the date they were made, or the location. Repeatedly they bear witness to the Lincean desire to look ever more closely into the interior of things that until then had been described only from the outside. This was done either with the aid of the microscope or by delicately dismantling the specimens that they had found or which had been sent to them by friends and colleagues.

Together these drawings represent the high-water mark of the belief in visual reproduction as a means of analysing and classifying the creations of nature. Other ambitious attempts had been made before to reproduce much of nature, and there would, of course, be more, but it is hard to think of any collection that matches the drawings from Cassiano's Paper Museum in quantity and scope, and, in so many cases, descriptive and artistic refinement. At the very height of the Lincean engagement with drawing as a tool of natural history research, however, their own fellow Galileo laid to rest the idea that the subjective qualities of things were capable of being recorded with the same objectivity as number, weight and size. And so the Lincei themselves began to lose faith in the possibilities of pictorial reproduction as an instrument of what we would now call scientific research. Cesi would bury himself in his efforts to classify the natural world not by means of drawing but in tabular form, and the basis of this effort, he realized, had to be geometrical and schematic, not densely descriptive and pictorial. But neither he nor any of his fellow Lincei ever felt the same hostility to picture-making that Linnaeus did, and whatever scepticism they may have had about the possibilities of reproduction in visual form lies silent beside the observational intensity, descriptive beauty and analytic closeness of the drawings reproduced in the volumes of this corpus.

THE *ERBARIO MINIATO* AND THE ACCADEMIA DEI LINCEI

Fabio Garbari and Lucia Tongiorgi Tomasi

THE *ERBARIO MINIATO* ('illuminated herbal') is an early seventeenth-century album of 211 botanical drawings that takes its name from the inked title on its spine.[1] The album is preserved in the Royal Library at Windsor Castle along with the greater part of Cassiano dal Pozzo's 'Paper Museum'. It entered Cassiano's collection in 1633 together with many other *libri dipinti* ('painted books') that he acquired from the widow of Federico Cesi, prince of Acquasparta (1585–1630) and founder of the Accademia dei Lincei (see pp. 10ff).

Native and exotic species are represented in the *Erbario Miniato* along with medicinal plants, vegetables and fruit-bearing species, garden varieties, weeds, fungi (**33–51**) and even a specimen of coral (**176**). Most of the drawings were inscribed, probably by Cesi himself, with the name of the plant and notes on its medicinal properties, extracted largely from the 1568 Italian edition of Pietro Andrea Mattioli's commentaries on Dioscorides, *I Discorsi di M. Pietro Andrea Matthioli . . . nelli sei libri di Pedacio Dioscoride Anazarbeo della materia medicinale.*

In addition to the *Erbario Miniato*, sixty-seven loose sheets of botanical drawings (**212–277**) have been identified to date that seem to be the *disjecta membra* of a companion volume to the *Erbario*. That volume was presumably broken up and remounted in the eighteenth century, after the dal Pozzo collection had entered the Royal Library under George III, and the drawings were dispersed from the Royal Library around 1920 (though a number have since been reacquired – see pp. 2–3). A putative third volume (on which more below) appears never to have entered the Royal Collection and is untraced.

Also catalogued here are sixteen further botanical drawings from the Paper Museum (**278–293**) that do not belong to the *Erbario Miniato* series. Some may have been made for Cesi (e.g. **293**) but most seem to have been executed for Cassiano (or even for his younger brother, Carlo Antonio dal Pozzo), many years after completion of the *Erbario.*

Herbals

The genre of the herbal has existed since classical times. It provided apothecaries and doctors with an encyclopaedia of 'simples', the raw materials of medical practice as codified by Galen (AD 129–200), which categorized plants and other *materia medica* according to their qualities and determined the use of these simples in combinations to ensure the proper balance of properties.[2] Such works were often accompanied by information on the habitat or origin of the plants, and the names by which they were known in various languages.

Since it is difficult to identify a specimen securely on the basis of a verbal description alone, in practice the botanical value of a herbal depends largely on its illustrations. Before the invention of printing, images of plants were often copied and recopied from one manuscript to the next, becoming schematic over the course of time and bearing little relationship to the real plants.

The oldest herbal to survive is the so-called *Codex Vindobonensis* of Juliana Anicia, produced in Constantinople in AD 512 [Fig. 4].[3] This manuscript, which contains more than 380 coloured drawings of plants, is a collation of texts on medicine and the natural sciences, including Περὶ ὕλης ιατρικῆς or *De materia medica*, written around AD 60 by the physician and pharmacologist Pedanius Dioscorides of Anazarbus in Cilicia (now southern Turkey). Dioscorides spent many years travelling around the Mediterranean area as a surgeon with the armies of the Emperor Nero, giving him ample opportunity to study the indigenous flora. *De materia medica* describes nearly 600 plants together with their medicinal properties, and was the standard reference work for pharmacological botany until well into the Renaissance.

From the second half of the fourteenth century, drawings in herbals began to display an increasing degree of accuracy and realism, a phenomenon that was particularly marked in northern Italy, where artists such as Giovannino de' Grassi (*fl.* 1389–98), Michelino da Besozzo (*fl.* 1388–1450) and Pisanello (1395–1455) portrayed plants and animals meticulously. Wealthy and discriminating patrons commissioned extraordinary herbals, such as the *Theatrum sanitatis*, produced in late fourteenth-century Milan as a gift for King Wenceslaus of Luxembourg;[4] the *Carrara Herbal*, produced in 1403 for Francesco II Novello da Carrara, lord of Padua [Fig. 5];[5] and the *Liber de simplicibus*, painted by the Venetian Andrea Amadio around 1445–8.[6]

It was the invention of printing, however, that heralded the most fundamental transformations in the genre. The rather crude and schematic illustrations in the first printed herbals, beginning with the *Herbarium Apulei* (Rome 1481, based on a medieval manuscript from Montecassino) [Fig. 6], compare poorly with manuscript herbals of the same period or with the remarkable nature studies produced by such artists as Leonardo da Vinci (1452–1519) and Albrecht Dürer (1471–1528). But during the first half of the sixteenth century, a series of publications profoundly modified the textual and iconographic tradition of the medieval herbal, and laid the foundations of modern botany. The first of these appeared in Strasbourg between 1530 and 1539, and the title – *Herbarum vivae eicones ad naturae imitationem summa cum diligentia et artificio effigiatae* – proclaimed its intended revolutionary nature. The author, Otto Brunfels (1488–1534), systematically gathered and described the flora of his native Germany, comparing his own observations with the knowledge handed down through Greek and Arab texts. To illustrate his work Brunfels availed himself of the skills of a talented artist, Hans Weiditz (*fl.* 1495–1536), who had drawn his subjects from life [Fig. 7]. This collaboration between naturalist and artist introduced a practice that would spread all over Europe from the mid-sixteenth century. It would be the role of the former to describe, interpret and classify the specimens, and of the latter to document them visually by means of direct observation.

In Basle in 1542, Leonhart Fuchs (1501–66), court physician and professor at the University of Tübingen, published *De historia stirpium*, whose aim – like that of the *Herbarum vivae*

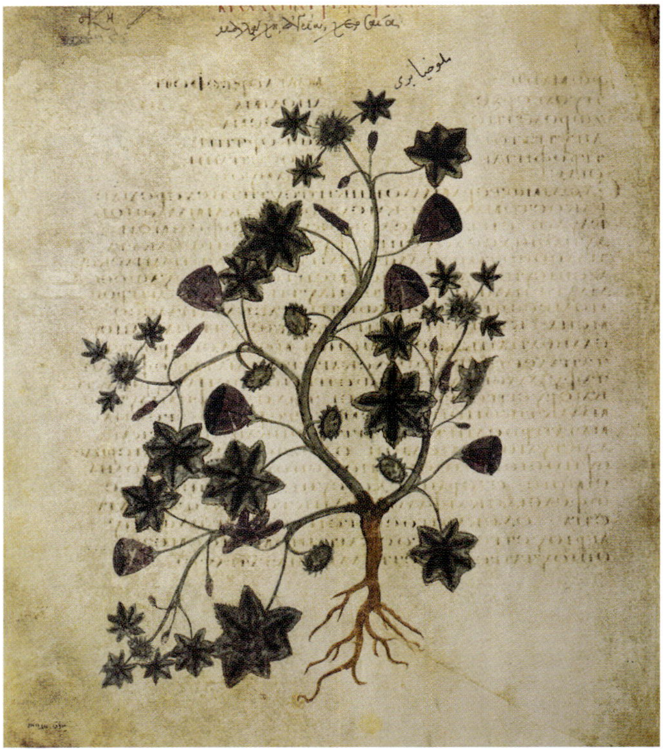

Fig. 4. High mallow (*Malva sylvestris*). *Codex Vindobonensis*, folio 228v. Vienna, Österreichische Nationalbibliothek, Med. Gr. 1

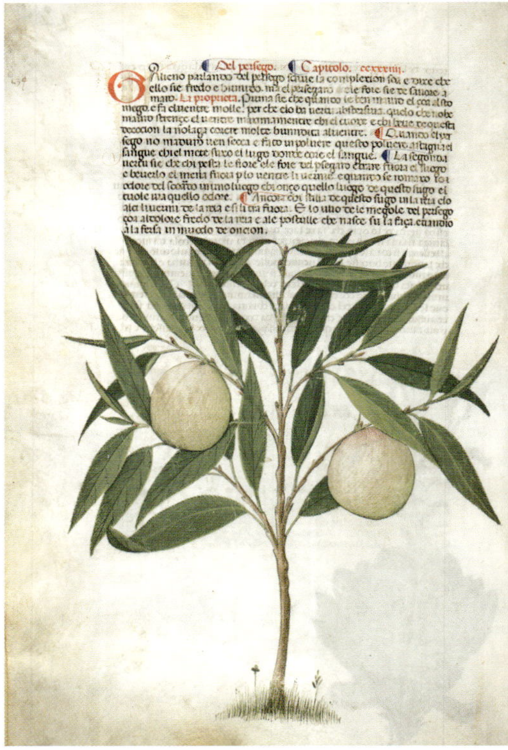

Fig. 5. Peach (*Prunus persica*). *Carrara Herbal*, folio 166v. London, British Library, MS Egerton 2020

eicones – was to present a systematic reordering of German flora, using as his point of departure Greek and Roman authorities, above all Dioscorides, Pliny the Elder (AD 23–79) and Galen. The accompanying woodcuts [Fig. 8] – in outline with little shading, as they were often coloured by hand, either by their purchasers, or by the authors for presentation to some prestigious client – were more important than the text, and in the preface Fuchs described the immense amount of work that went into their creation. In recognition of their contribution, the author included a portrait of each of his artists, dressed in doctoral robes and engaged in the production of the woodcuts.

The success of this new iconography was immediate and enduring. Many of the illustrations from the *De historia stirpium* would be copied in subsequent herbals produced throughout Europe, such as the 1546 edition of the *Kreutterbuch* of Hieronymus Tragus (Jerome Bock, 1498–1554), the *Cruydt-Boeck* (1554) of Dodoens (Rembert Dodoens, 1517–85) and the *New Herball* (1551–68) of William Turner (1508–68). The influence of Fuchs's work was such that the illustrations were still being copied in the mid-seventeenth century, in the first edition of Jean Bauhin's *Historia plantarum universalis* (1650), and even as late as 1774, in Salomon Schinz's *Anleitung zu der Pflanzenkenntniss*.[7]

In 1588 in Frankfurt, the physician Jacob Theodorus (1522–90), known as Tabernaemontanus (a Latinization of Bergzabern, his home town), published his monumental *Neuw Kreuterbuch*, the culmination of thirty-six years of study, followed two years later by the *Eicones*

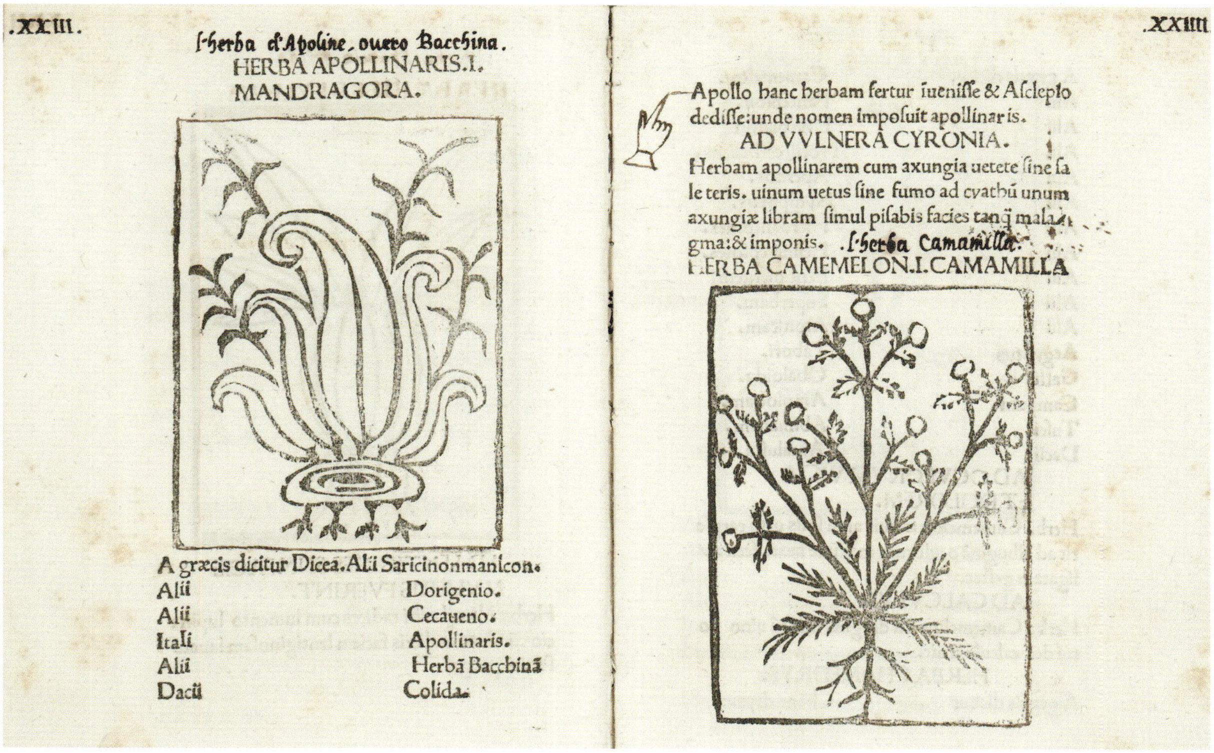

Fig. 6. Mandrake (*Mandragora officinarum*) and camomile (*Chamaemelum nobile*). *Herbarium Apulei*, Rome 1483

plantarum [Fig. 9], which reproduced more than 2,250 woodcuts from the original work without accompanying text. Some annotations in the *Erbario Miniato* refer to this work (**28**, **80**, **131**, **176**, **189–190**).[8] Meanwhile, the Antwerp publisher Christopher Plantin issued major works by Dodoens, Lobelius (Matthias de l'Obel, 1538–1616) and Clusius (Charles de l'Écluse, 1526–1609); sharing a common set of illustrations, these publications constituted one of the most important summations of botanical knowledge of the period, and Dodoens [Fig. 10] is cited three times in the annotations in the *Erbario* (**76**, **153** and **199**). These latter authors had begun to take account of their century's voyages of discovery, which had added many exotic species to the flora and fauna of Europe on which the writings of ancient authors were based. Clusius, for example, republished pioneering monographs on the flora of the Americas by Nicolas Monardes (1493–1588) and Cristobal Acosta (1515–94). Around the same time, the practice was emerging of drying plants between sheets of paper, allowing botanists to have specimens, even of rare or exotic species, available for study at all times.

Of greatest relevance to the *Erbario Miniato*, however, was the work of Pietro Andrea Mattioli (1501–78) of Siena, who spent much of his career as physician to the Emperor Ferdinand II. In 1544 Mattioli published (in Italian) his *Di Pedacio Dioscoride Anazarbeo libri cinque*, which offered a comprehensive review of contemporary botanical knowledge in the form of a commentary on the *De materia medica* of Dioscorides. Though Dioscorides' work had been published in the original Greek by Aldus Manutius in Venice in 1499, and translated into Italian by Ermolao Barbaro in 1516, Mattioli's work made the treatise accessible for the first time to

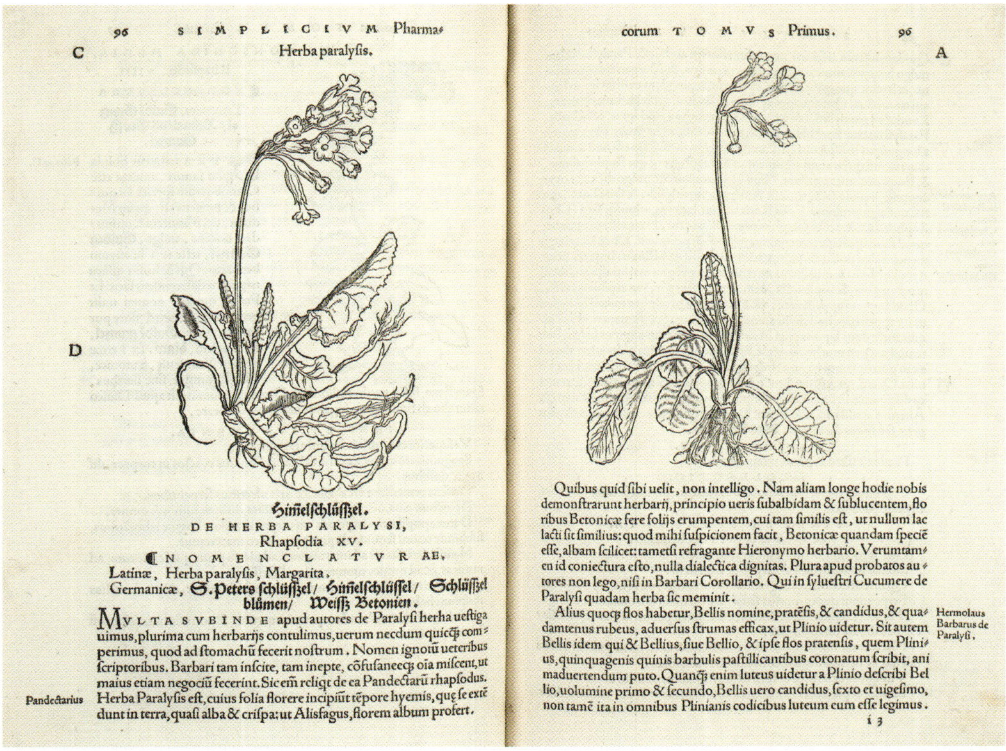

Fig. 7. Cowslip (*Primula veris*). O. Brunfels, *Herbarum vivae eicones*, Strasbourg 1530, p. 96

many European scholars, and it earned him international fame. The first edition presented the first five books of *De materia medica*, followed by a commentary which furnished corrections and supplementary information based on the author's own botanical studies and his reading of other classical authors, including Theophrastus (*c*. 372–287 BC), Galen and Pliny.[9] Mattioli integrated Dioscorides' herbal with other plants known to him, including some which did not possess any supposed medicinal virtues. Though it is described on the title page as 'truly not just useful but necessary',[10] this edition did not contain any illustrations.

The acclaim accorded his work encouraged Mattioli to prepare a second edition, augmented by the descriptions of 200 plants native to the region of Gorizia and the Istrian peninsula. This appeared in 1548 as *Il Dioscoride dell'Eccellente Dottor Pietro Andrea Mattioli*. So successful was this text that a pirated edition was printed in Mantua in 1549, and then two new authorized editions in Venice in 1550 and 1552. In 1554 two Latin editions were published, one by Vincenzo Valgrisi in Venice, embellished with 562 woodcuts produced in a collaboration between the artist Giorgio Liberale of Udine and the woodblock cutter Wolfang Meyerpeck of Meissen. In his dedicatory epistle Mattioli hailed Liberale as 'most skilled in the art of painting'.[11] These Latin editions were followed in 1555 by an Italian edition entitled *I Discorsi . . . nei sei libri della materia medicinale di Pedacio Dioscoride Anazarbeo di M. Pietro Andrea Matthioli senese medico cesareo*, which contained a completely revised commentary, Mattioli having benefited from the suggestions of two eminent colleagues, Luca Ghini of Imola (1490–1556) and Ulisse Aldrovandi of Bologna (1522–1605), with whom he corresponded frequently.

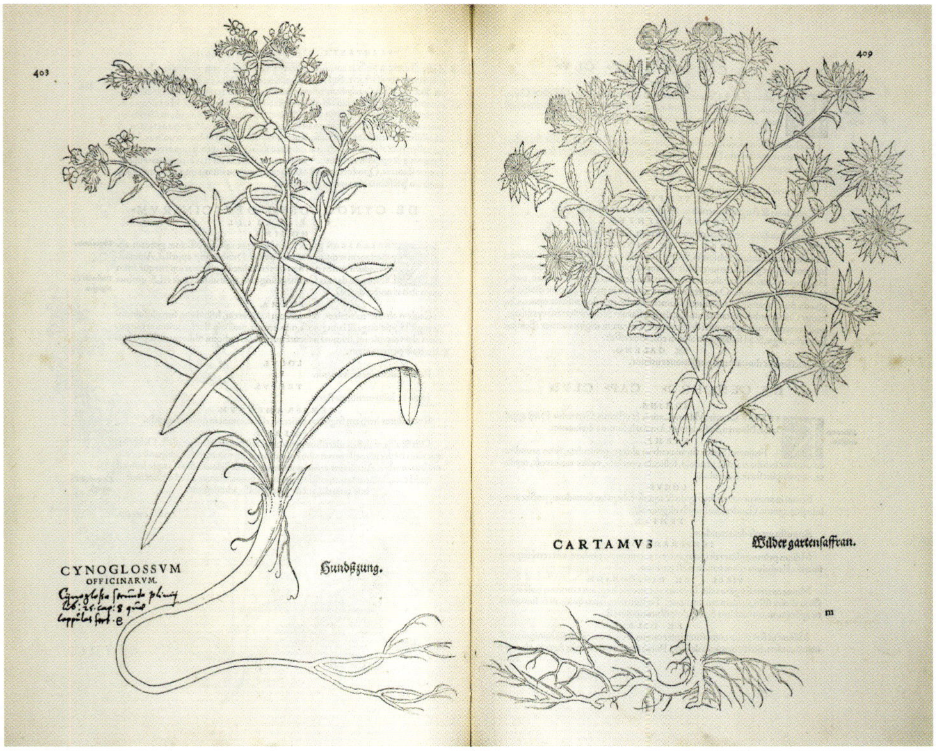

Fig. 8. Hound's tongue (*Cynoglossum officinale*) and safflower (*Carthamus tinctorius*).
L. Fuchs, *De historia stirpium*, Zurich 1542, pp. 408–9

Subsequent editions of the *Discorsi* in Latin, Italian, French, Bohemian and German followed in rapid succession. The most extensive were the Latin and Italian editions printed by Valgrisi in Venice in 1565 and 1568 respectively, each of which comprised more than 1,500 pages illustrated with over 1,000 woodcuts (see Figs 13 and 14). Mattioli's work was an authority for the study of medicinal plants well into the seventeenth century, and it was from the Italian edition of 1568 that most of the annotations in the *Erbario Miniato* were extracted.

Cassiano himself is known to have possessed *due tomi del Mattioli miniati* ('two illuminated volumes of Mattioli')[12] which are lost to us today and whose precise nature is unclear. A description of sorts may be provided by Cassiano's fellow Linceo Johannes Faber, who wrote to him in 1626 from Rome (while Cassiano was away in Spain) after having seen this work during a visit to Cassiano's brother Carlo Antonio: 'I saw to my great joy the illuminated Mattioli of your most illustrious excellency, a work in truth most worthy and curious, of which I think there is no equal in Europe, with such fineness are the illustrations made, and with such naturalness has the colour been given to the plants; those which are missing, most of which can be found in Rome, we will have painted by and by so that the work may be completed.'[13]

A new approach to the world of nature: the Accademia dei Lincei

The illustrated botanical texts produced during the sixteenth century testify to the growing importance assigned to the image in the study of the sciences. This was the background to the formation in 1603 of the Accademia dei Lincei (see pp. 10ff.), whose founding members were Federico Cesi, Francesco Stelluti (1577–1653), Anastasio De Filiis (1577–1608, a relative of Cesi) and the Dutch-born Jan van Heeck (1579–*c.* 1620, known as Johannes Heck or Heckius, or Giovanni Ecchio). The members of the Academy grasped the need for a new *pittura filosofica* or 'painting for knowledge' that aimed at a deeper understanding of natural phenomena.[14] This was a concept that the great botanists of the preceding century had already begun to formulate, demanding that their texts be accompanied by scientifically accurate illustrations, executed by skilled artists. Ulisse Aldrovandi – the professor of botany at the University of Bologna, who exerted a great influence on the study of natural history during the second half of the sixteenth century – established a *bottega artistica* or studio on his estate where artists could prepare botanical and zoological drawings under his direct supervision. This practice was adopted by other individuals and by progressive scientific institutions such as the Giardino dei Semplici in Pisa.[15] The importance of direct observation and the visual record may be traced through the entire history of the Accademia dei Lincei, culminating in the remarkable collections of Cassiano dal Pozzo. In a letter to Stelluti of July 1604, Cesi observed, regarding the science of plants, that

> more may be learned by oneself through direct contemplation (all the more when one is in the countryside) than by reading the books of others. In any case, since you are without books, what you already know is enough for you to contemplate with natural judgement, and from nature herself continue to learn.[16]

Each of the founding Lincei was initially assigned an academic speciality: Stelluti, astronomy and mathematics; De Filiis, history; Heckius, philosophy; and Cesi, botany. But their work at this stage was a common and shared experience, and botany appears to have been as much a key area of research for the physician Heckius, who routinely employed plants in his medical practice, as it was for Cesi. Almost every plant in the *Erbario* is associated through the accompanying inscriptions with its medicinal usage, and the initial impetus for creating the herbal – if not the physical process of compiling the manuscript – may well have come from Heckius.

Heckius was a scholar whose interest in botany and its medicinal applications, as revealed in his many letters to other Lincei, typifies the contemporary approach to the subject.[17] He was born in Deventer, where he received a humanist education. At the age of fourteen he embarked on his first trip to Italy, visiting various cities including Rome. He then returned to Holland, apparently remaining there until 1596 when, as a fervent Catholic, he was forced to seek refuge in Italy from religious persecution. In that year, inspired by the Neoplatonic philosopher Marsilio Ficino's *De triplici vita*, he wrote a manuscript treatise on hygiene, diet and the virtues of plants entitled *Liber de regimine sanitatis*.[18] Contained in the same manuscript are the undated works *De fructibus tractatus*, *Tractatus de radicibus herbarum diversarum* and *Tractatus de herbis*, which discuss topics relating to pharmacological botany and testify to his early interest in medicine. He studied at the University of Perugia, attending the lectures of the *lettore dei semplici* (teacher of simples) Annibale Camilli, and received a degree in medicine on 6 August 1601.[19]

Heckius then entered the service of the Orsini on their estates at Scandriglia, Ponticelli, Nerula and Montelibretti, gaining experience in the practice of medicine and, as he later wrote, conducting his *primiero saggio delli nostri semplici* ('first studies of our indigenous medicinal plants').[20] He became involved in a violent quarrel with a herbalist from Scandriglia, Raniero Consolini (or Casilini), regarding the merits of using costly medicines containing 'exotic' ingredients to treat patients, as Consolini regularly did. Heckius insisted that remedies prepared exclusively with native plants were just as effective, pointing to the 'many hundreds of sick patients' whom he had cured by these means.[21] In an altercation Consolini received a sword wound from which he died. Heckius was imprisoned, but the young Marquis of Monticelli, Federico Cesi, learned of the case and managed to have the sentence lifted on the grounds of legitimate defence.

Heckius was freed on 26 June 1603 and sent a deferential letter to Cesi from Spoleto, in which he expressed his gratitude and asked to be taken on 'among his other servants'. Aware of Cesi's keen interest in botany, Heckius enclosed with his missive

> some seeds of a medicinal plant that I found in a very deep cave in a deserted place in the mountains of Spoleto, and which I have never seen again since. And this plant is not dissimilar to the common melon, only its leaves are more deeply indented, its flowers vary and may be either yellow or white, [and] it produces fruit, some elongated, some rounded, some irregular.[22]

Aware that not only the form but other characteristics of a plant were fundamental to its identification, Heckius lingered over various details in his description of the fruit:

> some are at first blackish-green in colour, then becoming a colour deeper than gold, and they produce such a sweet and pleasing fragrance that they will fill with their perfume even the largest room; they are so lovely to the eye, so welcome to the nose, so soothing to the spirit that it is truly an astonishing thing.[23]

He closes with the observation: 'it appearing to me to be quite a new thing to find such a plant in those barren mountains, I was eager to share my discovery with Your Most Illustrious and Excellent Lordship, as I also hope to be able to do with many other things, both of plants and of seeds'.[24] That same summer Heckius entered Federico Cesi's service.

It is clear from his letters, which contain many references to Mattioli,[25] that Heckius was deeply concerned with the medicinal properties of plants. An undated but early letter addressed to Gerolamo Mercuriale, professor of medicine at the university in Pisa, contains observations on two simples, *zedoaria* (the rhizome of white turmeric, *Curcuma zedoaria*) and *agalloco* (the bark and root of agarwood, *Aquilaria agallocha*). In a letter sent in 1603 to his friend and patron Benedetto Gelosi on the subject of plants with aphrodisiac properties,[26] he quoted extensively from the texts of celebrated botanists, including Lobelius and Mattioli. Of even greater significance is a letter sent on 1 February 1603 to Pope Clement VIII, in which Heckius declared that he had personally gathered and assembled no fewer than 3,000 plants in a two-volume dried herbal.[27] Such collections frequently served as pendants to drawn herbals, and

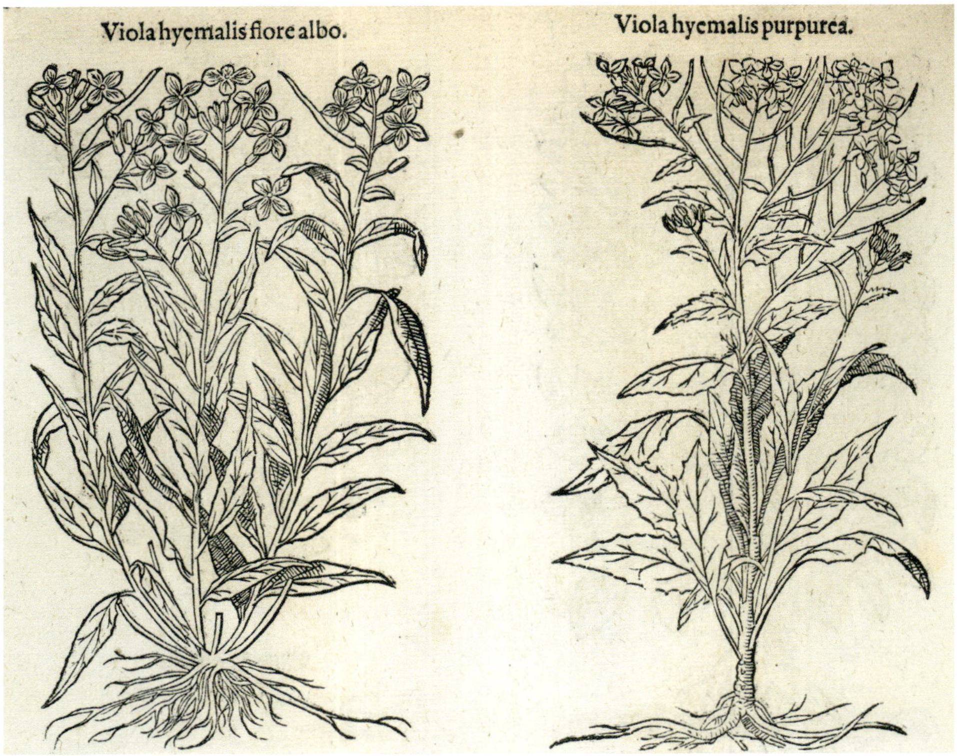

Fig. 9. Sweet rocket (*Hesperis matronalis*). J. Theodorus (Tabernaemontanus), *Eicones plantarum*, Frankfurt 1590, p. 308

Heckius's two volumes may well have complemented the *Erbario Miniato* and assisted the Lincei's early botanical researches.

Eager as ever to defend the belief that effective remedies could be prepared from indigenous plants,[28] the young physician wrote to Aldrovandi, by now retired but still one of the foremost experts in Italy on the subject of medicinal plants. In a letter of 14 November 1602, Heckius asserted in his imperfect but comprehensible Italian: 'the spirit of nature has provided us, no less generously than it has the barbarous Indians, with the most health-giving plants and minerals' – even though, as he continues, many physicians who have more regard for their personal enrichment than for the good of their patients 'make use of foreign plants, concocting false medicines, and including in a single prescription Asia, Africa, Europe and the New World all together'.[29]

Heckius sought to establish contact with the most notable botanists of the period, writing letters in February 1604 to Clusius, Lobelius, Caspar Bauhin and Thomas Mermann.[30] Another letter signed by all of the Lincei was sent to Bauhin, proposing an exchange of the plants that were being cultivated in their respective gardens.[31] Soon afterwards, however, the young scientists were prevented from frequenting one another for a time, at the insistence of Federico Cesi's family, concerned, it appears, by accusations of heresy. One of the results of this imposed separation was an even more voluminous correspondence between the members, with Cesi acting as the principal intermediary. He did everything in his power to maintain a network of communication and to provide 'beautiful books, writings, secrets and natural specimens most useful to the Lincei'.[32] He also devoted his time to writing the statutes of his academy, the 'Lyncaeographum'. Intended for circulation only among the

Lincei members and never published, these outlined the principles and goals of the Academy, dedicated to the pursuit and dissemination of knowledge.[33]

Cesi's family was disquieted by the influence exercised upon him by Heckius, and in 1604 Heckius left Rome. He travelled to meet the most renowned naturalists in Italy and abroad: in Bologna, Aldrovandi; in Pisa, Mermann, the physician Gerolamo Mercuriale and Francesco Malocchi, director of the Giardino dei Semplici;[34] in Genoa, the naturalist Bernardino Castelletti; in Paris, the physician Giuseppe Quercetano and the 'botanist-gardener' Vespasien Robin; in England, Lobelius; and in Leiden, Clusius.[35] Cesi reported to Stelluti and De Filiis in April 1605, that when Heckius had reached Prague:

> he immediately took on a young sculptor and engraver to make prints and drawings, something most useful to the work of the Lincei; [Heckius] hired him so that he might serve our order and keeps [the artist] with him, hoping that [the artist] will be taken into the service of the Lincei for ever . . . The engraver will be most useful to our order . . . we will be able thereby to illustrate our every observation.[36]

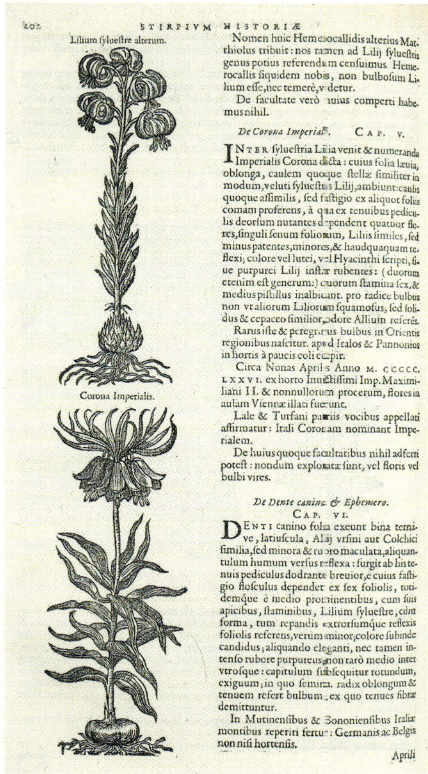
202 STIRPIVM HISTORIÆ

Lilium ſyluestre alterum.

Corona Imperialis.

Nomen huic Hemerocallidis alterius Matthiolus tribuit: nos tamen ad Lilij ſyluestris genus potius referendum cenſuimus. Hemerocallis ſiquidem nobis, non bulboſum Lilium eſſe, nec temerè, videtur.

De facultate verò huius comperti habemus nihil.

De Corona Imperiali. CAP. V.

INTER ſyluestria Lilia venit & numeranda Imperialis Corona dicta: cuius folia læuia, oblonga, caulem quoque ſtellæ ſimiliter in modum, veluti ſyluestris Lilij, ambiunt: caulis quoque aſſimilis, ſed faſtigio ex aliquot foliis comam proferens, à qua ex tenuibus pediculis deorſum nutantes dependent quatuor flores, ſinguli ſenum foliorum, Liliis ſimiles, ſed minus patentes, minores, & haudquaquam reflexi; colore vel lutei, vel Hyacinthi ſcripti, ſiue purpurei Lilij inſtar rubentes: (duorum etenim eſt generum:) quorum ſtamina ſex, & medius piſtillus inalbicant. pro radice bulbus non vt aliorum Liliorum ſquamoſus, ſed ſolidus & cepaceo ſimilior, odore Allium referẽs.

Rarus iſte & peregrinus bulbus in Orientis regionibus naſcitur. apud Italos & Pannonios in hortis à paucis coli cœpit.

Circa Nonas Aprilis Anno M. CCCCC. LXXVI. ex horto Inuictiſſimi Imp. Maximiliani II. & nonnullorum procerum, flores in aulam Viennæ illati fuerunt.

Lale & Turſani patriis vocibus appellati affirmatur: Itali Coronam nominant Imperialem.

De huius quoque facultatibus nihil adferri poteſt: nondum exploratæ ſunt, vel floris vel bulbi vires.

De Dente canino & Ephemero.
CAP. VI.

DENTI canino folia exeunt bina ternáve, latiuſcula, Allij vrſini aut Colchici ſimilia, ſed minora & rubro maculata, aliquantulum humum verſus reflexa: ſurgit ab his tenuis pediculus dodrante breuior, e cuius faſtigio floſculus dependet ex ſex foliolis, totidemq́ue è medio prominentibus, cum ſuis apicibus, ſtaminibus, Lilium ſyluestre, cùm forma, tum repandis extrorſumq́ue reflexis foliolis referens, verùm minor, colore ſubinde candidus; aliquando eleganti, nec tamen intenſo rubore purpureus, non rarò medio inter vtroſque: capitulum ſubſequitur rotundum, exiguum; in quo ſemina. radix oblongum & tenuem refert bulbum, ex quo tenues fibræ demittuntur.

In Mutinenſibus & Bononienſibus Italiæ montibus reperiri fertur: Germanis ac Belgis non niſi hortenſis.

Aprili

Fig. 10. Scarlet martagon lily (*Lilium chalcedonicum*) and crown imperial (*Fritillaria imperialis*). R. Dodoens, *Stirpium historia pemptades sex*, Antwerp 1583, p. 202

The academicians sent a letter to Heckius complimenting him on having found this unnamed artist and adding: 'since he will be most useful to the writings of the Lincei, we welcome him into our service; and when you can no longer afford to maintain him yourself, send him to the prince who will support him and give him things to do'.[37]

In time Heckius returned to Rome, but in 1607 he set off again, for Spain, from where he wrote to Stelluti: 'I have with me about one hundred plants gathered in Spain and never before described'.[38] He had also examined a dried herbal of plants from the Americas in the library of the monastery of the Escorial, perhaps part of the collection that was brought to Madrid from Mexico by the physician Francisco Hernández and which would later form the subject of the *Tesoro Messicano* published by the Academy.

In February 1615 Cesi received Heckius once again as a guest at his palace in Acquasparta, but Heckius's mental health was deteriorating. During a meeting of the Lincei held on 24 March 1616 (in which the academicians expressed their solidarity with Galileo, who had just been admonished by the ecclesiastical authorities for supporting the Copernican theory of the universe), they temporarily suspended Heckius's membership 'until he returns to health'.[39] But Heckius was never to return to the academy which he had helped to found thirteen years earlier, and he died, perhaps while staying at the abbey of Sant'Angelo in Capoccia, around the year 1620.

Authorship and structure of the Erbario Miniato

The origins and authorship of the *Erbario Miniato* are undocumented. The manuscript was first studied in 1929 by the great scholar of the early Lincei, Giuseppe Gabrieli, who cautiously thought that he could distinguish the hands of both Cesi and Heckius in the annotations.[40] Sixty years later Francesco Solinas posited two distinct phases of compilation for the *Erbario*, suggesting that the inscriptions of the first phase were corrected by both Cesi and at least two additional hands, one of them possibly being Cassiano's.[41] He later accepted Gabrieli's identification of Cesi as the author of the majority of the inscriptions, without discussing the possible identity of other hands.[42] Recently, David Freedberg also assigned the majority of the inscriptions to Cesi, and followed Gabrieli in hazarding the possible presence of Heckius's 'more distinctively foreign hand' in a few instances, while recording an alternative suggestion that the principal hand may instead be that of Giovanni Battista Winther (Cesi's physician from 1624).[43]

But while there are variations in the character of the inscriptions, these variations seem to be those of a single, informal hand writing at different times, with different pens and inks and at different speeds, rather than evidence of the presence of more than one hand. The bulk of the inscriptions do indeed seem to be in the hand of the young Cesi [Fig. 11], as the scholars cited above have thought, and the additions and alterations to the text are not sufficiently distinct in character to suggest the presence of a second hand in the bound *Erbario*. Only on some of the loose sheets is a different hand clearly visible (e.g. **252**, **259–260**), and – as will be seen – this appears to have been an eighteenth-century scribe recording the original inscriptions when the second volume of the *Erbario* was dismembered. Comparison with the known handwriting of Heckius and Winther rules out the possibility that either was responsible for any of the annotations in the *Erbario*.[44]

The authorship of the drawings is unknown. Several of the Lincei were amateur artists: Heckius observed during a visit to Stelluti in Parma that his host 'drew the illustrations for almost all of his books'.[45] During his travels through northern Europe in 1604–5, Heckius had compiled a series of notebooks entitled *Fructus itineris ad Septentrionales*, the fourth of which, *De vegetabilibus*, contains illustrations of plants, flowers and roots, many drawn by Heckius himself [Fig. 12].[46] Each drawing includes the botanical name of the plant, written in Italian chancery script, and a description of its characteristics (sometimes with citations from Mattioli's *Discorsi*, and information on where the plant had been gathered), written in Dutch in a cursive script. From the evidence of Heckius's drawings in those manuscripts it is clear that he was not the artist of the *Erbario Miniato*, and it is likely that Cesi recruited an artist (or artists) with whom he worked in close collaboration, just as Aldrovandi had during the previous century.

Most of the drawings in the *Erbario* (**1–211**) and from the dismembered volume (**212–277**) were constructed from quick outlines in black chalk or graphite, over which watercolour and bodycolour were applied in a rapid, fluid manner, sometimes with touches in more intense tones to emphasize a particular quality such as the fleshiness of a leaf. The great majority appear to be by a single artist, though a few, such as **160**, **192** and **242a**, are by different hands.

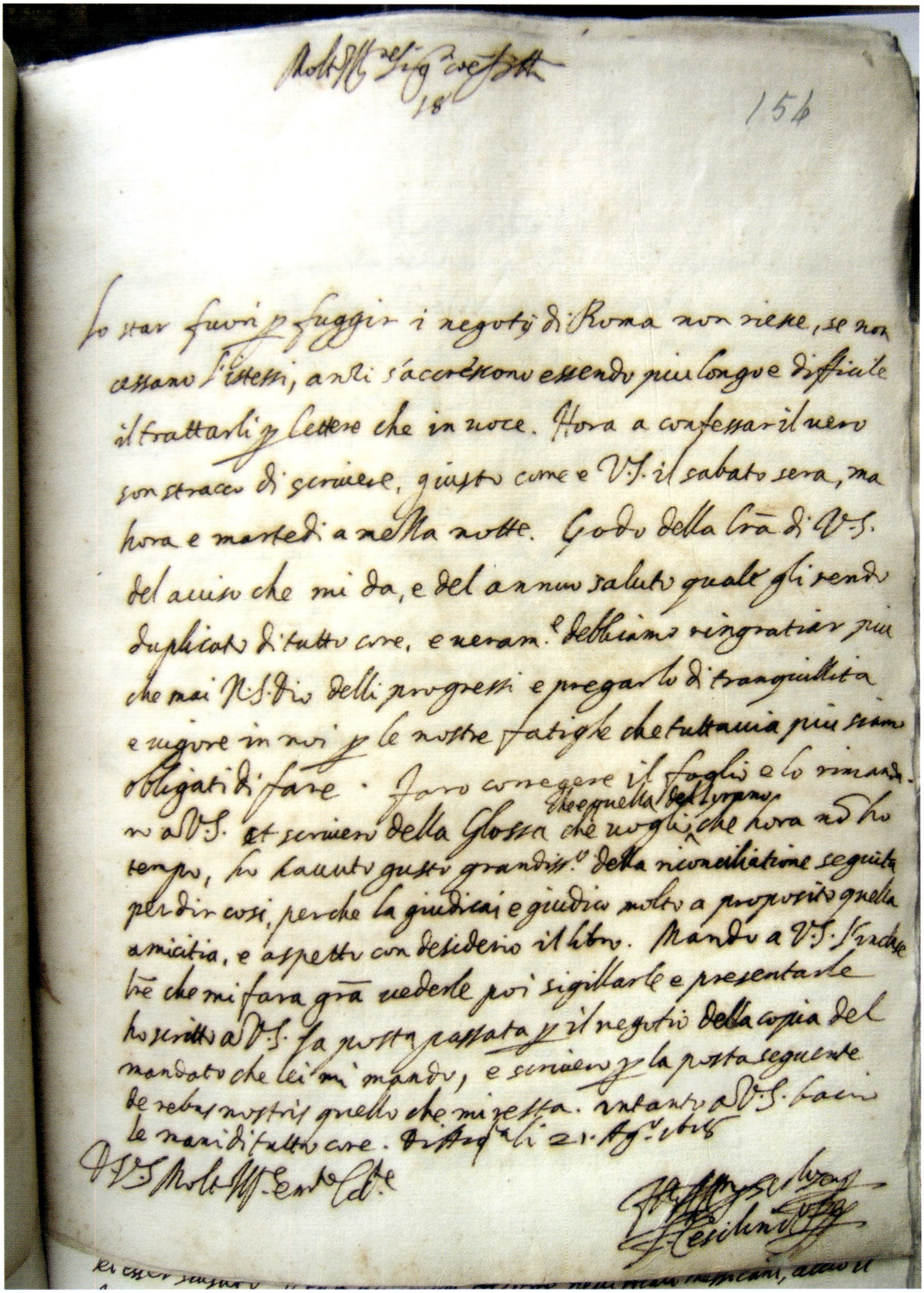

Molto Ill.re Sig.r [illegible]
18
154

Lo star fuori per fuggir i negotii di Roma non riesce, se non cessano l'istessi, anzi s'accrescono essendo piu longo e difficile il trattarli per lettere che in voce. Hora a confessar il vero son stracco di scrivere, giusto come è V.S. il sabato sera, ma hora è martedì a mezza notte. Godo della lettera di V.S. del aviso che mi da, e del annuo saluto quale gli rendo duplicato di tutto core, e veram.te debbiamo ringratiar piu che mai N.S. Dio delli progressi e pregarlo di tranquillità e vigore in noi per le nostre fatighe che tuttavia piu siamo obligati di fare. Farò corregere il foglio e lo rimando a V.S. et scriverò della Glossa che voglio [illegible] che hora non ho tempo, ho hauuto gusto grandiss.o della riconciliatione seguita per dir così, perche la giudicai e giudico molto a proposito quella amicitia, e aspetto con desiderio il libro. Mando a V.S. l'incluse tre che mi farà gratia vederle poi sigillarle e presentarle. ho scritto a V.S. la posta passata per il negotio della copia del mandato che lei mi mandò, e scriverò per la posta seguente de rebus nostris quello che mi resta. Intanto a V.S. bacio le mani di tutto core. D'Acquasparta li 21 Ag.to 1613

Di V.S. Molto Ill.re [illegible]

[illegible]

Fig. 11. Letter by Federico Cesi to Johannes Faber, 21 August 1613. Rome, BANL, Fondo Faber vol. 423, folio 154

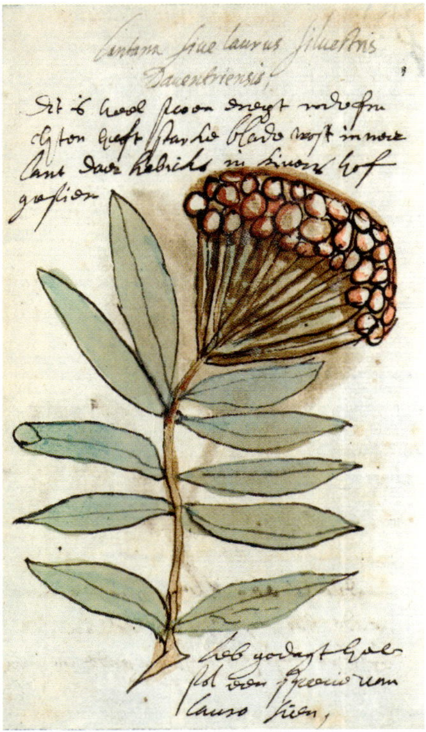

Fig. 12. Laurustinus (*Viburnum tinus*). Johannes van Heck (Heckius), *Fructis itineris ad Septentrionales*, folio 86v. Montpellier, BEM, MS H.507

Solinas suggested that the drawings were produced in two distinct phases, a 'group A' begun in the first years of the century (e.g. **1**, **46** and **74**), and a more sophisticated 'group B', closer to 1620 (e.g. **129**, **246** and **253**).[47] He more recently attributed the drawings of his 'group A' to Cesi himself, *c*. 1610–15 (giving **227**, **231** and **274** as examples), without adducing any comparative material to justify this attribution, while dating three drawings from his 'group B' (**221–223**) to 1615–20.[48] While it is clear that the drawings vary in degree of finish, it does not seem possible to divide them into distinct groups in this way.

The material does, however, seem to have been built up over time before it was bound in its present order, with the inclusion of drawings by other hands, some perhaps received as gifts from fellow naturalists. The compilation of the material may well have begun in the early years of the Lincei. Only one drawing (**242a**) bears a date – 1620 – and that sheet appears to be a later insert into the sequence. Occasionally drawings and parts of drawings were inlaid in the original folios (**199**, **201**), and a few of the folios (**36**, **152**, **248**) are composed of two separate sheets. Parts of a drawing or slips of paper bearing a name were also occasionally cut from other sheets and pasted on to the folios to complete or correct an illustration. The drawing of a peony (**253**) is notable in that the artist depicted a flowering branch of *Paeonia mascula*, while pasted to its base are the roots of *Paeonia officinalis*.

Cesi's annotations record variant names (see, for example, **196**) and medicinal uses of the plants, taken mostly from the 1568 Italian edition of Mattioli's *Discorsi* [Figs 13 and 14], though citing on occasion Tabernaemontanus, Dodoens or Monardes.[49] The inscriptions usually end with the relevant page number of the *Discorsi* and occasionally the words *Matt*, *Mathiolo*, *nel mio Mattiolo*, or, most fully, *nel mio Mattiolo grande* (the reference is to a 'large' Mattioli because the 1568 edition was the lengthiest version of the text available, printed as a pair of massive folios, and physically larger than previous editions). In some cases Cesi wrote *non scritto da Mattiolo* ('not mentioned by Mattioli'), if he could not find the plant in the *Discorsi*. On occasion he would correct himself, as on **65** and **80**, where initial identifications are cancelled or scratched out and superseded by new ones. On **121** the inscription 'my book does not mention it' is struck through and followed by 'page 1297 in my large Mattioli'.

Most of Cesi's citations are of the page in the *Discorsi* bearing the illustration of the relevant plant, rather than the pages carrying the passages from which the inscriptions were copied out. Many of the page citations were added at a later stage and in a different ink, occasionally taken from Mattioli's botanical name index. A sheet depicting a hop ('lupulo'), for example (**112**), carries an incorrect reference to p. 458 of the *Discorsi*; this was taken from the adjacent

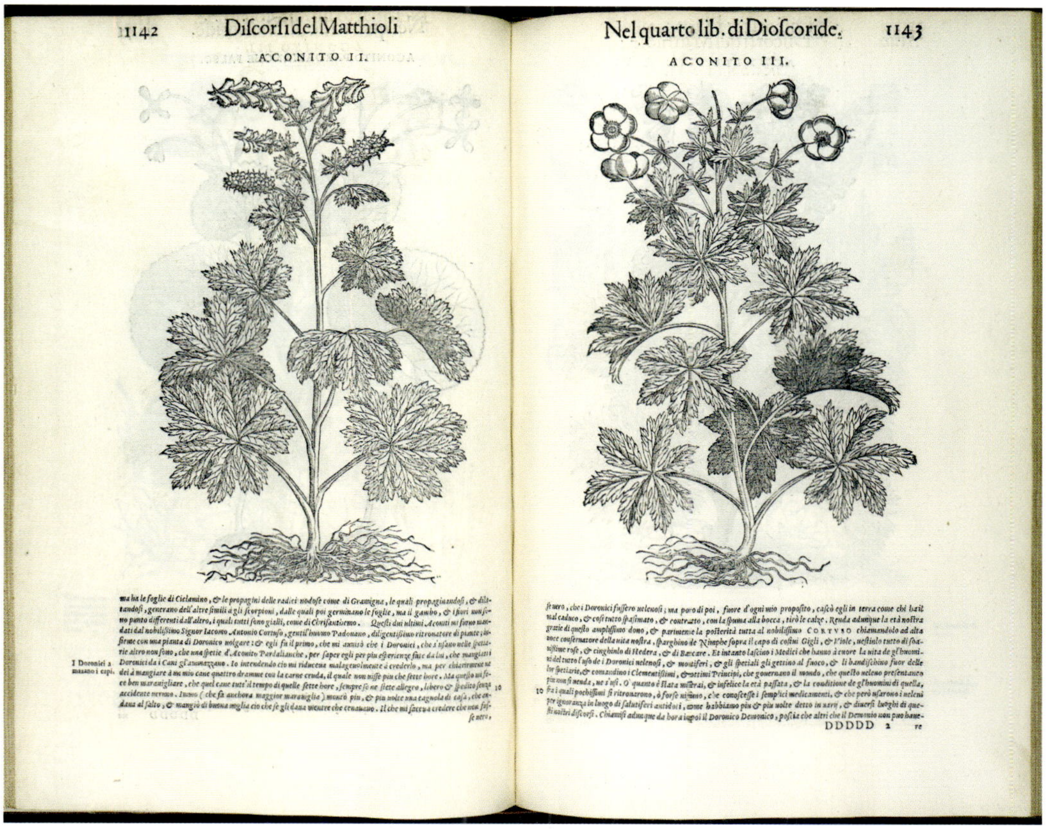

Fig. 13. *Aconitum lycoctonum* and *Ranunculus aconitifolius*. P. A. Mattioli, *I Discorsi*, Venice 1568, pp. 1142–3

entry in Mattioli's index, the lupin ('lupino'), and was subsequently corrected to p. 1273 (where the 'lupulo' is discussed).

The annotations are usually not straightforward transcriptions of passages from the *Discorsi*, but often conflate elements of Dioscorides' text and of Mattioli's commentaries. The inscription on **56**, for example, is taken from p. 1171 of the *Discorsi*. There we read the text of Dioscorides (our underlining):

> *La alsine, la quale chiamano alcuni anthillio, & altri miosota, per rassembrarsi le sue frondi alle orechie de i topi, nasce nelle selve ombrose, & luoghi opachi, dal che è stata chiamata alsine. Sarebbe questa stata la medesima, che l'helsine, se non fusse piu picciola, & non havesse frondi minori, & non pelose. pesta respira odore di cocomero. Ha virtù di ristagnare, & d'infrigidire. Impiastrasi con polenta per le infiammagioni de gli occhi. Il suo succo distillato nell'orecchie, ne cava il dolore, & vale a tutte quelle cose, che l'helsine.*

This is followed by Mattioli's commentary, which begins:

> *Chiamasi l'Alsine in Toscana Centone: della quale se ne veggono però piu spetie, ritrovandosi la maggiore, & la minore, quantunque una sola ne recitasse Dioscoride. Altri la chiamano in Italia Pavarina, altri Pizza gallina, & altri Centonice.*

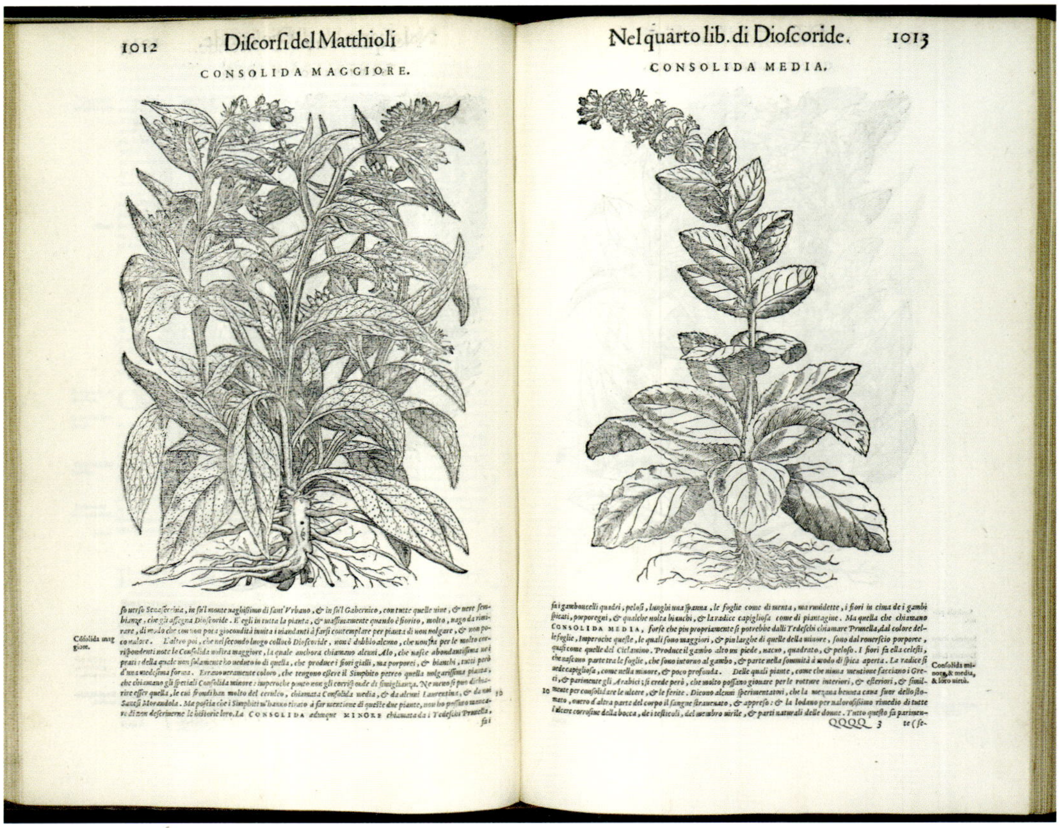

Fig. 14. Common comfrey (*Symphytum officinale*), and pyramid bugle (*Ajuga pyramidalis*). P. A. Mattioli, *I Discorsi*, Venice 1568, pp. 1012–13

The underlined passages in the texts were rearranged to give Cesi's inscription:

> *Alsine. la quale chiamano alcuni Antillio, e' altri miosotta / in Toscana si chiama Centone. altri Pavarina, altri pizza gallina, e' altri Centonice, à virtu de ristagnare. e' infrigidire. impiastrasi con polenta à li infiamagioni de li occhi.*

With one minor exception,[50] the drawings in the bound *Erbario* run in the order in which the plants are found in Mattioli's *Discorsi*, from p. 1112 (on **1**) to p. 1375 (on **157**). Sheet **157**, depicting a bunch of grapes, is the last illustration in the *Erbario Miniato* to cite the *Discorsi* directly; **158** and **159** also bear drawings of grapes and would have been understood as a continuation of **157**, with the inscription 'Agresto' on **159** probably drawn from Mattioli's p. 1379 (the chapter 'Dell'Omphacio, cio è Agresto').

Sheet **159** is the last in the volume to bear an old pen-and-ink foliation at upper right, often fragmentary or absent due to the trimming of the sheets in an early binding operation. From the dozen or so cases where this early foliation is fully visible, it can be seen that it follows the current order of the sheets, from **6**, foliated in ink *463*, to **151**, foliated in ink *577*. But this range of numbers implies that around thirty sheets were inserted into the original pen-and-ink foliated sequence before it was bound (perhaps including the block of drawings of fungi, **33–51**, three of which – **38** and **50–51** – are noteworthy in bearing their annotations turned through

90 degrees). Following these 159 folios that bear (or bore) a pen-and-ink foliation at upper right are a further 52 that bear no ink foliation and do not cite Mattioli (though **165**, **169** and **176** do specify that the plants were *not* to be found in Mattioli), beginning with **160**, the drawing of a Chinese rhubarb that is exceptional in being a direct copy of another work.

Almost all the 211 folios of the bound *Erbario* also bear a small pen-and-ink numeral at upper centre that runs sequentially from *499* to *705* (**78**, **158**, **197** and **211** are unnumbered). These are of the type found throughout the Paper Museum (see p. 14) and were applied while the drawings were in dal Pozzo ownership later in the seventeenth century. The four index sheets at the end of the volume refer to these 'Pozzo' numbers, and the index must therefore have been compiled after the manuscript entered Cassiano's possession. Though neatly written, these indexes are not in the 'scribal' hand found in most of the other indexes to Cassiano's albums (see pp. 13–14).

Among the loose drawings (**212–277**), the citations of Mattioli range from p. 685 (on **213**) to p. 1109 (on **276**). While only seventeen of these cite the *Discorsi* directly, many of the other sheets depict species that do appear in Mattioli, and as these have mostly been cut down, it is possible that annotations were trimmed off. The 'Pozzo' numbering (from *279* to *498*) demonstrates that those sheets citing Mattioli were also arranged in Mattioli page-number order (with other sheets intercalated according to unknown criteria), and they have thus been catalogued here in the order of the surviving 'Pozzo' numbering.

As well as corrections and additions to the annotations, there are other indications that the *Erbario* was compiled over an extended period. There seems to be no pattern to the style of entitling the sheets – the names of the plants are sometimes given in large capitals between ruled lines (and sometimes pasted on to the folio), sometimes written freehand as a single word or phrase, and sometimes as part of an extended annotation. The watermarks are notably varied, indicating that the artist was not gradually working his way through a single stock of paper. The annotations on two sheets reproduce the same passage in Mattioli (**156–157**). Several of the folios bear on their versos offsets of drawings (usually of the graphite or black chalk outlines) that are no longer adjacent. In some cases it is clear that a sheet has been inserted: **24** has on its verso an offset of **26**, and it seems that the reference to Mattioli on **25** was added some time after the main body of the inscription. Drawing **119** has on its verso an offset of **121**; **120** is annotated *no*[*n*] *scritta dal Matiolo* and so did not form part of Cesi's original sequence in Mattioli order, but being a 'Spetie de Ginestra' it was eventually placed after **119**, a 'Genestra' found in Mattioli. In other cases the offsets are evidence of a more radical reorganizing: for example, the verso of **120** has an offset from **195**; an offset of the graphite outlines of **206** is found on the verso of both **184** and (less strongly) **203**; and conversely **203** has on its verso offsets of both **206** and **211**.

Also suggestive of an earlier arrangement is an inked numbering of the form *No. 43* (as on **65**) at the bottom of thirteen of the folios in the bound *Erbario* (and presumably trimmed off some of the dispersed sheets). The numbers range between 4 and 59 and are now in no order.[51] Their significance has not been elucidated: they may reflect the order of the first wave of material before a concordance with Mattioli was established, or may have been a concordance with some other reference material used by Cesi.

While many of the loose drawings (**212–277**) bear annotations in the hand recognizable as Cesi's in the bound *Erbario*, five of the sheets (**242, 246, 252, 259–260**) are annotated in whole or in part by a later, apparently eighteenth-century hand. These later annotations seem to make an attempt to emulate the handwriting of the original annotations, and are probably conscientious records of earlier inscriptions that had been excised when the sheets were cut down. The 'Pozzo' numbers on most of the loose sheets are also in this later hand, and in several cases we find both the original 'Pozzo' number and the same number repeated by the later hand. The cutting down of these sheets probably occurred when the drawings were mounted for George III, though why one volume was dismembered and the other allowed to remain intact is unknown.

All the cut-down sheets were mounted on the pages of George III's *Natural History* volumes, of which five survive at Windsor (see pp. 2, 12ff). 'Inventory A' of *c.* 1810 (see p. 8) lists six *Natural History* volumes dedicated to *Plants* (nos VIII to XIII), containing a total of 366 folios. These were sold from the Royal Library in the early twentieth century and their contents dispersed (see pp. 2–3). It is very likely that the 83 drawings catalogued here as **212–293** were contained within these volumes, suggesting that as many as 284 botanical drawings formerly at Windsor remain untraced.

In summary, therefore, it appears that there were originally three volumes of the *Erbario Miniato*. The third of these is the surviving *Erbario Miniato* volume at Windsor (**1–211**), with 'Pozzo' numbers from *499* to *705* and covering the species found in Mattioli from pp. 1112 to 1375. The second volume bore 'Pozzo' numbers from around *279* to *498*, and covered plants in the *Discorsi* from around pages 681 to 1111. The pages of this album were cut down in the eighteenth century and remounted for George III; most of the drawings were sold and dispersed in the early twentieth century and sixty-seven have since been identified (**212–277**). A putative first volume, bearing 'Pozzo' numbers up to about *275* and covering plants up to around p. 680 of the *Discorsi*, is wholly untraced and probably did not enter the Royal Collection. It may have remained in the Albani collection along with other Paper Museum material retained by Cardinal Albani, and since dispersed or destroyed.[52]

Most of the sixteen loose botanical drawings catalogued here that are not part of the *Erbario Miniato* group (**278–293**) were probably executed for Cassiano or his brother, Carlo Antonio dal Pozzo, many years after the *Erbario*. Over half bear 'Pozzo' numbers from a distinct but highly fragmentary sequence, ranging from *216* to *984* (**278–288**). Several may be attributed to Vincenzo Leonardi (*fl.* 1621–46; see pp. 15–16), including a number of teratological specimens which were much prized by collectors of the period. Drawings **285–286** and **291**, depicting a red cabbage and an anomalous inflorescence of broccoli, are by a distinct hand whose identity is not known. It is conceivable that these works were by a later artist commissioned by Cassiano or Carlo Antonio after the death of Leonardi (at an unknown date, but after the mid-1640s), to work in his style for the Paper Museum. The pen-and-ink study of a deformed artichoke (*Cynara scolymus*, **293**) is close in style to the work of the artist who executed the drawings of fossil woods for Cesi that also passed to Cassiano.[53]

The species depicted

Unfortunately the total loss of a putative first volume and the dispersal and partial loss of a second prevent us from forming a precise idea of the original contents of the collection as a whole.[54] Among the 293 drawings catalogued here, 239 species can be identified (including 17 species of fungi), 190 of which grow spontaneously in Italy.[55] Most of the plants are 'simples' which were included in Dioscorides' treatise and in the *Erbario* because of their supposed pharmacological properties. Three of the plants are endemic to Italy – *Cymbalaria pallida* (**63**), *Centaurea centaurium* (**215**) and *Pulmonaria vallarsae* (**271**). About twenty may be considered garden forms, whether derived from native European or from exotic species, and thirty-seven exotic species are represented. In six cases the subspecies or botanical variety has been identified (**26**, **70**, **111**, **272**, **285** and **291**).

About sixty of the plants were widely cultivated in the seventeenth century for human consumption, as animal fodder, or as sources of substances ranging from cosmetic ingredients to dyes and flavourings. No fewer than six cultivated varieties of the artichoke (**222–226** and **284**) and four varieties of the grape (**156–159**) are illustrated, together with two cabbage varieties (**285–286** and **291**), and the exotic pineapple (**279**) and cashew (**288**). Also included are about thirty-seven ornamental species, ranging from bulbous flowering plants (*Muscarimia*, *Lilium*, *Convallaria*, *Fritillaria*, *Sternbergia* spp.) to herbaceous (*Delphinium*, *Antirrhinum*, *Mirabilis*, *Matthiola* spp.) and woody species (cedar, holly and yew). Of interest are three anomalous specimens – two Scotch or pot marigolds, the 'Calta pulianta' (**151**) and the 'Calendola prolifera II' (**193**), and a stock or gillyflower (*Matthiola* sp., **188**) – that appear to have flowers growing directly out of other flowers.

While the inscriptions are mainly (though not solely) concerned with the medicinal properties of the plants, the purpose of the illustrations was strictly botanical. This is especially evident in drawings which show the entire plant complete with its roots[56] and others that illustrate the flowers or fruit at various stages of development.[57] A drawing of the hop (**112**) is unusual in that it represents the plant as a 'bouquet' rather than in its natural state. Also noteworthy are the drawings of a twig from a pear tree (**278**), with cut sections of the fruit depicted below, and of a branch loaded with fruit which appear to be medlars (**282**).

A few botanical errors can be identified. The flowers of the red nightshade (**15**) are drawn with six petals instead of five, and the flowers of the red hemp-nettle (**101**) are shown growing from short pedicels when they are actually sessile. The annual mercury (**146**) is illustrated with both its male and female flowers, but the annotation confuses them. In about a dozen instances the annotation mistakenly identifies a plant on the basis of Mattioli's text. For example, the red dead-nettle (*Lamium purpureum*, **65**) is identified as the 'Ortica seconda' on p. 1184 of the *Discorsi*, whereas Mattioli's plant is actually a specimen of *Urtica dioica*, and a narcissus (**125**) is mistakenly identified as the *Pancratium maritimum* found on p. 1303. Similar errors were made with the lesser burdock (*Arctium minus*, **75**); the ribbed melilot or yellow sweet clover (*Melilotus officinalis*, **82** – the inscription at first correctly identified the plant as the 'Loto domestico' illustrated on p. 1221 of the *Discorsi*, but was later changed to 'Loto salvatico', illustrated on p. 1222); the milfoil or yarrow (*Achillea millefolium*,

83); and the drooping brome (*Bromus tectorum*, **106**) and goat grass (*Aegilops neglecta*, **107**), the latter two being simple grasses whose identification posed a genuine challenge.

There is no attempt to categorize the plants in the terms familiar from Galen, who classified simples according to their qualities (cold/warm, wet/dry, and so on) so that they could be used in combination to achieve the right balance of qualities for the particular ailment. It has been argued that Dioscorides' work was thus demoted into a textbook of raw materials rather than a manual for medical practice itself.[58] In the sixteenth century, Paracelsus (Theophrastus von Hohenheim, 1493–1541) campaigned against Galenic medicine, proclaiming that all simples were themselves in fact complex, and that attention ought to focus on the specific qualities of the individual substances, rather than their use in combination.[59] The Lincei proclaimed an allegiance to Paracelsus ('dedicated to the Paracelsian disciplines'),[60] and it is unsurprising that Cesi should have relied on Mattioli, whose aim was the correct identification of plants and the description of their specific medicinal qualities.

There are also no direct references in the *Erbario Miniato* to the doctrine of signatures, according to which the physical form of certain plants reflected the part of the body on which they would act (for example, the walnut, whose surface resembles the brain, as a specific for brain diseases).[61] One of the major proponents of the doctrine, Giovanni Battista della Porta (*c.* 1535–1615), was inducted into the Accademia dei Lincei in his latter years, but the *Erbario Miniato* says nothing about such matters.

Cesi's later botanical work

In the years after the compilation of the *Erbario Miniato*, Cesi was to embark on still more ambitious programmes of botanical illustration. The preparation of the *Tesoro Messicano* [Fig. 15] (see pp. 15, 17–19) engaged him for much of the rest of his life. Around 1611 Cesi commissioned Isabella Parasole to prepare engravings for a *Libro dell'herbe*,[62] and in December of that year Markus Welser wrote from Augsburg to his fellow Linceo in Rome, Johannes Faber, of the imminent publication of Basilius Besler's monumental *Hortus Eystettensis* [Fig. 16], commenting that 'apart from the charm of its copper engravings, for curiosity and for every other consideration it cannot be compared to the volume of the Most Excellent Marquis Cesi'. Cesi's work on the *Tesoro* clearly attracted much attention: in May 1612, Galileo – also a Linceo – wrote to Pietro Dini, Bishop of Fermo:

> In the past few days, when I was in the house of my lord, the Most Illustrious and Excellent Marquis Cesi, I saw the pictures of 500 Indian plants, and doubted that they could be real; and even if they were, might one not affirm that they were perhaps vain and superfluous, since neither I nor any of the others around me knew their qualities, virtues and effects?[63]

A few years later, around 1618, Cesi hired the German engraver Giorgio Nuvolstella 'to engrave the figures of the animals for the book on Mexico'.[64] The first, incomplete edition of the *Tesoro Messicano* was published in 1628, and the monumental undertaking (which also

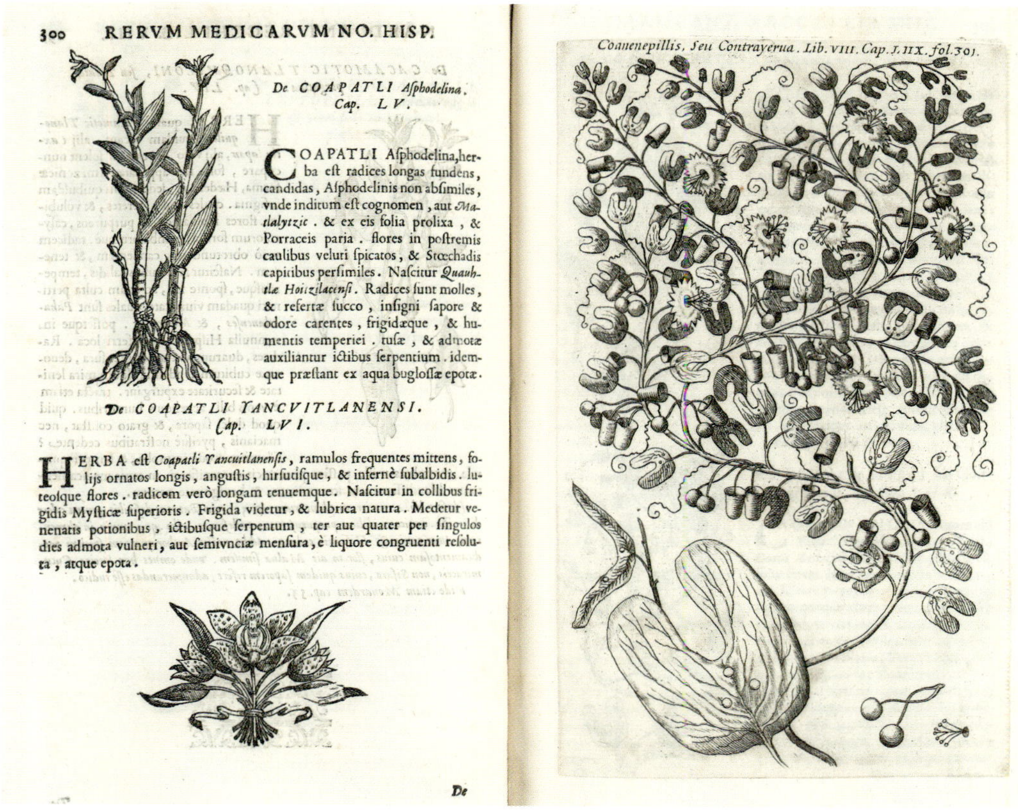

Fig. 15. Dayflower (*Commelina* sp.), *Stanhopea tigrina*, and Mexican passionflower (*Passiflora mexicana*). F. Hernández, *Rerum medicarum Novae Hispaniae thesaurus*, Rome 1651, pp. 300–1

included much non-botanical material) was completed only in 1651 thanks to the efforts of Cesi's successors, especially Cassiano and Stelluti, long after his death in 1630.

The first edition of the *Tesoro Messicano* also included a part of Cesi's proposed system of classification, the *Tabulae Phytosophicae . . . seu rei herbariae syntaxis* (see pp. 16–17), the objective of which was to establish the foundations of a science of plants, or *phytosophia*. This emerges clearly from the index to the *Tabulae*, which ranges from the *substantia* (substance) to the *vita, vires, usus, energia . . . partes, diversitas, nomina* ('life, properties, uses, energy, parts . . . differences, names') of plants, without neglecting their symbolic and emblematic meanings. The twentieth *Tabula* was devoted to the *phytoiatria* or medicinal uses of plants. The complex schemata, abounding in learned citations, diagrams, cross-references and parentheses, were accompanied by lengthy digressions in which Cesi demonstrated his learning, both literary and scientific. There are numerous references to the works of Pliny, Virgil, Theophrastus, Galen and Dioscorides, as well as to Mattioli. Of the twenty *Tabulae*, the first twelve and part of the thirteenth – all dedicated to the classification of plants – were published in the 1628 edition of the *Tesoro Messicano*, and the complete version, revised by Stelluti, in the 1651 edition.[65]

Many of the plants portrayed in the *Erbario Miniato* were incorporated into the *Tabulae*'s complex system. There is a reference to the 'cardo mostruoso di Imperato' (see **293**) in the sixth

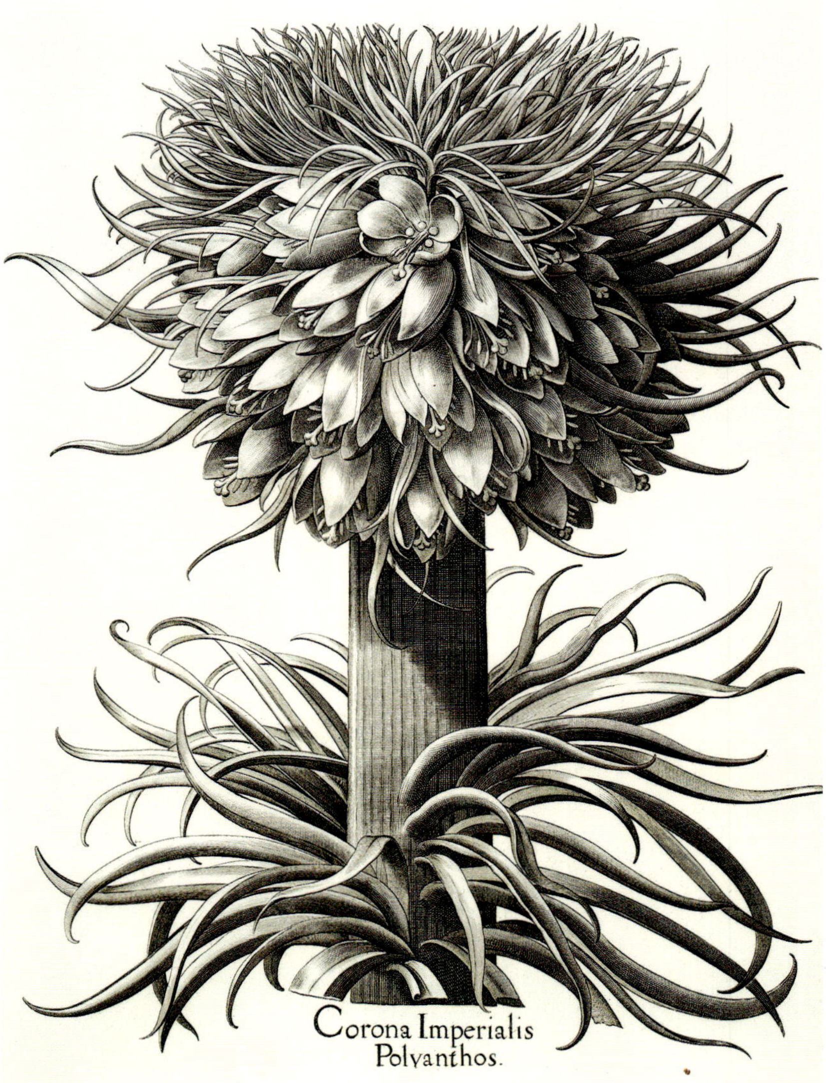

Fig. 16. Crown imperial (*Fritillaria imperialis*). B. Besler, *Hortus Eystettensis*, Nuremberg 1613

Tabula [Fig. 17], where the peony, amaranth, anemone and tulip are also mentioned, providing the opportunity for some reflections on the surprising variations in colour that a single species may exhibit.[66] The subject of botanical illustration is raised in *Tabula* 19, where Cesi remarks on the role played by illustrated herbals, even antiquated ones, in a scholar's studies: 'There lie hidden in the corners of old libraries manuscripts from which one may retrace the vestiges of antique plants.'[67] He goes on to observe that artists seem unable to resist prettifying whatever plant they have been asked to draw, a tendency, he says, that must be understood and forgiven.[68]

The extent of Cesi's reliance on illustrations (as well as the standard reference works) for his classificatory work on the *Tabulae* is made clear in a letter of 1622 to Faber:

> The commentaries of Tabernaemontanus and Bauhin on Mattioli that you lent me have been of great use and assistance in the course of my revision of this uncountable army

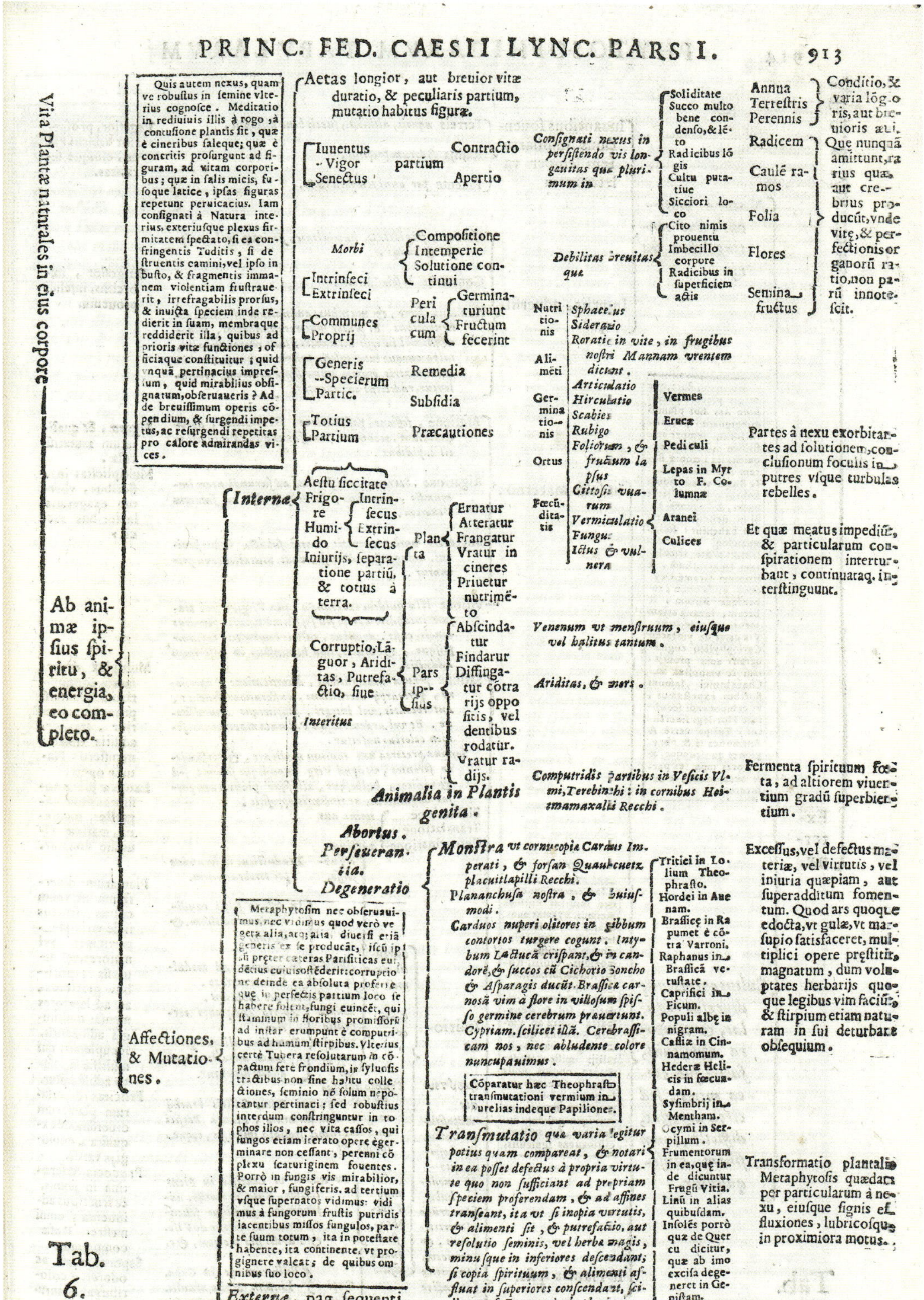

PRINC. FED. CAESII LYNC. PARS I. 913

Vita Plantæ naturales in eius corpore

Quis autem nexus, quam ve robustus in semine vlterius cognosce. Meditatio in rediuiuis illis à rogo, à contusione plantis fit, quæ è cineribus saleque; quæ è concretis prosurgunt ad figuram, ad vitam corporibus; quæ in salis micis, fusoque latice, ipsas figuras repetunt peruicacius. Iam consignati à Natura interius, exteriusque plexus firmitatem spectato, si ea confringentis Tuditis, si de struentis camini, vel ipso in busto, & fragmentis immanem violentiam frustrauerit, irrefragabilis prorsus, & inuicta speciem inde redierit in suam, membraque reddiderit illa, quibus ad prioris vitæ functiones, of ficiaque constituitur; quid vnquã pertinacius impressum, quid mirabilius obsignatum, obseruaueris? Ad de breuissimum operis cõpendium, & surgendi impetus, ac resurgendi repetitas pro calore admirandas vices.

Aetas longior, aut breuior vitæ duratio, & peculiaris partium, mutatio habitus figuræ.

Iuuentus, Vigor, Senectus — partium — Contractio, Apertio

Morbi — Compositione, Intemperie, Solutione continui

Intrinseci, Extrinseci

Communes, Proprij — Pericula cum — Germinaturiunt, Fructum fecerint

Generis, Specierum, Partic. — Remedia, Subsidia

Totius, Partium — Præcautiones

Ab animæ ipsius spiritu, & energia, eo completo.

Interna — Aestu siccitate, Frigore, Humido — Intrinsecus, Extrinsecus; Iniurijs, separatione partiũ, & totius à terra.

Planta — Eruatur, Atteratur, Frangatur, Vratur in cineres, Priuetur nutrimẽto

Pars ipsius — Abscindatur, Findatur, Diffingatur cõtra rijs oppositis, vel dentibus rodatur. Vratur radijs.

Corruptio, Languor, Ariditas, Putrefactio, siue Interitus

Animalia in Plantis genita.

Abortus. Perseuerantia. Degeneratio

Affectiones, & Mutationes.

Metaphytosim nec obseruauimus, nec vidimus quod verò vegeta alia, atq; alia diuersi eiũ generis ex se producat, iscũ ip ... præter cæteras Parisiticas eui... dictus cuiuis ... corruptio ... deinde ea absoluta proferre ... quæ in perfectis partium loco se habere solent, fungi euincẽt, qui staminum in floribus promissori ad instar erumpunt è compuctibus ad humum stirpibus. Vlterius certè Tubera resolutarum in cõpactum ferè frondium, in syluosis tractibus non sine habitu collectiones, seminio nõ solum nepotantur pertinaci; sed robustius interdum constringuntur in tophos illos, nec vita cassos, qui fungos etiam iterato opere egerminare non cessant, perenni cõ plexu scaturiginem fouentes. Porrò in fungis vis mirabilior, & maior, fungiferis. ad tertium vsque supernatos vidimus: vidimus à fungorum frustis putridis iacentibus missos fungulos, parte suum totum, ita in potestate habente, ita continente, vt progignere valeat; de quibus omnibus suo loco.

Externa. pag. sequenti.

Consignati nexus in persistendo vis longæuitas quæ pluri-mum in — Soliditate, Succo multo bene condenso, & lẽto, Radicibus lõgis, Cultu putatiue, Sicciori loco

Debilitas breuitas quæ — Cito nimis prouentu, Imbecillo corpore, Radicibus in superficiem actis

Annua, Terrestris, Perennis — Radicem, Caulẽ ramos, Folia, Flores, Semina fructus — Conditio, & varia lõgioris, aut breuioris æui. Quę nunquã amittunt, rarius quæ, aut crebrius producũt, vnde vitę, & perfectionis organorũ ratio, non parũ innotescit.

Nutritionis — Sphacelus, Sideratio, Roratio in vite, in frugibus nostri Mannam vrentem dicunt.

Alimenti — Articulatio, Hirculatio

Germinationis — Scabies, Rubigo, Foliorum, & fructuum la ... plus

Ortus — Cittosis vuarum, Vermiculatio

Fœcunditatis — Fungus, Ictus & vulnera

Vermes, Erucæ, Pediculi, Lepas in Myrto F. Columnæ, Aranei, Culices

Partes à nexu exorbitantes ad solutionem, conclusionum foculis in putres vsque turbulas rebelles.

Et quæ meatus impediũt, & particularum conspirationem intercurbant, continuataq. interstinguunt.

Venenum vt menstruum, eiusque vel halitus tantum.

Ariditas, & mors.

Computridis partibus in Vesicis Vlmi, Terebinthi: in cornibus Hoitzmamaxalli Recchi.

Fermenta spirituum fœta, ad altiorem viuentium gradũ superbientium.

Monstra vt cornucopia Cardui Imperati, & forsan Quauhcuetz placuitlapilli Recchi. Plananchusa nostra, & huiusmodi. Carduos nuperi olitores in gibbum contortos turgere cogunt. Intybum Lactucã crispant, & in candorẽ, & succos cũ Cichorio Soncho & Asparagis ducũt. Brassica carnosã vim à flore in villosum spisso germine cerebrum præuertunt. Cyprium. scilicet illã. Cerebrassicam nos, nec abludente colore nuncupauimus.

Cõparatur hæc Theophrasto transmutationi vermium in Aurelias indeque Papiliones.

Transmutatio quæ varia legitur potius quam compareat, & notari in ea posset defectus à propria virtute quo non sufficiant ad propriam speciem proferendam, & ad affines transeant, ita vt si inopia virtutis, & alimenti fit, & putrefactio, aut resolutio seminis, vel herba magis, minusque in inferiores descendant; si copia spirituum, & alimenti affluat in superiores conscendant, scilicet perfectas magis, & pleniores.

Tritici in Lolium Theophrasto. Hordei in Auenam. Brassicę in Rapum et cõtra Varroni. Raphanus in Brassicã vetustate. Caprifici in nigram. Populi albę in nigram. Cassiæ in Cinnamomum. Hederæ Helicis in fœcundam. Sysimbrij in Mentham. Ocymi in Serpillum. Frumentorum in ea, quę inde dicuntur Frugũ Vitia. Linũ in alias quibusdam. Insolẽs porrò quæ de Quercu dicitur, quæ ab imo excisa degeneret in Genistam.

Excessus, vel defectus materiæ, vel virtutis, vel iniuria quæpiam, aut superadditum fomentum. Quod ars quoque edocta, vt gulæ, vt maximo stupio satisfaceret, multiplici opere prestitit, magnatum, dum voluptates herbarijs quoque legibus vim faciũt, & stirpium etiam naturam in sui deturbare obsequium.

Transformatio plantalis Metaphytosis quædam per particularum à nexu, eiusque signis efluxiones, lubricosque in proximiora motus.

Tab. 6.

Hhhh

Fig. 17. *Tabula Phytosophica* 6, in F. Hernández, *Rerum medicarum Novae Hispaniae thesaurus*, Rome 1651, p. 913

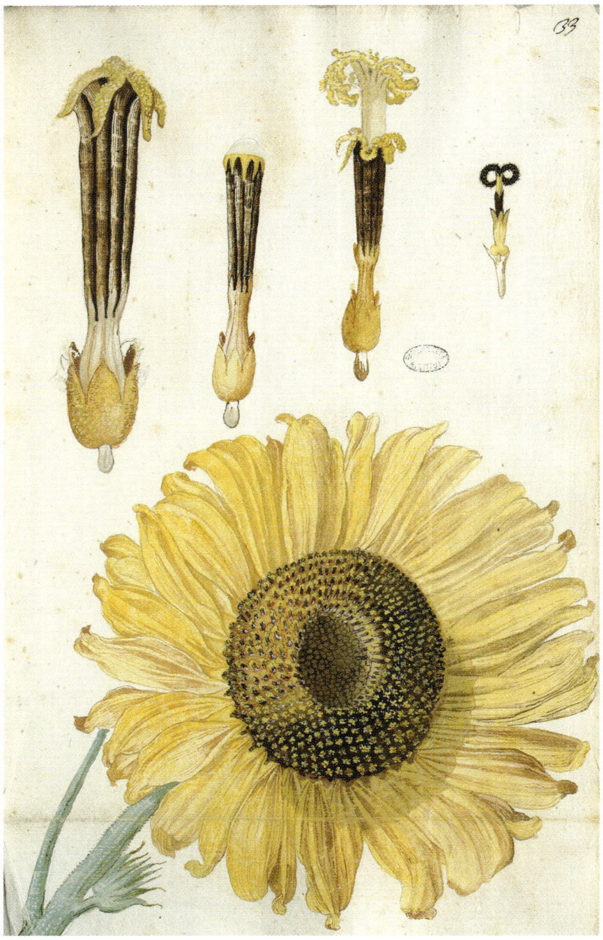

Fig. 18. Sunflower (*Helianthus annuus*). Paris, BIF, MS 975, folio 33

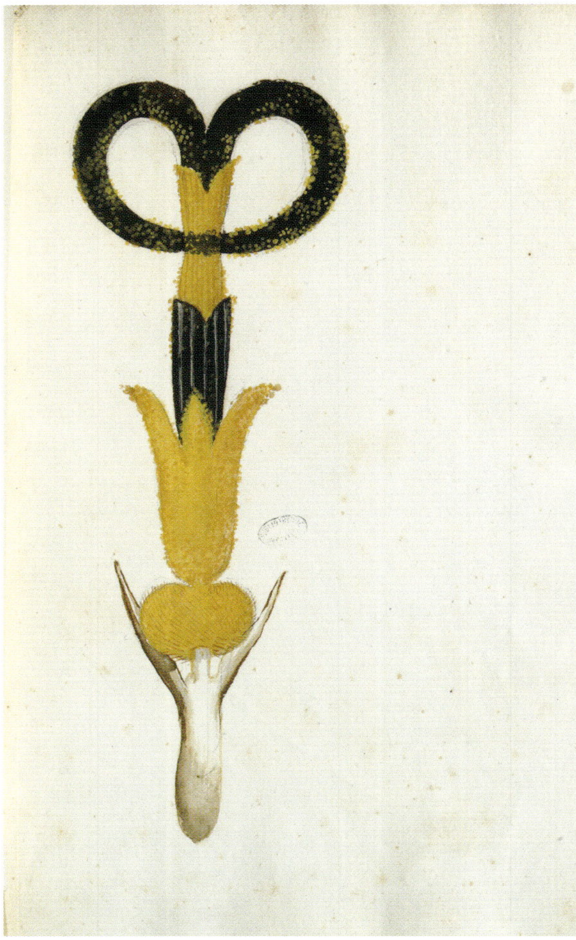

Fig. 19. Details of a sunflower (*Helianthus annuus*). Paris, BIF, MS 975, folio 34

> of plants; but the most convenient in terms of placing and ordering so huge a plantation would be Lobelius's two volumes of pictures of plants, the *Icones Lobellianae*, as an aid to memory; [I would like to] cut up all the pictures and place them in the manner you know . . . ; so please get me two unbound copies of these books . . . of the best edition that can be found.[69]

By this time, Cesi was compiling a new collection of drawings, eight volumes of which also passed into the collection of Cassiano dal Pozzo and are now conserved in the Bibliothèque de l'Institut de France in Paris. Rediscovered only recently and first brought to notice in 1980, these volumes – three devoted to fungi (see Part B.II of the present catalogue series) and five mostly to plants and flowers (Part B.VII, forthcoming) – constitute an astonishing corpus of about 1,900 drawings.[70] Their subjects are depicted in minute detail, frequently from more than one angle and sometimes as observed through a microscope.[71] Cesi had been sent his microscope by none other than Galileo, who wrote in a celebrated letter of 23 September 1624: 'I am sending Your Excellency a little glass to see the minutest things close up, which I hope

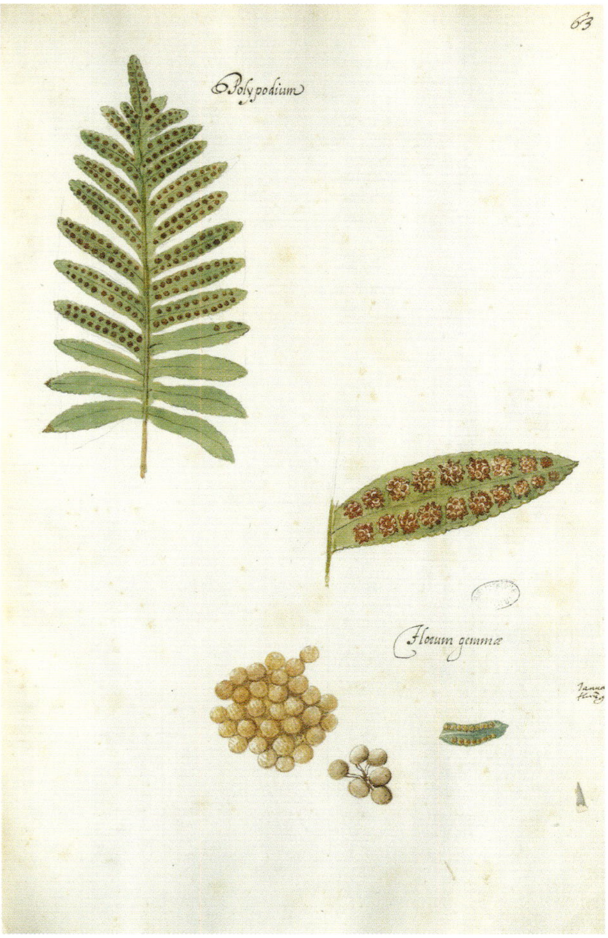

Fig. 20. Wall fern (probably *Polypodium vulgare*). Paris, BIF, MS 976, folio 63

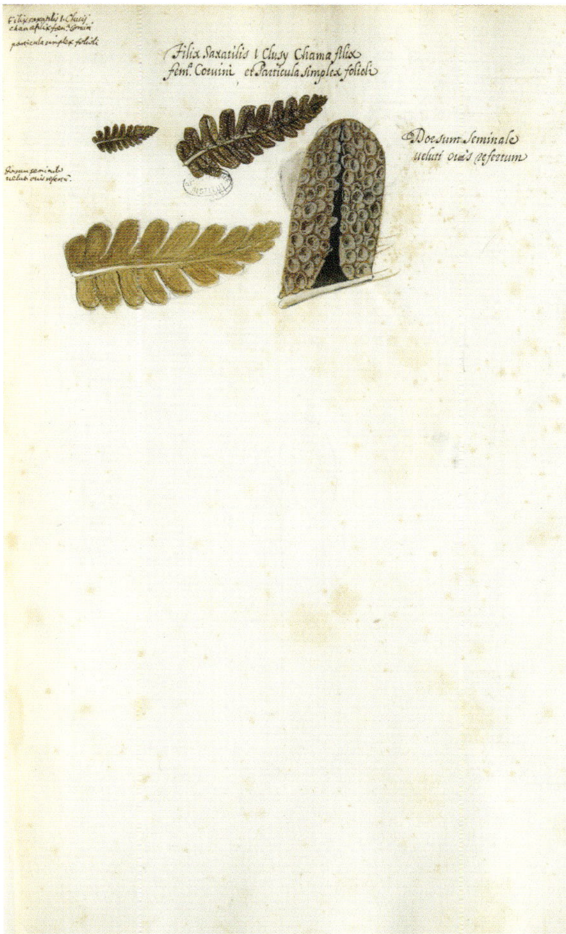

Fig. 21. Details of a fern (probably *Polypodium vulgare*). Paris, BIF, MS 976, folio 64

that you will take no small pleasure in using, as I have. I put off dispatching it to you until I had first brought it to perfection, having experienced difficulty in finding the way to finish the crystal lenses perfectly'.[72]

The eagerness with which Cesi turned the lens of this 'little glass' (*occhialino*) on his botanical specimens is evident throughout the pages of the Paris manuscripts. These bear frequent notes by Cesi describing the plant and its habitat, usually the countryside around his ancestral home at Acquasparta or one of the many private gardens in Rome where exotic plants were cultivated, though no observations are made on medicinal usage. Occasionally the season and the date on which the specimen had been gathered are mentioned, the earliest year being 1623 and the latest 1628. Some drawings of dissected insects examined under the microscope are also scattered amongst these pages. Produced by a number of talented artists whose identity remains to be established,[73] the Paris drawings employ a virtuoso technique quite unlike that used in the *Erbario Miniato*, which instead had adopted an economical approach intended to capture the most obvious identifying characteristics of the plants. While the illustrations in the *Erbario* often show isolated leaves, flowers and so on as an aid to identification, the detail in the Paris manuscripts is of a wholly different order. Many of the plants that appear in the *Erbario Miniato* are also depicted in the Paris manuscripts, but the two bodies of drawings have little else in common. Two examples will suffice to illustrate these differences.

If we compare the sunflower (*Helianthus annuus*, **196**) in the *Erbario Miniato* with the studies of the same plant on folios 33 and 34 of Paris MS 975 [Figs 18 and 19], it becomes clear that in the *Erbario* the artist has merely sought to capture the general appearance of the flower head without conveying any of the details of its complicated structure. In contrast, attention has been devoted in the Paris drawings to the various types of flowers making up the centre and the surrounding rings of the capitulum. Some of the details recorded by the artist could have been seen only with the aid of a magnifying glass or a microscope; these include the ovary, the basal sections of the still immature anthers, marked with dark striations, the bifid, reflexed-arcuate stigma whose two apices touch one another, and the grains of pollen scattered over the stigma and other surfaces.

A fern (probably *Polypodium vulgare*) is likewise illustrated in both the *Erbario Miniato* (**143**) and the Paris corpus (MS 976, fols 63 and 64). Once again the *Erbario* drawing provides the characteristic form of the plant's frond and root, whereas in the later manuscript [Figs 20 and 21] the polypodium's unusual reproductive structures – which were invisible to the naked eye and therefore unknown to botanists before the advent of the microscope – are carefully documented. The pedicelled sporangia and tiny sori (spore-producing receptacles) are depicted in these sheets, while folio 65 shows the unusual spore-producing structures of other ferns with a detail that could only have been obtained from painstaking microscopic studies.

The two sets of drawings reflect different periods of Cesi's botanical investigations. There is little to link the *Erbario Miniato* with the theoretical framework and natural philosophy developed in the *Tabulae* (which articulated the notion of the 'botanist-mathematician', echoing the Galilean concept of a universe 'expressed in the language of mathematics'),[74] and similarly none of the probing into the anatomy of plants that is found in the Paris manuscripts. The *Erbario* grew out of the young botanist's desire to acquaint himself with the known flora of Italy and its medicinal applications. The Paris manuscripts document the work of a mature scientist, in which the conventions of the herbal tradition and its emphasis on *materia medica* are abandoned. Identification and naming are merely the starting points for an enquiry whose chief concern is the desire to understand not only the form but also the function of different plant structures. The entirely new visual language that informs these drawings is as distant from the *Erbario* as it is from the elaborate flower books of the period, such as the florilegium produced in 1639 by the artist Francesco Mingucci for Cardinal Francesco Barberini, patron of Cassiano (see p. 1) and himself a member of the Accademia dei Lincei.[75]

The aim of this exuberant work was to document the most spectacular flowers – particularly rare bulbous species – that could be found in the gardens of the cardinal and other wealthy families in Rome. Cesi's Paris manuscripts, by contrast, show the plants and flowers not in all their flamboyant beauty, but dissected and magnified for the penetrating gaze of the Lincei, thus laying the foundations for the modern science of botany.

NOTES

1 On the *Erbario Miniato* see especially Gabrieli 1929; Solinas 1989; *Cassiano* cat. 1993, pp. 190–200; *Cassiano* cat. 1997, pp. 31–3; Freedberg 2002, pp. 195–218.
2 On the influence of Galen, see Temkin 1973.
3 Vienna, Österreichische Nationalbibliothek, MS Med. Gr. 1; Blunt/Raphael 1989, pp. 14–21; Tongiorgi Tomasi 1994; Lack 2001, pp. 22–31.
4 Rome, Biblioteca Casanatense, MS 459.
5 London, BL, Egerton 2020.
6 Venice, Biblioteca Nazionale Marciana, MS lat. VI, 59.
7 Arber 1986, p. 70.
8 Ibid, p. 76. The illustrations to Tabernaemontanus's *Eicones plantarum* were not original, having been borrowed from various sources, including Fuchs, Bock, Mattioli, Dodoens, Clusius and Lobelius. The woodblocks were borrowed by the English printer John Norton, who used them to illustrate the first edition of John Gerard's *Herball*.
9 Ferri 1997, pp. 17–18.
10 *veramente non manco utile che necessaria*: Mattioli 1544.
11 *Adiuvit nos quoque mirum in modum Georgius Liberalis homo in artis pingendi peritissimus et post ipsum Volfang Meierpeck Misnesis, qui dum assidue plantarum et animalium imagines delinearent, nulli quidem labori, ac diligentiae pepercerunt* ('We were helped in an excellent fashion by Giorgio Liberale, most skilful in the art of painting and, after him, by Wolfang Meyerpeck of Meissen, [both of] whom assiduously drew images of the plants and animals, sparing themselves neither effort nor diligence'): Mattioli, *Commentarii, Epistula Nuncupatoria*, 1565, no pagination. Meyerpeck prepared the woodblock engravings together with the wood engraver Georg van Sichem of Basle. Another engraver, Hans Minich, collaborated on the Bohemian edition of the work. See also Tongiorgi Tomasi 1997, p. 367, and Lenzi 1997, p. 92. Liberale accompanied Mattioli to Prague, where he had gone on the accession of his patron to the imperial throne; Mattioli reported with great satisfaction that 'his painter' *di continuo disegna figure grandi di piante e animali, tanto belle quanto possa far la natura* ('is continually drawing large figures of plants and animals, as beautiful as anything Nature could create'). These drawings first appeared in the 1562 edition of the *Discorsi*, published in German with the collaboration of Georg Handsch: see Raimondi 1906, p. 33, and Blunt/Raphael 1989.
12 From the deed of sale of the dal Pozzo library to Cardinal Alessandro Albani by Clement XI, 1714: Archivio di Stato di Roma, Notai RCA Tartaglia, vol. 1962, fol. 19.
13 13 April 1626: *Ho visto con mio grandissimo gusto il Matthiolo miniato da V.S. Ill.ma, opera invero degnissima et curiosissima, che di certo credo non si trovi cosa simile in Europa, con tanta finezza sono fatti l'intagli, et con tanta naturalezza fu dato il colore alle piante; quelle che mancano, della quale bona parte habbiamo a Roma, faremo che di mano in mano si dia la miniatura e si compisca affatto l'opera*: Rome, BANL, Archivio Linceo IV, fols 178–179; Gabrieli 1938–42, pp. 1114–15.
14 *Pittura filosofica*, wrote Cesi, was the *indirizzo della pittura, e suo studio, non solo a dilettation semplice, il che è vanissimo abuso, ma a giovamento di viva et efficace disciplina e piacer di molta utilità*: Naples, Biblioteca Nazionale, MS XII.E.4, fol. 24v (Gabrieli 1989, I, p. 49). Quoted in Olmi 1992, p. 374 n. 225.
15 See Tongiorgi Tomasi 1980; Garbari/Tongiorgi Tomasi/Tosi 2002, pp. 51–60.
16 *la scienza dei vegetativi, quale più si acquista da se stesso speculando (massime essendo in campagna) che leggendo libri altrui. Del resto non havendo libri, quello che lei sa gli basta per poter con il giudizio naturale speculare et dal istessa natura di continuo imparare*: Cesi to Stelluti from Rome, 17 July 1604: BAV, Vat. lat. 9684, fols 52–57 (Gabrieli 1938–42, p. 39); Olmi 1992, p. 320.
17 On Heckius see *DBI*, XLII, 1993, pp. 277–81; Gabrieli 1989, II, pp. 1053–1115; Alessandrini 1976; Rienstra 1968; Conti 1990; Freedberg 2002.
18 Rome, BANL, Archivio Linceo XXIX, fols 27–191.
19 On Heckius's academic training see, in addition to the already cited *DBI*, p. 278, his own account, *Modus studendi*: Rome, BANL, Archivio Linceo XXV, fol. 5.
20 From a letter to Ulisse Aldrovandi, 14 November 1602: Rome, BANL, Archivio Linceo XVIII, fol. 23, reproduced in Gabrieli 1989, II, pp. 1084–6.
21 Ibid. On Heckius's medical activities, see in particular: Rome, BANL, Archivio Linceo XXII (*Adversus Romanorum medicorum deliramenta*) and Archivio Linceo XXIII (*Experimenta Scandriliae* ..., on experiments he conducted between 1602 and 1603); Gabrieli 1989, II, pp. 1064–6.
22 *alquanto seme di un semplice che mai più ho visto, il quale ho trovato in una profundissima grotta — d'un loco deserto delle montagne di Spoleti. E' questa pianta niente dissimile dal volgar melone, solo fa più intagliate le foglie, varia nel fiore, il quale fa or giallo or bianco, fa frutti alcuni longi, alchuni tondi, alchuni azzaccati*, from Spoleto (?July 1603): Rome, BANL, Archivio Linceo XVIII, fol. 46; Gabrieli 1938–42, p. 24.
23 *alchuni sonno in prima di color e verde negro, poscia deventano di colore più che aurei, et danno sì grato et suave odore, che impiono della loro fraganza ogni gran cammera; sonno sì belli agli occhi, così grati al naso, talmente di lor si pasce l'animo che è cosa incredibile*: Rome, BANL, Archivio Linceo XVIII, fol. 46; Gabrieli 1938–42, p. 24.
24 *apparendomi cosa nova trovar simil semplici in così aspere montagne, n'ho voluto far parte a V. S. Ill.re et Ecc te, come anche spero di fare d'alchun altre cose, così de piante, come de semi*: Rome, BANL, Archivio Linceo XVIII, fol. 46; Gabrieli 1938–42, p. 24. The botanist Enrico Chiovenda had suggested to Gabrieli that this plant might be 'Cucumis melo cantalupensis', a variety quite similar to the species illustrated on **290**.
25 See Gabrieli 1989, II, pp. 1060 and 1061. The importance of the works of Mattioli and other 16th-century botanists is discussed by Heckius in a text titled *Ambitioni maledictam salutem*: Rome, BANL, Archivio Linceo XVIII, fols 41–44.
26 26 February 1603: Rome, BANL, Archivio Linceo XVIII, fols 33–36; see Gabrieli 1989, II, p. 1060.
27 *De stirpium varietatibus duos maximos libros, in quibus his manibus ter mille stirpium differentias ex diversis mundi partibus collectas glutine affixeram* ('Two large books of various

plants into which I personally had glued three thousand plants gathered in various parts of the world'): Rome, BANL, Archivio Linceo XVIII, fols 27–28; see Gabrieli 1989, II, p. 1060. Chiovenda also attributed to Heckius an *Index herbarum* which Fabrizio Cortesi had discovered among the papers of Johan Faber in the Archivio degli Orfani, Rome (now Rome, BANL), but ascribed to Faber (Cortesi 1908): see Gabrieli 1989, II, p. 1099.

28 See *Epistolarum medicinalium . . . liber*: Rome, BANL, Archivio Linceo XVIII, in Gabrieli 1989, II, pp. 1059–61.

29 Ibid, p. 1085: *non meno a noi provista ha l'alma natura di salutissime piante et minerali, che alli barbari Indiani* [...] *adoprar piante straniere, falsificate droghe, et fare in una ricetta l'Asia, l'Africa, L'Europa, et il mondo novo insieme*.

30 See the letters dated 17 February 1604 (Rome, BANL, Archivio Linceo XVIII, fols 59v–61) in Gabrieli 1938–42, pp. 27, 29 and 30.

31 Rome, BANL, Archivio Linceo XVIII, fol. 63, in Gabrieli 1938–42, p. 28.

32 *bellissimi libri, scritti, secreti et cose naturali per i Lyncaei necessarissime*: BAV, Vat. lat. 9684, fols 64–66; Gabrieli 1938–42, p. 61.

33 An abridged version of this document was sent in the form of a *lettera circolare* to Stelluti and De Filiis in April 1605: BAV, Vat. lat. 9684, fols 64–66; Gabrieli 1938–42, pp. 59–70.

34 Gabrieli 1989, I, p. 434. On this Pisan botanist, see Garbari/Tongiorgi Tomasi/Tosi 2002, *passim*.

35 Heckius to his fellow Lincei, 19 December 1604: BAV, Vat. lat. 9684, fols 96–97; Gabrieli 1938–42, p. 47.

36 *immediatamente provvisto di un giovane scultore et disegnatore in rame per far stampe e figure, cosa utilissima alli componimenti Lyncaei, quale pigliò con animo che servisse all'ordine et lo tiene seco, se debba riceversi al servizio de' Lyncaei per sempre . . . Utilissimo sarà il disegnatore in rame per il nostro ordine . . . . onde potremo figurare ogni nostra osservazione*: BAV, Vat. lat. 9684, fols 64–66; Gabrieli 1938–42, pp. 64, 68.

37 *Perchè è utilissimo ai componimenti Lyncaei lo riceviamo al nostro servitio; et quando lei non possa mantenerlo appresso sé, lo mandi al principe che lo manterrà, et le darà da fare*: BAV, Vat. lat. 9684, fol. 75; Gabrieli 1938–42, pp. 78–80. On the role of images in the work and thought of the Lincei, see Raimondi 1974, pp. 25–40; Olmi 1992, pp. 273–5; Freedberg 1993, pp. 141–53; Freedberg 2002, pp. 1–10; Baldriga 2002, pp. 235–7.

38 *sunt apud me circiter centum Plantae non editae in Hispania observatae*: letter of Heckius to Stelluti dated 2 June 1608: BAV, Vat. lat. 9684, fol. 101; Gabrieli 1938–42, p. 110.

39 *donec ad suam sanitatem redeat*: see Gabrieli 1938–42, p. 544.

40 Gabrieli 1929, p. 534.

41 Solinas 1989, pp. 53, 60, 63.

42 *Cassiano* cat. 1993, pp. 198, 200; *Cassiano Segreti* 2000, p. 94; *Cassiano Segreti* 2001, p. 252.

43 Freedberg 2002, pp. 207, 445 n. 26. The suggestion that the inscriptions are by Winther was ascribed to Solinas in the Christie's auction catalogue, New York, 28 January 2000, under lot 18.

44 For Winther's hand (unpublished) see, for example, his letter from Acquasparta to Faber in Rome, 17 July 1624: Rome, BANL, Archivio degli Orfani di S. Maria in Acquiro, MS 413, fols 50–53, and others cited in Gabrieli 1938–42, pp. 1353–4. For Heckius see Fig.12 here, Montpellier, BEM, MS H.507 (*Fructus itineris ad Septentrionales*), fols viiiff, or the examples published in *Lincei* cat. 2002–3, pp. 67 (Rome, BANL, Archivio Linceo IV, fol. 252), 75 (Rome, BANL, Archivio Linceo XX, fol. 85v, *De circulis sphaere*) and 78 (Montpellier, BEM, MS H.507, *Fructus itineris ad Septentrionales*, fols 126v–127).

45 *apud quem adhuc iucunde maneo, qui fere omnes huius libri pictures delineavit*, from a letter to his fellow Lincei in Rome dated 1 October 1605: Montpellier, BEM, MS H.506; Gabrieli 1938–42, pp. 90–1.

46 Montpellier, BEM, MS H.507.

47 Solinas 1989; *Cassiano* cat. 1993, pp. 191–2, 199.

48 First posited in *Cassiano* cat. 1993, p. 199; more firmly stated in *Cassiano Segreti* 2000, cat. nos 88–93; *Cassiano Segreti* 2001, cat. nos 166–171.

49 Tabernaemontanus is cited on **28**, **80**, **131**, **176** and **189–190**; Dodoens on **76**, **153** and **199**; and Monardes on **184**. Gabrieli erroneously believed that the annotation referred to Lobelius's *Icones stirpium* (Antwerp 1591): see Gabrieli 1929, pp. 533–4.

50 In the *Erbario* the black bryony (**137**) appears before the white bryony (**138**), reversing the order in *I Discorsi*, pp. 1347–8.

51 On **1**, no. 57; on **33**, no. 11; on **35**, no. 7; on **65**, no. 43; on **67**, no. 44; on **79**, no. 55; on **90**, no. 30; on **93**, no. 28; on **112**, no. 34; on **125**, no. 32; on **149**, no. 59; on **156**, no. 4; on **163**, no. 40.

52 See Alessandrini 1978, pp. 21–46.

53 Catalogued in Part B.III of the present catalogue series: see Scott/Freedberg 2000.

54 Gabrieli 1989, I, pp. 273–93. Nor is any help to be found in the information drawn up by the German Martin Fogel (1643–75), who had received his degree from the university in Padua and was the first historian of the Lincei: see Gabrieli 1989, I, pp. 273–93. One of his many *schede* lists the manuscript works on the subject of botany contained in the Academy's library, but does not shed any light on the original arrangement of the *Erbario*; it does, however, furnish us with precious information regarding the volumes of *figure miniate* owned by the Academy, which must have included more than 2,000 drawings (Fogel's listing is published in Gabrieli 1989, I, p. 287):

Un libro in fog.º con varie figure di semplici o fiori, etc. figure tra grandi e piccole 320, le figure sono miniate.
Un altro libro in fog.º, figure miniate grandi e piccole 240.
Un altro libro in fog.º, figure miniate grandi e piccole 910.
Un altro libro in fog.º figure miniate grandi e piccole 590.
Una cartella in fog.º con varie figure miniate grandi e piccole 67.
Una cartella in fog.º, con diverse figure di fonghi, Animali dell'India et altri fig. min. 55.
Due fiori grandi miniati in due pezzi di rame.
Libellus de medicinalibus Indorum Herbis

[this is the second herbal from the Paper Museum in the Royal Library at Windsor: see Gabrieli 1929, pp. 534–5].

55 Four plants cannot be identified (**168**, **171**, **210** and **273**), in four cases the identification is uncertain (**126**, **249**, **257** and **282**), while in about a dozen cases only the genus can be distinguished with certainty (**59**, **134–135**, **152–153**, **164**, **187**, **188**, **194**, **208**, **211**, **233** and **235**).

56 For example, **25**, **52**, **54**, **72**, **90**, **108**, **154–155**, **183**, **214**.

57 For example, **13**, **14**, **19**, **23**, **248**.

58 Riddle 1985, esp. pp. 168–76.

59 Pagel 1982.

60 *Linceae Accademiae condiscipuli arcanarum sagacissimi indagatores scientiarum, et Paracelsicae dediti disciplinae*, wrote Heckius to Thomas Mermann on 17 February 1604: Rome, BANL, Archivio Linceo XVIII, fol. 61; Gabrieli 1938–42, p. 30; Freedberg 2002, p. 67.

61 There has not yet been a thoroughgoing history of the doctrine of signatures, and opinions differ as to its antiquity. Some scholars, following Walter Pagel (1982, p. 149), assert that it is 'an ancient principle', though Pagel gives only one classical instance, and that an anomalous one (burnt crayfish as a remedy for cancer, the Greek for crayfish, *karkinoi*, resembling the word carcinoma – verbal rather than anatomical similarity). Others (e.g. Maclean 2002, pp. 324–5) argue that while scattered instances of a supposed relationship between the shape of a plant and that of the organ it affects may be found before the 16th century, no general principle seems to have been proposed until Paracelsus and G.B. della Porta, and their proposals by no means met with universal acceptance. Dodoens (1583, p. 16) condemned the idea as a recent invention (*nonnullorum posterioris aetatis et nostril saeculi recentiorum haec inventa*). Mattioli certainly offered one instance (1568, p. 1050, 'Echium italicum'), but his rhetoric suggests that he saw the signature relationship as a single or at least rare instance, rather than the exemplification of a general principle: *non è picciola maraviglia il pensare, che la sagacissima natura habbia prodotto l'Echio con teste di vipera, notificando cosi à gli huomini, de i quali è alla amorevolissima protettrice, esser cotal pianta valoroso rimedio à I morsi di cosi velenosi.*

62 Baglione 1642, pp. 394–5. See also Solinas 1989, p. 60.

63 *Adunque io li giorni passati quando in casa dell'Illustrissimo ed Eccellentissimo marchese Cesi, mio signore, vidi le pitture di 500 piante indiane, affermare o quelle esser al mondo, ovvero, se pur vi fossero, esser frustratorie e superflue, perché né io né alcuni de' circostanti conosceva le lor qualità, virtù ed effetti?*: Carutti 1883, p. 55. Galilei 1890–1909, XI, pp. 107–8: letter 532 dated 21 May 1611.

64 *per intagliare le figure dell'animali del libro Mexicano*: Rome, BANL, Archivio Linceo IV, fols 374–375, quoted in Olmi 1992, p. 374 n. 227.

65 The *Tabulae Phytosophycae* also appear in the rare 1649 edition.

66 Hernández 1651, p. 913; see also Pirotta 1904, pp. 11–12.

67 *Latent in Bibliothecarum angulis codices, in quibus antiqua vestigia plantarum recolere possit*: Hernández 1651, p. 949.

68 Ibid; Pirotta 1904, p. 80.

69 Rome, BANL, Archivio degli Orfani di S. Maria in Acquiro, MS 423, fols 198–199; Gabrieli 1938–42, pp. 778–9: *La commodità che V.S. m'ha data delli doi libri prestatimi, Tabernemontano e Bauhino sopra il Mattiolo, m'è stata di molto agevolamento alla revisione di questo innumerabil quasi esercito plantare; ma per più comodo nel locare e ordinare per il fine di questa gran Plantamentatione, haverei bisogno di doi volumi delle Icones Lobelliane per aiuto della memoria, con la universal rappresentatione tagliandole e locandole come V.S. sa* [...] *prego dunque V.S. a procurarmi a tal effetto doi libri tali sciolti* [...] *e che li libri siano compiti della miglior editione che possa haversi* (translation from Freedberg 2002 (p. 377), where possible titles and editions are also discussed: p. 472, nn 52–54).

70 The three mycological codices were first identified by Andrea Ubrizsy (see Ubrizsy 1980, the first publication to announce the rediscovery). The other five codices were discussed shortly afterwards in Alessandrini/de Angelis/Lanzara 1985 and de Angelis/Lanzara 1986. They have been most fully treated in the recent Cesi, *Atti* 2006.

71 Many of the sheets carry inscriptions mentioning the use of the microscope: *Microscopio observato*, *Microscopio spectatus* and *Ex microscopio*.

72 *Invio a V.E. un occhialino per veder da vicino le cose minime, del quale spero che ella sia per prendersi gusto e trattenimento non piccolo, ché così accade a me. Ho tardato a mandarlo, perché non l'ho prima ridotto a perfezzione, havendo hauto difficoltà in trovare il modo di lavorare i cristalli perfettamente*: Rome, BANL, Archivio Linceo XII, fol. 157; Gabrieli 1938–42, p. 942.

73 The names of Isabella and Leonardo Parasole have been suggested. Isabella Parasole collaborated on the *Tesoro Messicano*: see Baglione 1642, pp. 394–5; Solinas 1989, p. 60.

74 See Guerrini 2006, pp. 153–231.

75 BAV, MS Barb. lat. 4326, dated 1639. See Tongiorgi Tomasi 1986, pp. 293–306, and MacDougall 1994.

NOTES FOR THE READER

The following notes are intended to clarify the meaning of key terms, headings and typographical conventions used in the catalogue.

CATALOGUE NUMBER: each catalogue entry has a unique number composed of the SERIES letter (A = Antiquities and Architecture, B = Natural History), the PART number in roman numerals and the ENTRY number in arabic numerals, for example, B.III.32. Cross-references to entries within the same part are indicated by the arabic number only, in **bold** type. References to entries already published in other parts of the catalogue raisonné are to the full catalogue number; references to entries in forthcoming parts are by series letter and part number only. Where a part is divided into several volumes, these are indicated by an arabic numeral after a forward slash, for example, A.IX/1 and A.IX/2. The present volume is B.VI/1. A list of all planned parts in the series appears in B.VI/1, p. vi.

LOCATIONS AND ORDER: drawings with catalogue numbers **1** to **211** are in the Royal Library at Windsor Castle, bound in the *Erbario Miniato* album, and follow the order of the album. The Royal Library inventory number (RL) is also given in each case. Eighty-three loose sheets (**212–293**) follow, with the present whereabouts indicated (if known). Sixty-seven of the loose sheets (**212–277**) are from a dispersed companion volume to the *Erbario Miniato*, and follow the 'Pozzo' numeration of that album (see NUMBERING below, and pp. 13–14, 35–6). The remaining sixteen drawings (**278–293**) are not related to the *Erbario Miniato* and follow a separate 'Pozzo' numeration, where present, with the unnumbered sheets last.

PLANT NAMES: the common English name is given first, followed by the scientific name with its authority. The authorities cited are listed on pp. 635–8. The scientific, English and Italian common names are indexed on pp. 647–55.

MEDIUM: all the drawings (with the exception of **242a** and **293**) are executed in watercolour and bodycolour over black chalk or graphite, occasionally heightened with gum. Drawings **242a** and **293** are executed in pen and ink over black chalk.

SIZE: the dimensions of the drawing sheet are given in millimetres, height followed by width, for **212–293**. The bound *Erbario Miniato* folios (**1–211**) all measure 420 × 275mm.

WATERMARKS: the watermarks are discussed, listed and illustrated on pp. 618–31.

ARTISTS, DATES: the artists of the *Erbario Miniato* and related sheets (**1–277**) are not known (see pp. 30–2). Four of the non-*Erbario* sheets (**279**, **280**, **281** and **292**) have been attributed to Cassiano's artist-collaborator Vincenzo Leonardi (see pp. 15–16 and 36). Drawings **1–277** are thought to have been produced during the first two decades of the seventeenth century, and **278–293** some decades later (see pp. 30–2, 36).

PROVENANCE: all the drawings share a common provenance into the twentieth century: see p. 2. As discussed on pp. 35–6, **212–277** probably formed part of a companion volume to the *Erbario Miniato*, which was broken up in the library of George III. The folios were cut down, remounted with wash borders, and bound as part of a series of around twenty albums collectively entitled *Natural History*, together with many other drawings, including **278–293**. Most of these albums were sold from the Royal Library shortly after the First World War, and by the outbreak of the next war the drawings were in the hands of the London dealer Jacob Mendelson, who may have been responsible for breaking up the albums. A number of the drawings suffered damage, including water staining, at this time, apparently following air raids. All of **212–293** may be assumed to share this provenance, which is therefore not noted under each entry, and provenance is given only from this point in time onwards, when known.

Many of Mendelson's drawings were bought by Sir Rex Nan Kivell, a partner of the Redfern Gallery on Cork Street. Nan Kivell gave some of the drawings away to friends but retained the bulk for himself, and in 1976 he generously gave 118 of these drawings to The Queen (to be followed a year after his death in 1977 by a further five sheets, one of which was **293**). Drawings from this group are noted in the provenance line simply as 'Sir Rex Nan Kivell'. Another large group had been purchased, also probably from Mendelson, by the American collector James R. Herbert Boone. On his death in 1983 Boone bequeathed his collection to the Johns Hopkins University, Baltimore, which sold the greater part of it at Sotheby's, New York, on 16 September 1988. Drawings from this group are noted in the provenance line as 'Boone sale', followed by the lot number. Five further drawings (**229**, **233**, **235**, **236**, **237**), purchased probably from Mendelson by Eliette Bostrom, were returned to the Royal Library at some unknown date during the 1940s or 1950s. The ownership of several other drawings was known to Anthony Blunt in the 1950s, but their present whereabouts is mostly unknown.

NUMBERING: *italic* is used to indicate 'Pozzo' numbers (see p. 14).

ANNOTATION: transcriptions are given in *italic*, followed by translations in parentheses, with the source (when known) cited in square brackets. Any lacunae, interpolations or interpretations of illegible passages in the transcriptions are indicated between square brackets. Line breaks are marked with an oblique stroke, and distinct annotations are divided by a semi-colon. The translations respect as far as possible the sixteenth- and seventeenth-century meaning of medical, pharmacological and botanical terms, and are thus not always literal. [Square brackets] indicate that the original was not entirely comprehensible. Uppercase [M] in square brackets gives the corresponding word or passage in Mattioli's 1568 edition of *I Discorsi*, where the transcription in the *Erbario* differs significantly.

MOUNT: **1–211** are drawn directly on the folio sheets. A number of the loose drawings (**212–293**) retain their George III 'Type D' mounts, being laid down on a two-ply sheet measuring roughly 586 × 435mm (if not cut down), watermarked D&C Blauw (see p. 618) and with wash borders. See A.IX/1, pp. 74–5, for a description of all the mount types of the dal Pozzo corpus.

ENTRY COMMENTARY: in the body of the entry the description refers to the specimen drawn, and not in general to the species to which it belongs. A botanical glossary is found on pp. 632–4. The entries on the mycological drawings (**33–51**) have been written by David Pegler, author of B.II (*Fungi*).

LITERATURE: this pertains to the drawing, and not to the specimen depicted. Publications are cited in abbreviated form; a bibliography is given on pp. 639–42.

PHYSICAL DESCRIPTION OF THE *ERBARIO MINIATO* ALBUM (**1–211**)

The *Erbario Miniato* [Fig. 22] is a paper codex measuring 425 × 285mm, fully bound in vellum, all edges green. Stamped in gold on both front and back boards is a large crown with the letters G III R. Crudely inscribed in ink on the spine are the title *Erbario / Miniato* and, at the bottom, *VI*; Gabrieli (1929) also recorded the presence of a number *58* on the spine, no longer visible. The volume comprises a total of 221 folios: three flyleafs at the front; 211 folios bearing drawings on the rectos (and in one case, **188**, on the verso); four index folios; and three further flyleafs at the back. An offprint of Gabrieli's article (1929) on the volume is attached between the second and third front flyleafs. Folio 1 bears a red wax seal with the coat of arms of Anna Teresa Benzoni, the daughter-in-law of Carlo Antonio dal Pozzo. Many of the folios bear on their versos pencil identifications of the plants by W.T. Stearn (1911–2002) and other botanists. The indexes on folios 212–215 list the species first in alphabetical order, then in the order of the manuscript (see pp. 607–17 for a transcription).

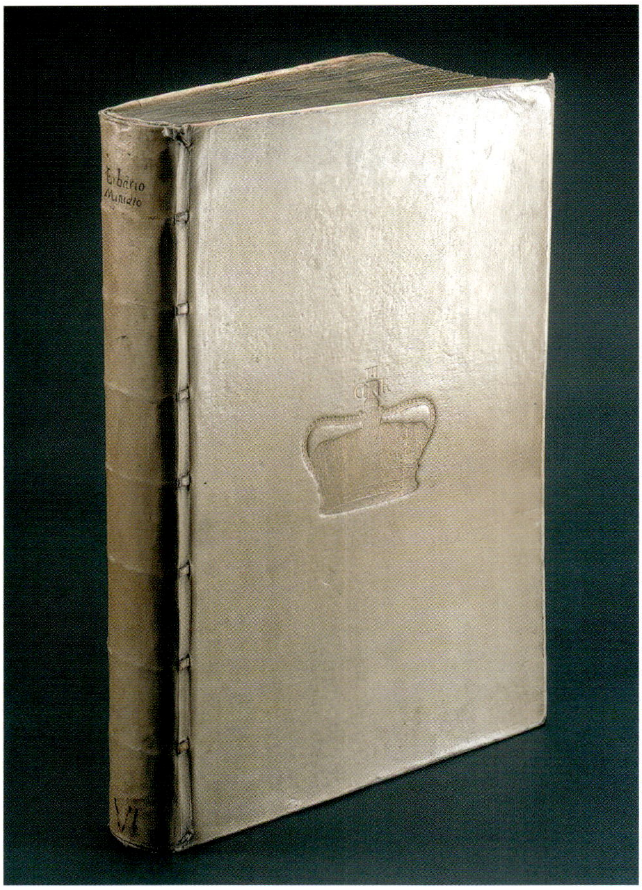

Fig. 22. *Erbario Miniato*, Royal Library, Windsor Castle

CATALOGUE

The *Erbario Miniato*: entries 1–154

1. Corn poppy or common red poppy, *Papaver rhoeas* L.

Erbario Miniato, fol. 1 (RL 27691)

Seal of Anna Teresa Benzoni at lower centre. *Watermark*: Crown 47

NUMBERING: *499*

ANNOTATION: *il papavero salvatico ôvero / Rhea, dassi la decotione / di cinque, overo sei de i suoi / capi fatta in tre ciathi di vino / alla consumatione della metà, à / bere p*[*er*] *fare dormire, beuto il / seme con acqua melata alla / misura d'uno acetabolo, molifica / leggiermente il corpo. ~~129~~ / Spargendo la decotione de le foglie. sopra il capo. fa dormire. 1112 N:º 57.* ('The wild poppy or *Rhea*. A decoction of five or six of its flower heads made in three cups of wine and reduced by half is administered as a drink for inducing sleep. Drinking the seed in honey water in the amount of one *acetabulum* slightly softens the body. ~~129~~ Spreading a decoction of the leaves on the head makes one sleep. 1112. No. 57.'). [From Mattioli 1568, pp. 1111–12]

LITERATURE: *Quaderni Puteani* 1, pp. 53, 55 (fig. 36)

The common red or corn poppy, a member of the family Papaveraceae, is a herbaceous annual native to the semi-arid regions of the Near East, and now widespread in central and southern Europe, central and western Asia and northern Africa, in fields of grain or on abandoned land (see also **8**). It was known to the Egyptians, and the young leaves were eaten as a salad by the Greeks. The poppy contains large amounts of an alkaloid with a wide range of physiological effects. Its expectorant and sudorific properties can be used to treat ailments of the respiratory system, and the petals and dried capsules have long been employed to treat insomnia and convulsions.

This specimen has an erect stem and narrow, lanceolate, toothed leaves, lobed near the stem. The solitary flower on its long peduncle has four petals which (in this specimen) lack the black spots that are usually found at their base. From the axils of the leaves spring two other peduncles, each ending in a bud with enveloping sepals; the dense covering of short hairs on both the peduncles and the buds can be seen. The mature fruit, shown in a detail in the lower right corner, consists of a poricidal capsule containing the tiny black seeds.

Although the characteristics of the flower shown here are somewhat different from the 'Papavero salvatico' in Mattioli's *Discorsi* (p. 1112), both are clearly specimens of *Papaver rhoeas*, which shows a wide range of morphological variations.

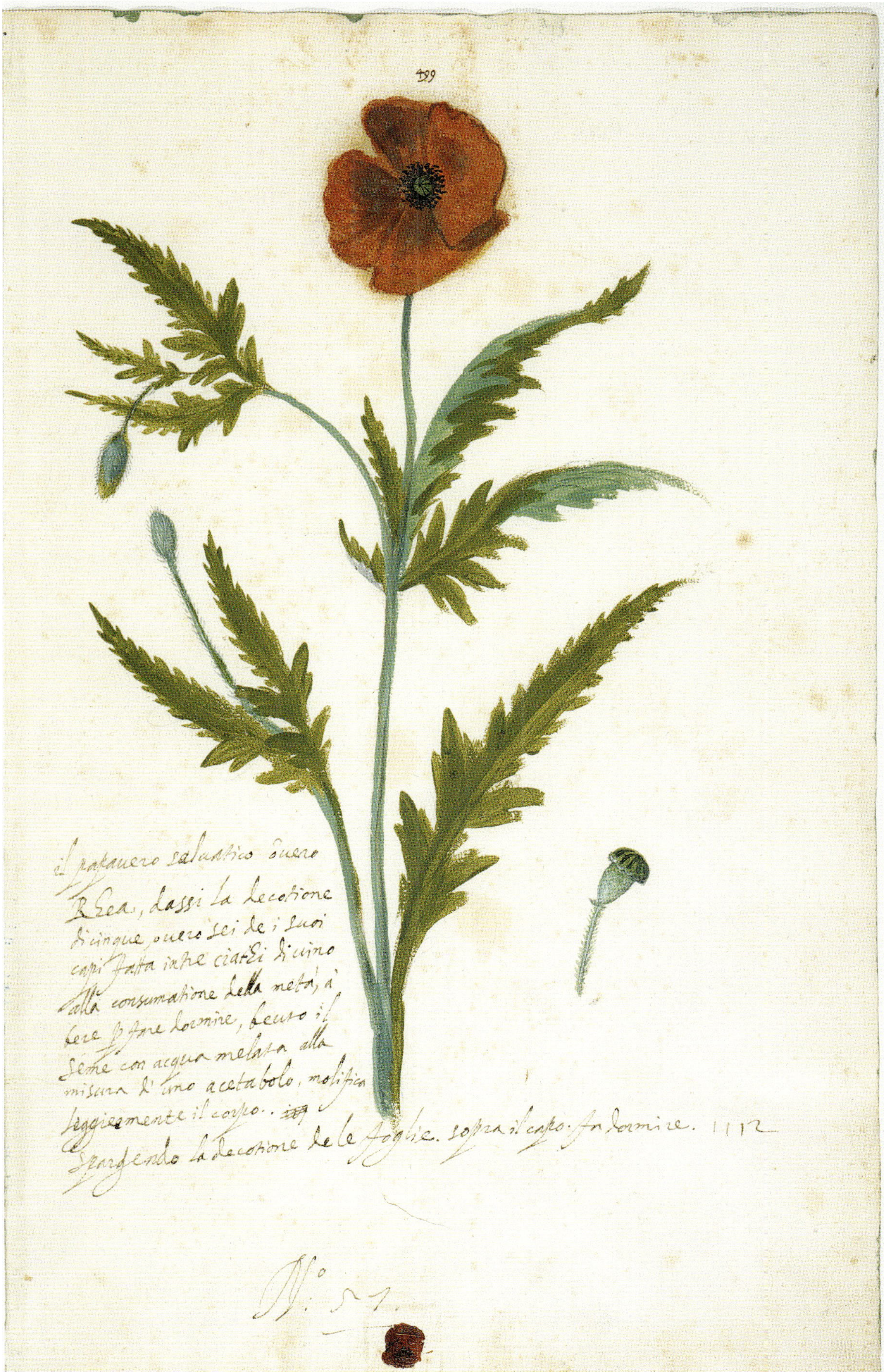
499
il papauero saluatico ouero
Rhea, dassi la decotione
di cinque, ouero sei de i suoi
capi fatta in tre ciathi di vino
alla consumatione della metà, à
bere p fare dormire, beuto il
seme con acqua melata alla
misura d'uno acetabolo, molifica
leggiermente il corpo.
Spargendo la decotione de le foglie. sopra il capo. fa dormire. 1112
N° 51.

1

2. Opium poppy, *Papaver somniferum* L.

Erbario Miniato, fol. 2 (RL 27692)

NUMBERING: *500*

ANNOTATION: *Papavero domestico./ Ha natura de infrigidire / pigliando il fumo dove / bolla le frondi e i, capi / fanno agevelmente dormire./ bevesi la loro decotione p[er] fare / dormire. Si cuoce li capi nelle / acqua sino che rientra la meta, / e mesevi il mele e' ~~cosi~~ e si cuocano / insieme che si faccia in forma / di latuario. è buono p[er] levare i do= / lori, p[er] la testa, p[er] il catarlo, p[er] i / flussi stomacale dassi il seme del / papavero negro.'trito p[er] li flussi del corpo. / Ell'opio che si fa del papavero è utilissimo / a' molte infirmità. como raconta il Matthiolo / 1113.* ('Domestic poppy. Has a cooling effect. Inhaling the smoke from the boiling of the flower heads and leaves sends one easily to sleep. Drinking their decoction makes one sleep. The heads are cooked in water until reduced by half, and mixed with honey are cooked together until they become a form of preparation. This is good for relieving pain, for the head, for catarrh, for discharges of the stomach. The ground seeds of the black poppy are given for discharges of body fluids. The opium made from the poppy is very effective against many illnesses, as Mattioli relates. 1113'). [From Mattioli 1568, pp. 1112–13]

Like the corn poppy (**1**), the opium poppy is native to Asia and now grows wild throughout southern and central Europe, and has become naturalized in the Americas (see also **5–7**, **9–12**). It is impossible to determine whether its spread was accidental or due to its medicinal properties. The opium is harvested by slitting the immature capsule to release a milky fluid which is dried to form the base from which morphine, heroin, codeine, narcotine and papaverine are derived. These alkaloids have a variety of effects on the central nervous system, and can induce acute or chronic drug intoxication. Morphine is a powerful painkiller, while codeine and narcotine are used as sedatives and papaverine as a spasmolytic agent. The Assyrians, Sumerians and Egyptians were all familiar with opium. In Greece the drug was prized for its medicinal properties and was considered sacred to the goddess Demeter, and it was used in the preparation of food and drink for initiates into the Eleusinian mysteries. Pliny recommended its use for eye infections.

Here a long erect peduncle springs from a thick stem bearing two large sessile leaves, shaped like ovate blades with toothed, scalloped edges. The peduncle curves slightly at its apex; the flower has four broad petals of a pale pink that becomes darker towards the base of the flower, where we can glimpse the immature capsule. The poppy's fruit, shown in an enlarged detail, consists of a subspherical poricidal capsule culminating in a disc made up of twelve stigmatic rays.

The image on p. 1113 of the *Discorsi* is entitled 'Papavero domestico', but is clearly a specimen of *Papaver somniferum*.

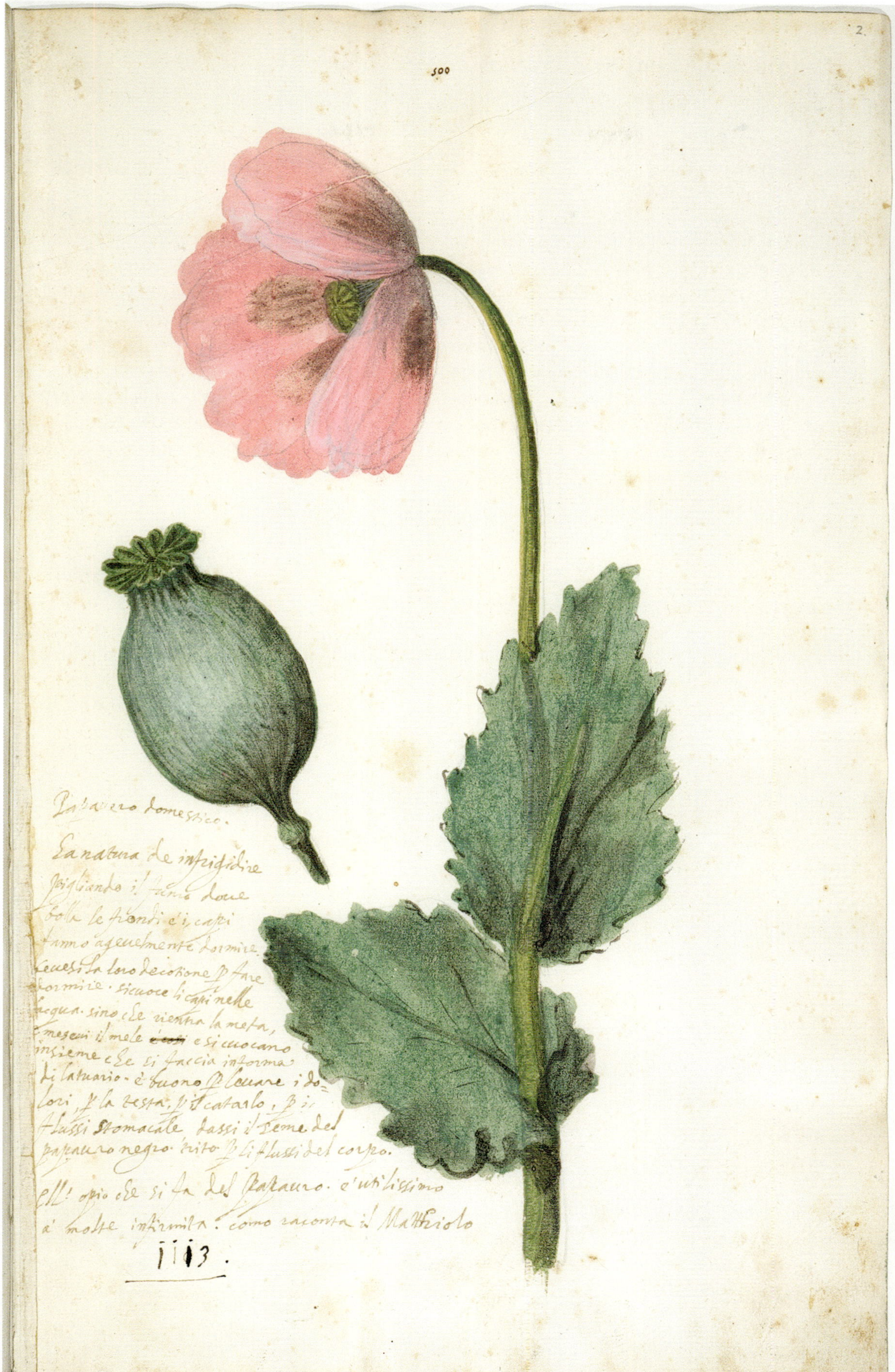
2.
500
Papavero domestico.
Ea natura de infrigidire
pigliando il fumo doue
bolle le frondi e i capi
fanno agevolmente dormire.
Beuesi la loro decotione p fare
dormire. si cuoce li capi nelle
acqua. sino che vienta la meta,
mescoui il mele ~~così~~ e si cuocano
insieme che si faccia informa
di latuario. è buono p levare i do=
lori, p la testa, p il cataralo, p i
flussi stomacale dassi il seme del
papauro negro trito p li flussi del corpo.
ell' opio che si fa del papauro. e' utilissimo
a molte infirmita. como raconta il Matthiolo
1113.

3. Yellow horned poppy, *Glaucium flavum* Crantz

Erbario Miniato, fol. 3 (RL 27693)

NUMBERING: *501*

ANNOTATION: *Papavero cornuto. nel Ma: 1116* ('Horned poppy. In Mattioli 1116'). [From Mattioli 1568, p. 1116]

The yellow horned poppy is a herbaceous biennial of the family Papaveraceae (see also **4**). It grows along the coasts of Europe and Asia Minor, where it thrives in sandy or rocky soil and on fertile, uncultivated land. All the green parts of the plant contain the alkaloid compound glaucine, along with various resinous and mucilaginous substances. The yellowish sap obtained when the plant is pressed was once used for the treatment of cutaneous ulcers in humans and animals, and the oil from the seeds for cooking and in lamps.

The artist has depicted the same specimen twice, with its flower half open and then fully open. The thick, erect stem bears two deeply lobed, fleshy, stem-clasping leaves. The golden-yellow flower crowning the short, thick peduncle is composed of four petals, with the pistil and stamens barely suggested. The stem also carries a fruit consisting of a linear, glabrous capsule extending from a glabrous peduncle, half as long as the capsule itself.

4. Yellow horned poppy, *Glaucium flavum* Crantz

Erbario Miniato, fol. 4 (RL 27694)

Watermark: Eagle 19

NUMBERING : *502*

ANNOTATION: *PAPAVERO CORNUTO* ('Horned poppy')

VERSO: black chalk sketch for **123** (Mock orange, *Philadelphus coronarius* L.)

This stalk of a yellow horned poppy (see **3**), with no apparent hairiness, bears two deeply lobed, stem-clasping leaves and a flower of four large, golden-yellow petals on a short peduncle. Many short yellow stamens surround the flower's gynoecium (ovary, style and stigma), which is twice as long as the stamens. The fruit consists of a linear, glabrous capsule on a glabrous peduncle that is one-third as long as the capsule itself, with a bilobed stigma at its apex.

5. Opium poppy, *Papaver somniferum* L. cv.

Erbario Miniato, fol. 5 (RL 27695)

Watermark: Crown 43

NUMBERING: *503*

ANNOTATION: *Papavero* ('Poppy')

This is the first of a series of folios showing different garden varieties of the opium poppy (see **2** for the wild variety). The single bloom on its long, hairless stalk is made up of innumerable fimbriate petals. These finely fringed petals are the result of a transformation of the stamens, a phenomenon seen in cultivated plants exposed to strong changes in temperature and light.

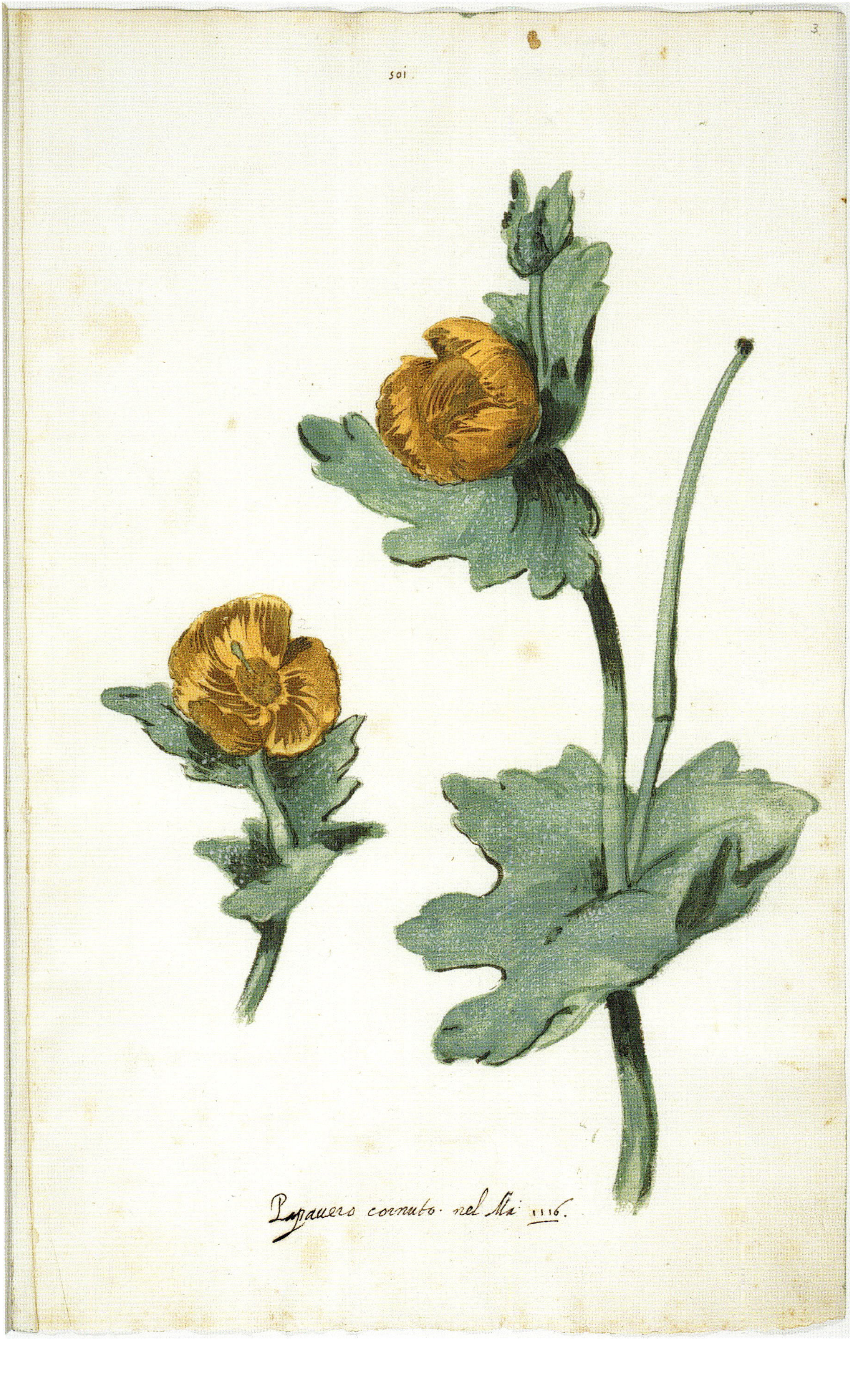
3.
501.
Papauero cornuto. nel Mi. 1116.

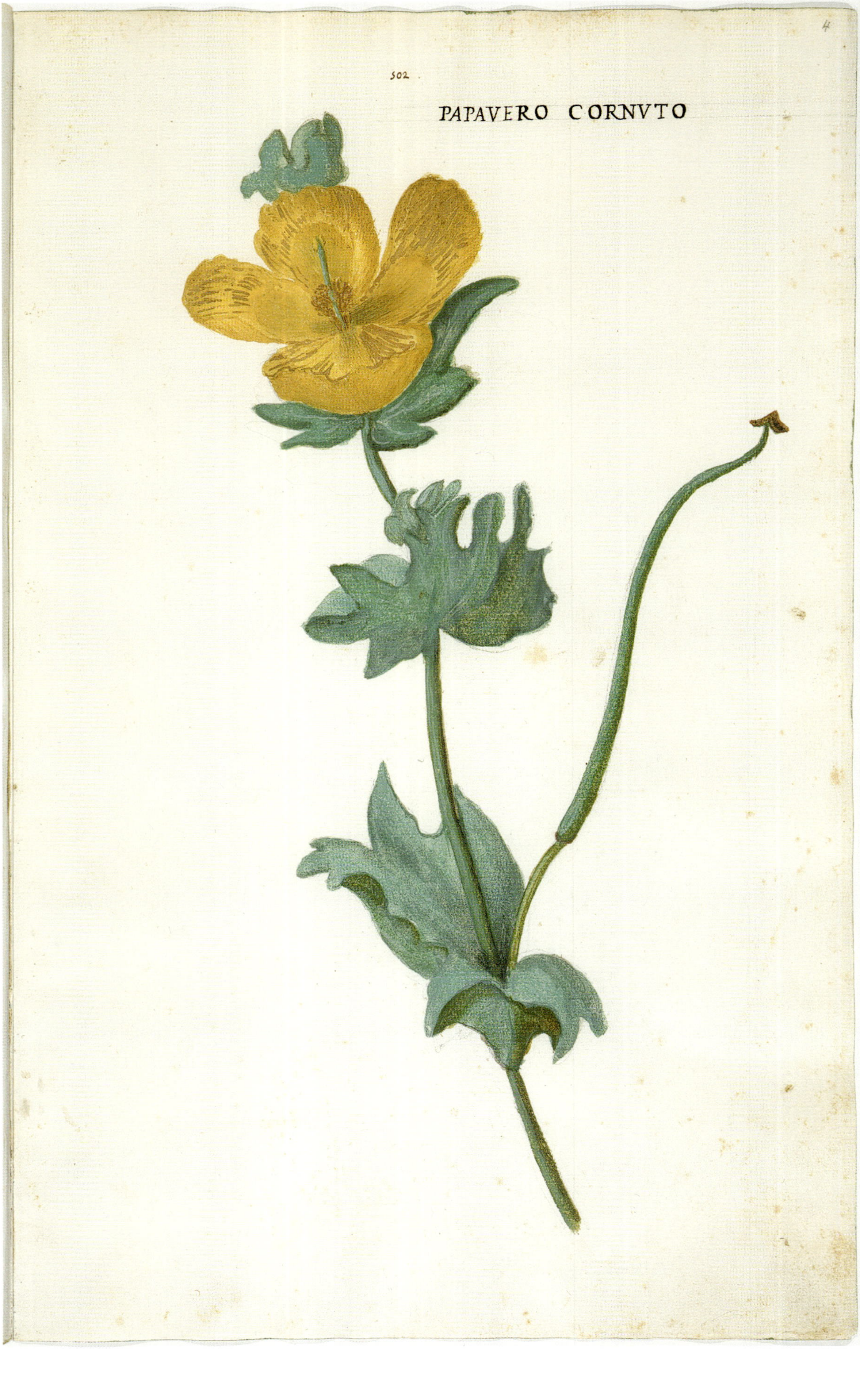

4

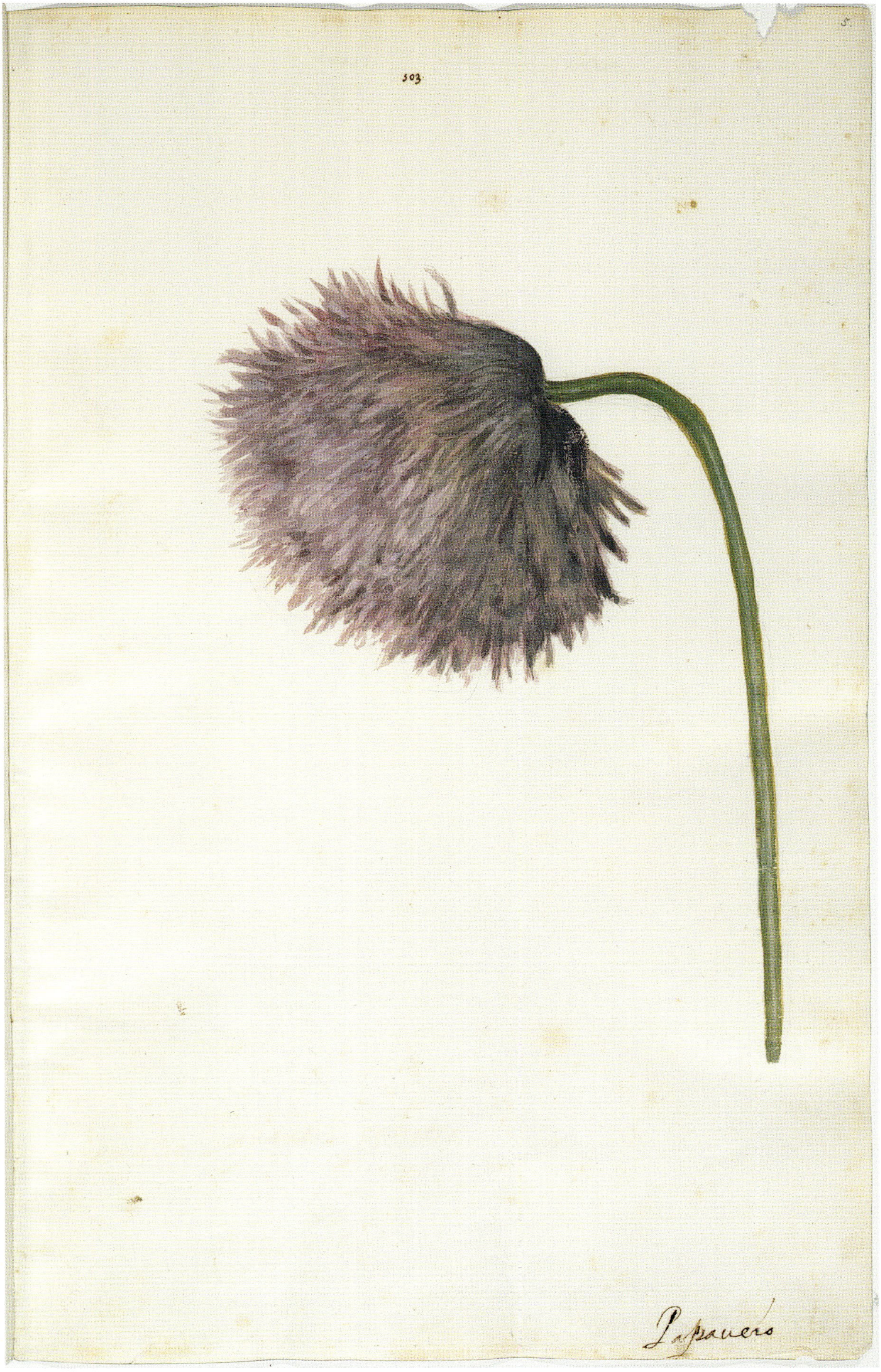
503
Papauero

6. Opium poppy, *Papaver somniferum* L. cv.

Erbario Miniato, fol. 6 (RL 27696)

Watermark: Fleur de lys 50

NUMBERING: *504*

ANNOTATION: *Unaltro Papavero. pulianto* ('Another poppy, many-flowered')

This cultivar has an upright stem bearing two alternate, deeply lobed, sessile leaves. The long peduncle is crowned by a carmine-coloured flower whose fimbriate petals completely hide the gynoecium and androecium. Double varieties such as this were described as *poliante* or *puliante* ('polyanthos', Greek for 'many-flowered').

7. Opium poppy, *Papaver somniferum* L. cv.

Erbario Miniato, fol. 7 (RL 27697)

Watermark: Fleur de lys 52

NUMBERING: *505*

ANNOTATION: *Papavero Pulianto. no*[*n*] *scritto dal matiolo* ('Many-flowered poppy. Not mentioned by Mattioli')

In this cultivar three alternate leaves with lobed and toothed edges spring from closely spaced nodes. The glabrous stem and peduncle end in a flower composed of numerous pale pink fimbriate petals that conceal the stamen and pistils.

8. Corn poppy or common red poppy, *Papaver rhoeas* L. cv.

Erbario Miniato, fol. 8 (RL 27698)

Watermark: Fleur de lys 50

NUMBERING: *506*

ANNOTATION: *Unaltro Papavero* ('Another poppy')

This drawing shows a garden variety of the corn or common red poppy (see **1**). The slender, glabrous stem bears two widely separated leaves, narrowly lanceolate with dentate margins and three deep incisions. The flower on its long peduncle has variegated fimbriate petals, bright red along the edges and white in the inner portions. Between the petals appears the immature capsule with its stigmatic disc.

The flower is similar to the varieties known today as the Shirley poppies, which were raised in the 1880s by the Revd William Wilks (1843–1923) in his garden at Shirley in Surrey. The petals of these varieties range from deep red through pale pink to white, with no trace of black.

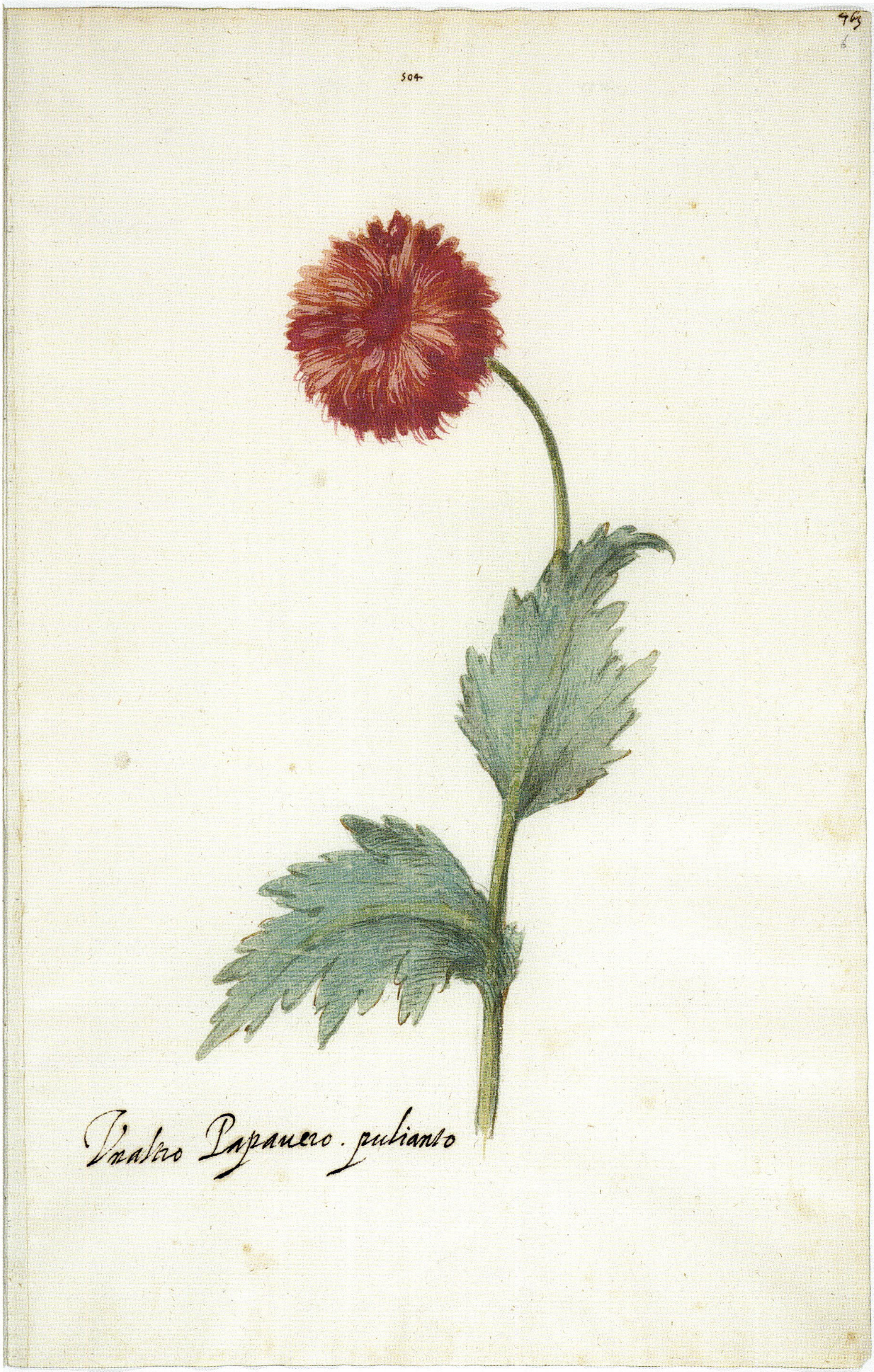
504
Vnaltro Papauero . puliante

505

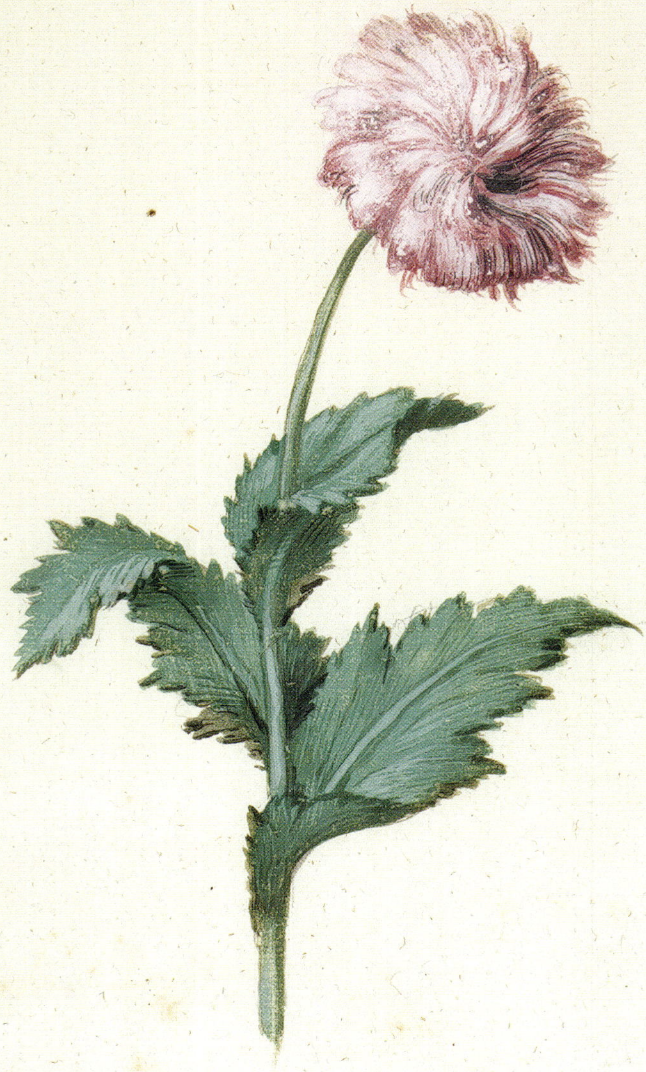

Papauero Pulianto. nō scritto dal matiolo

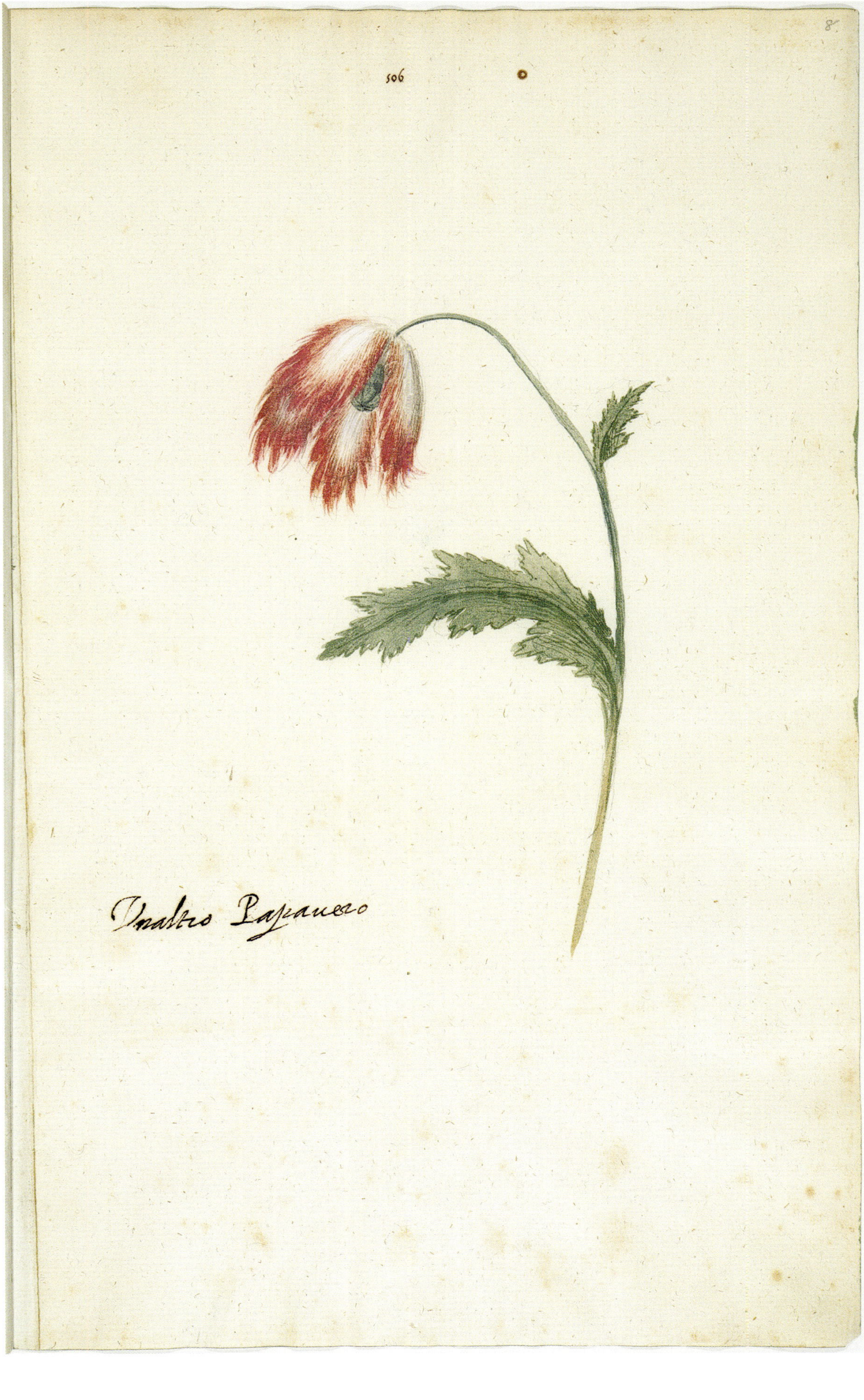
506
8
Vnaltro Papauero

9. Opium poppy, *Papaver somniferum* L. cv.

Erbario Miniato, fol. 9 (RL 27699)

NUMBERING: *507*

ANNOTATION: *Papavero* ('Poppy')

The long stalk of this cultivar, emerging from an enveloping bracteate leaf, appears to be covered with tiny hairs. The large flower is made up of numerous bright pink fimbriate petals.

10. Opium poppy, *Papaver somniferum* L. cv.

Erbario Miniato, fol. 10 (RL 27700)

NUMBERING: *508*

ANNOTATION: *PAPAVERO PULIANTO* ('Many-flowered poppy')

This cultivar has a bloom composed of two different types of petal. The broad outer petals are bright red with darker bands of colour running through their centres, while the numerous internal petals, of the same intense red, have fimbriate edges (see **5** for this phenomenon).

11. Opium poppy, *Papaver somniferum* L. cv.

Erbario Miniato, fol. 11 (RL 27701)

Watermark: Eagle 20

NUMBERING: *509*

ANNOTATION: *UNALTRO PAPAVERO PULIANTO* ('Another many-flowered poppy')

The flower consists of many laciniate, fimbriate petals, bright orange-red in colour, at the centre of which lies the bright green sixteen-rayed stigmatic disc of the capsule. The stamens are completely absent. A similar many-petalled poppy was depicted by Jacopo Ligozzi for the Medici collections (Florence, Uffizi, 1926 Orn.).

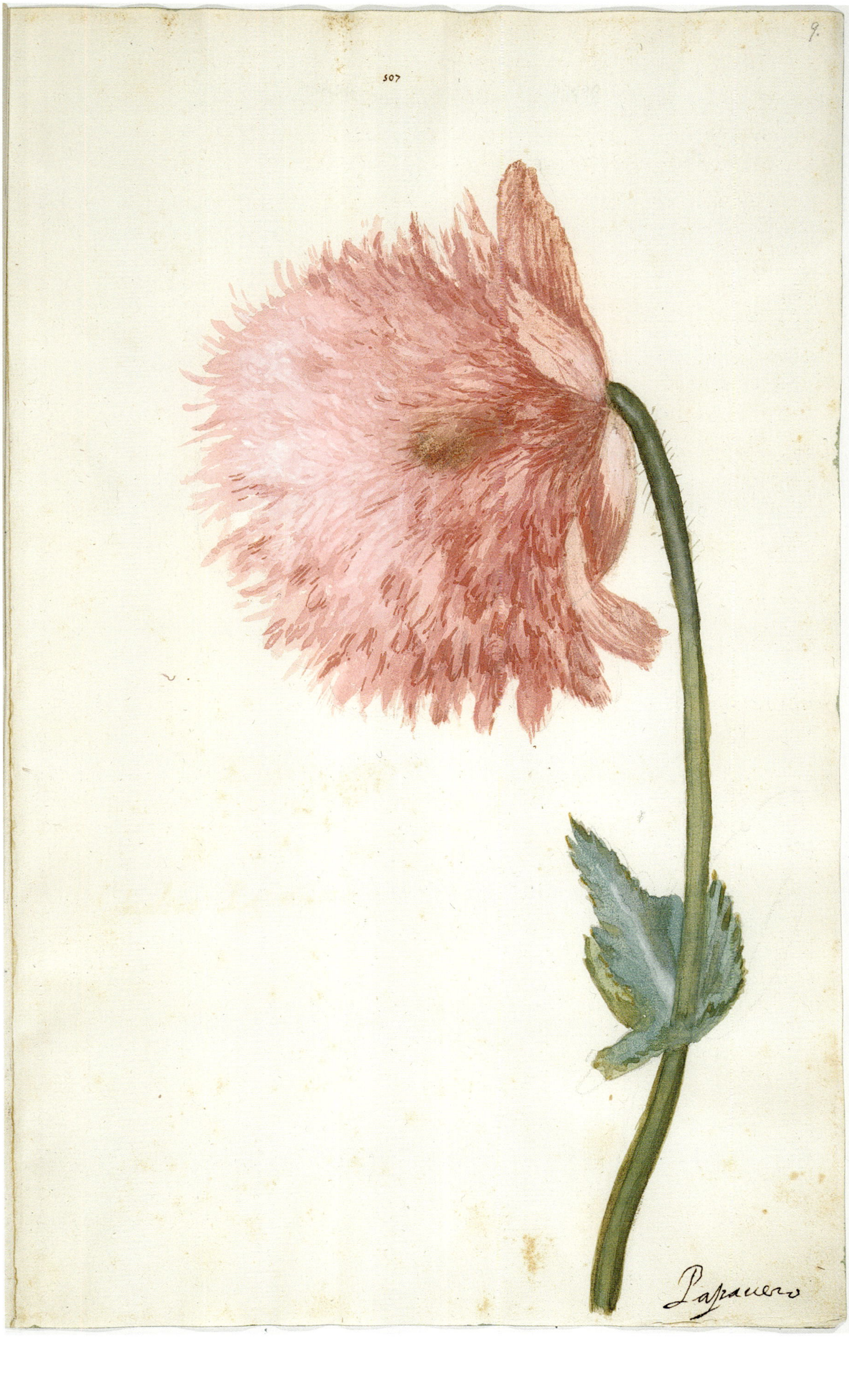
507
9.
Papavero

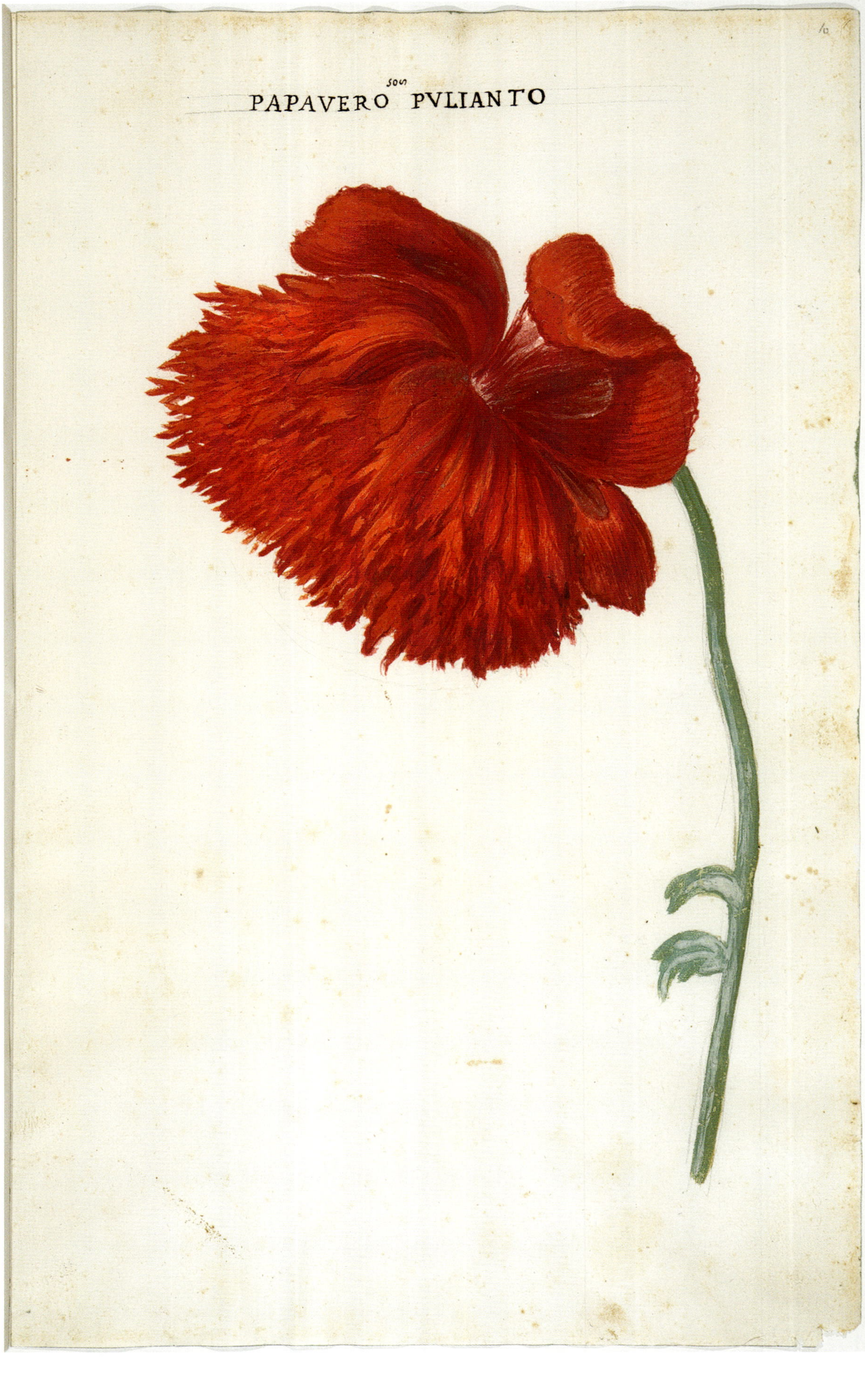
sou
PAPAVERO PVLIANTO

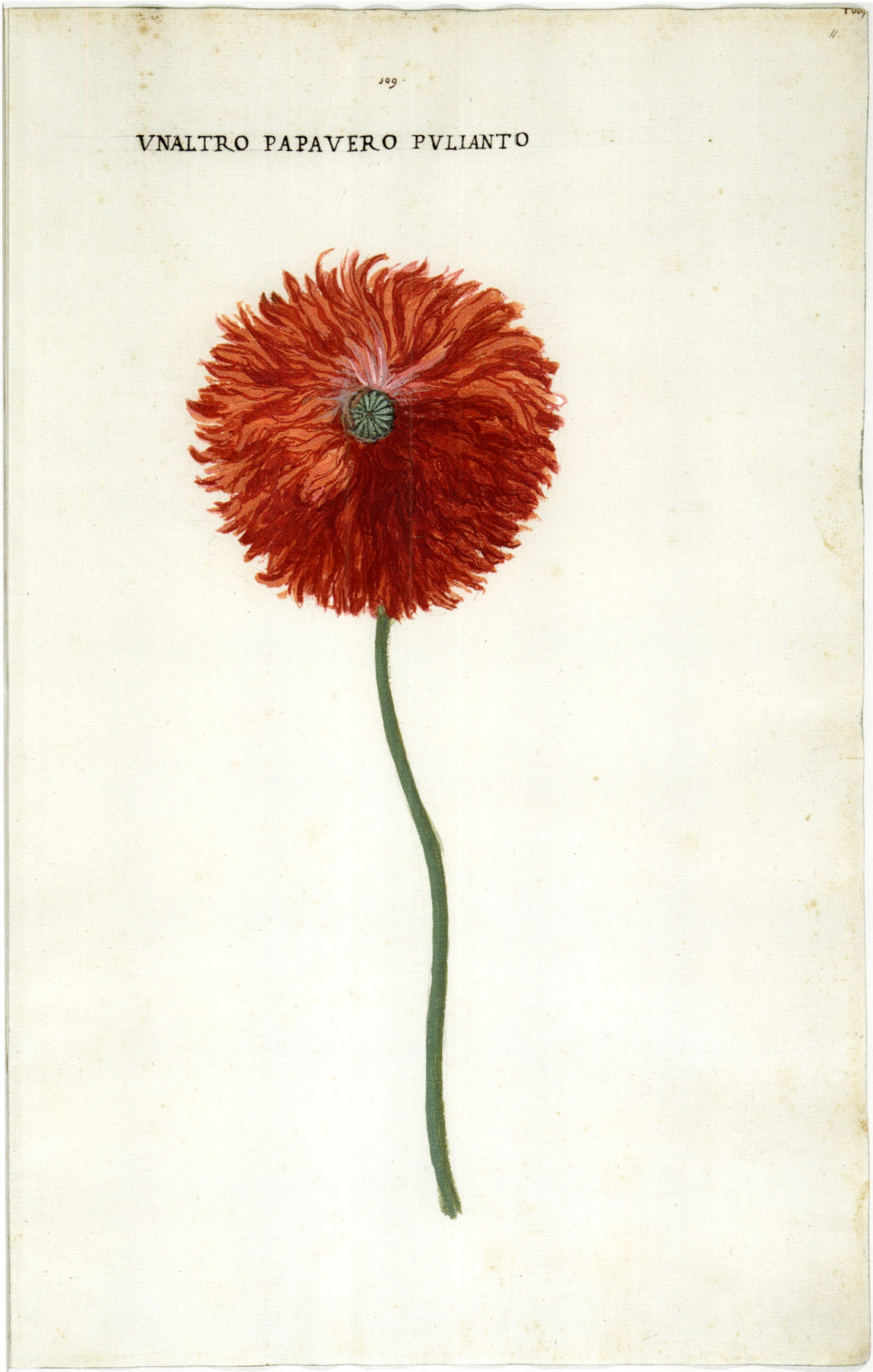
509
VNALTRO PAPAVERO PVLIANTO

12. Opium poppy, *Papaver somniferum* L. cv.

Erbario Miniato, fol. 12 (RL 27702)

Watermark: Eagle 20

NUMBERING: *510*

ANNOTATION: *UNALTRO PAPAVERO PULIANTO* ('Another many-flowered poppy')

As in **10**, the flower of this cultivar is composed of two different types of petal – four complete external petals with a typical spot of intense colour at their base, together with laciniate, fimbriate inner petals that hide the stamens and pistil. The large corolla is shown bending towards the earth, as if too heavy for its slender stem.

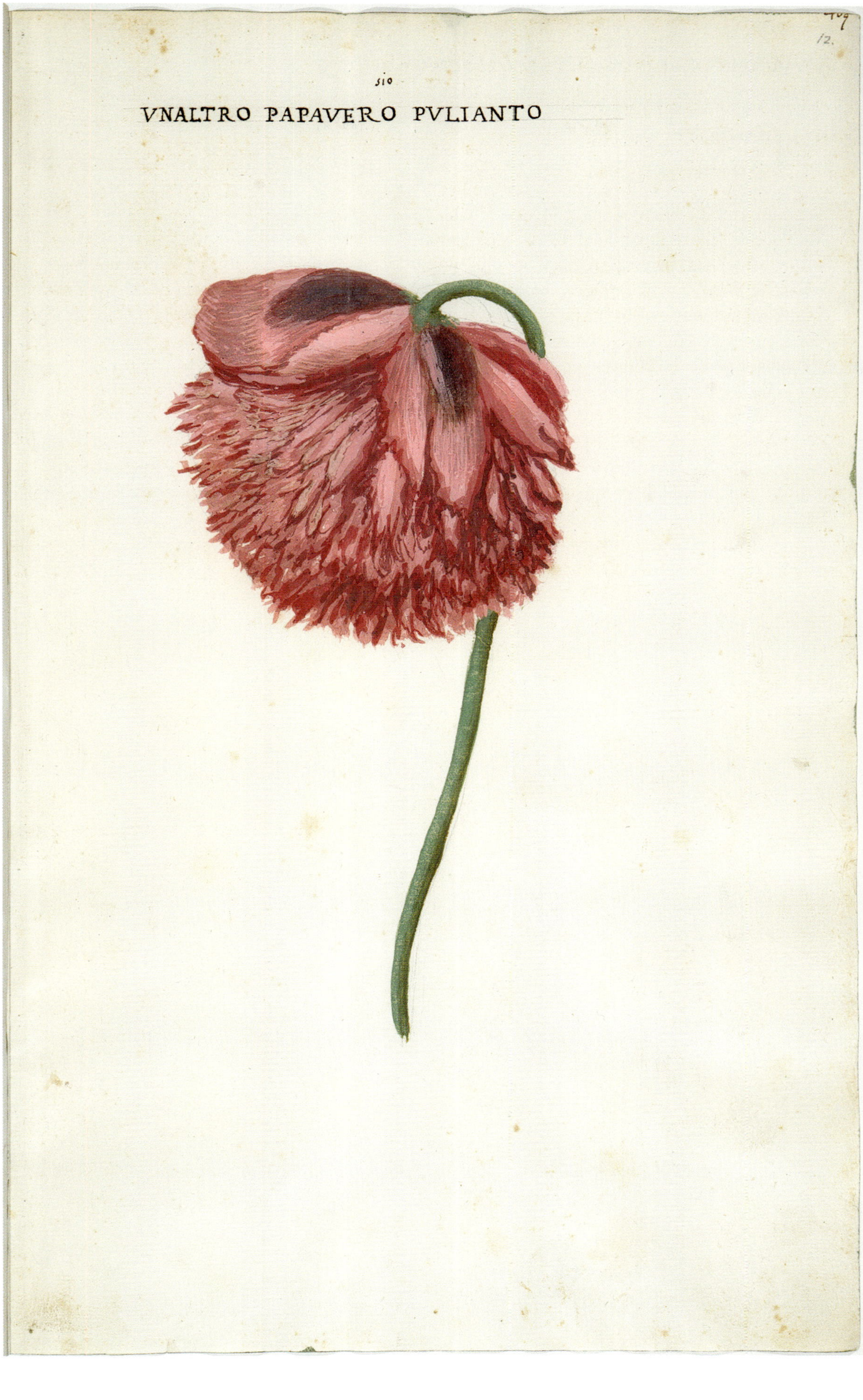
VNALTRO PAPAVERO PVLIANTO

13. Flower-of-an-hour, *Hibiscus trionum* L.

Erbario Miniato, fol. 13 (RL 27703)

NUMBERING: *511*

ANNOTATION: *Hipecoo. 1117.* [From Mattioli 1568, p. 1117]

The hibiscus is a herbaceous species of the family Malvaceae, native to the warmer temperate, subtropical and tropical regions of the world, where it flourishes in muddy terrain or under irrigated cultivation. In Italy it is an adventitious, naturalized, but fairly uncommon species. *Hibiscus trionum* is native to central Africa; when in bloom the flowers remain open for only a short period each day, hence its common name 'flower-of-an-hour'. While some species of hibiscus have been prized for their showy blossoms since the end of the sixteenth century, and the Chinese hibiscus *Hibiscus rosa-sinensis* in particular has yielded hundreds of cultivars, *Hibiscus trionum* is of only limited interest and in America the plant is considered a weed.

This drawing shows a plant in flower, complete with its root system. The stem of the plant is erect and covered with tiny hairs, the leaves are palmate-partite with lobes and the taproot runs almost horizontally, as often seen in medieval herbals. The specimen has five branches, each bearing three or four flowers shown in stages from a tightly closed bud to the fully opened blossom. The colour of the petals accords with that described by Mattioli: 'flowers whose white tends towards yellow, tinted, however, with red in their early stages, and at whose centre there is a cluster of gold' (*I Discorsi*, p. 1118). The pedicels are twice the length of the sepals, and the characteristic structure of the calyx can be clearly distinguished, with two whorls of sepals, an inner circle of ovate segments and an outer circle of acute linear segments (the epicalyx). The fruit, which takes the form of a large capsule, is not shown.

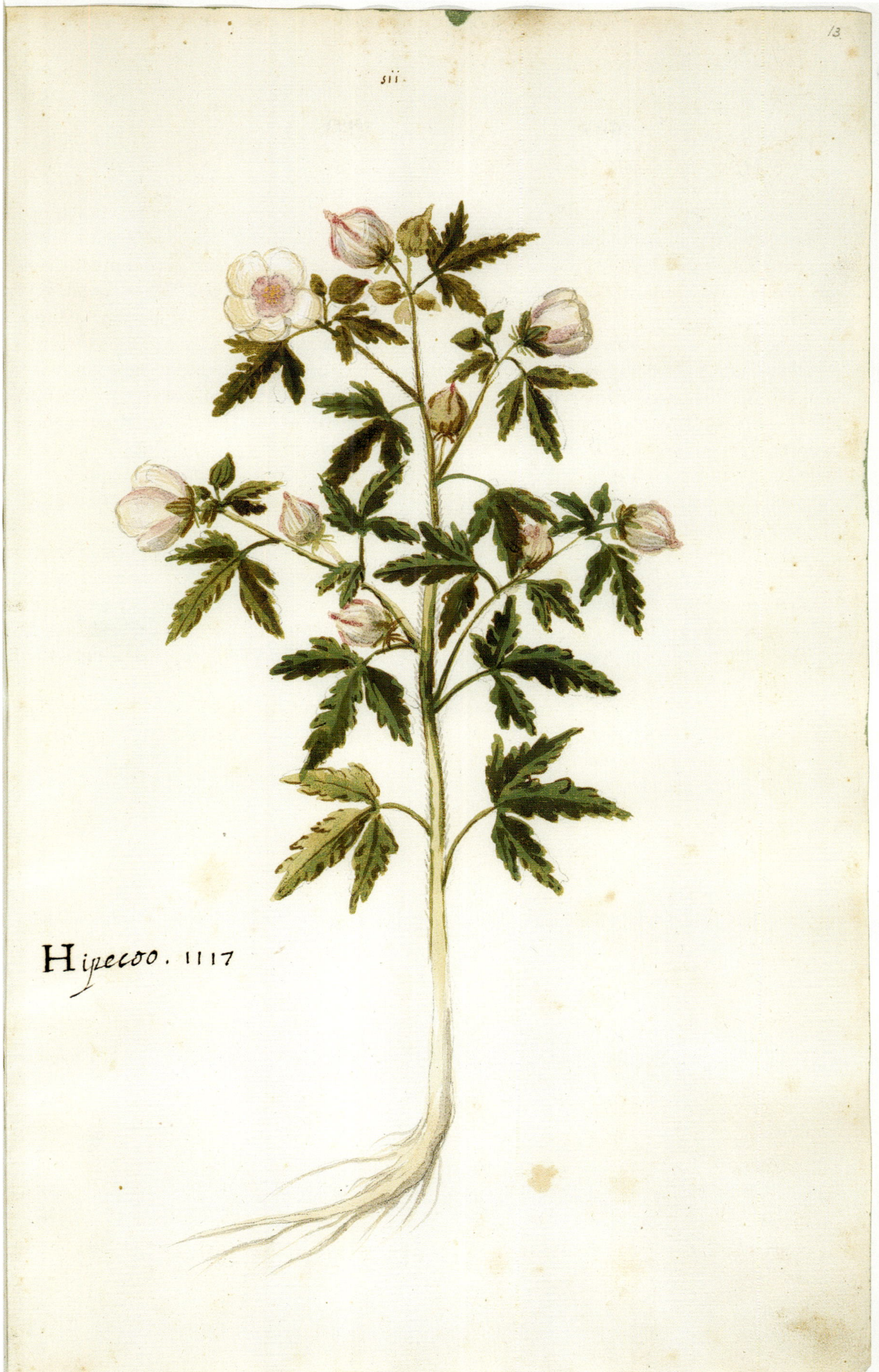
13
sii
Hipecoo. 1117

14. Henbane, *Hyoscyamus niger* L.

Erbario Miniato, fol. 14 (RL 27704)

NUMBERING: *512*

ANNOTATION: *Hiosciamo. 1119.* [From Mattioli 1568, p. 1119]

This drawing is the first of a series in the *Erbario Miniato* showing plants of the family Solanaceae, which includes about 90 genera and at least 2,300 species, many of importance as sources of food and drugs.

Henbane is a herbaceous biennial, common on disturbed ground throughout Europe, Asia and northern Africa, from sea level to high altitudes. It contains alkaloids whose medicinal properties were known in antiquity. Administered in minute doses, henbane has a tranquillizing effect and was used to treat cases of insomnia, cramps and convulsions. During the ninth century the plant was used, together with opium, hemlock and mandrake, to prepare the first anaesthetic, the *spongia somnifera* ('sleep-inducing sponge').

The vernacular name for the plant in Italian, *giusquiamo*, is derived from the Greek words ὗς (*hys*), 'pig', and κύαμος (*kyamos*), 'bean', as pigs were supposedly the only animals that could eat this poisonous plant without suffering any ill effects.

The drawing shows two flowering stems of black henbane. The specimen on the right is in full bloom, with each funnel-shaped corolla made up of five pale yellow petals with a dense tracing of veins that become darker towards the centre and the base of the blossom. Although the calyx of this species typically has five teeth, the calyxes shown here have several more. The details of the reproductive structures are not visible.

In the specimen on the left, the petals have dropped, leaving the mature fruit. The thick, grey, villose stem bears numerous calyxes in the fruiting stage and alternate, bluntly toothed, lanceolate leaves. The lower calyxes and leaves are large with short peduncles and petioles; both gradually become smaller and sessile towards the apex of the stem, which ends in a wilted flower. The mature calyxes, which are villous like the stem, have swelled in size and assumed their characteristic pitcher-like shape with toothed orifices.

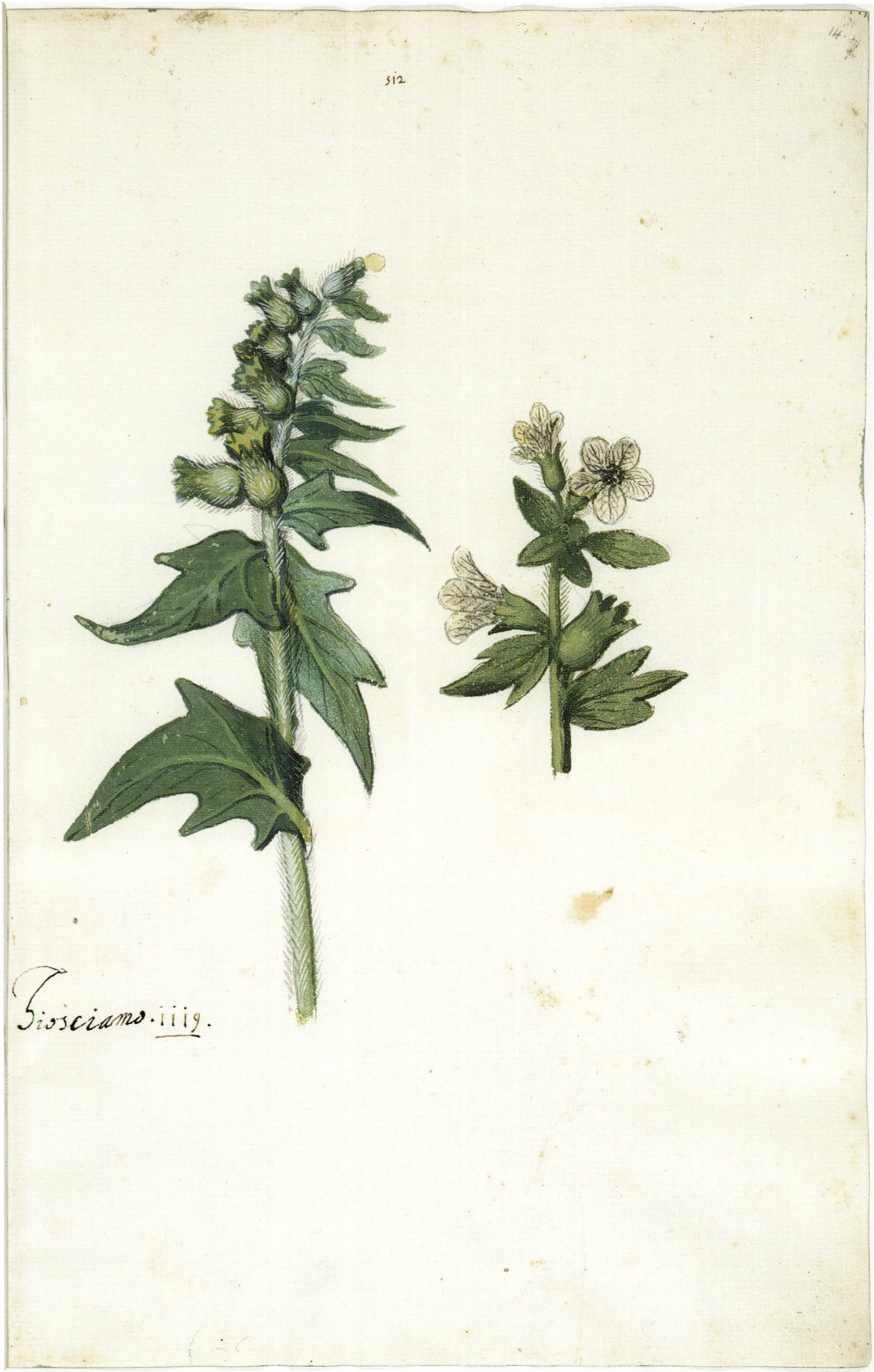
512
14
Iosciamo. iiiig.

15. Red nightshade, *Solanum villosum* Mill.

Erbario Miniato, fol. 15 (RL 27705)

NUMBERING: *513*

ANNOTATION: *Di molti e' diversi, / ~~sonno le~~ sorte / sonno i, solatri; Solatro hortolano. Ha virtù di rifrescare: le sue fronde / impiastrate con fiore di polenta giovano al fuoco sacro, è / al'ulcere serpigiose: sanano trite, e aplicate p[er] se sole, / le fistole lagrimali, e' i, dolori de la testa, conferiscono al / ardore de lo stomaco: trite con sale, e fattone impiastro riso= / lvano le posteme che vengano dopo le orecchie. il / succo mescolato con olio rosato. cerusa, e spiuma de / argento, conferisce al fuoco sacro. all'ulcere corosive: / e, incorporato con pane alle fistole lagrimali, fassene / utilmente linimento in su'l capo a' i fanciulli con olio ro=/ sato, per le infiamagione del li panicoli del cervello. di=/ stilato nelle orecchie leva via il dolore. aplicato di sotto / con lana. ristagna il flusso del mestuo. il succo mesco=/ lato con sterco giallo di gallina, che stia nei, cortili, e impi=/ astrato con tela, è rimedio presentaneo delle fistole lagri=/ mali 1125* ('There are many and diverse types of *solatri*. Garden *Solatro*. It has a cooling faculty. Its leaves applied with pearl barley flower are beneficial for holy fire [erysipelas] and serpiginous ulcers. The leaves, ground and applied alone, cure fistulas of the tear ducts and headaches and soothe a burning stomach; ground with salt and made into a poultice they cure the mumps. The juice mixed with rose oil, wax and silver foam [crystallized lead monoxide] relieves holy fire and corrosive ulcers; mixed with bread, it relieves fistulas of the tear ducts. A liniment can usefully be made for application with rose oil to the head of children for inflammations of the meninges of the brain. Dropped in the ears it relieves earache. Applied from below with wool it staunches menstrual flows. The juice mixed with the yellow dung of chickens and applied with a cloth provides an instant remedy for fistulas of the tear ducts. 1125'). [From Mattioli 1568, pp. 1124–5]

Red nightshade is a herbaceous annual of the family Solanaceae, and can be found in cultivated and abandoned fields all over the world. The vernacular name for the genus *Solanum* is 'nightshade' because of the poisonous properties of many of the species. All the green parts and the fruit contain poisonous alkaloids: tropeine, a substance which can cause mydriasis (excessive dilation of the pupil of the eye), and solanine, a highly toxic glucoalkaloid that has a narcotic effect on the central nervous system and can cause convulsions and death when ingested in large doses. The quantity of the active compounds in the plant varies, depending on the growing conditions, and the young leaves are eaten as a vegetable in some parts of Central and South America. In the past the juice extracted from this plant was used as an analgesic and sedative, and nightshade was one of the medicinal plants named after St John, because it was believed that they were most potent when gathered at the summer solstice, close to the feast day of the Baptist (24 June).

The stem of the nightshade may be either simple or branched at its base. This drawing illustrates a stem of the plant without its roots but with both fruit and flowers. The alternate leaves are ovate with long petioles and wavy margins, and taper to sharp points. The flowers, sprouting in widely spaced clusters from reflexed peduncles, are white with five or six petals each. The berries borne on long peduncles are green when young and bright red when mature; this plant may thus be identified as the red nightshade, *Solanum villosum*, rather than the closely related black nightshade, *Solanum nigrum*.

Mattioli identified and illustrated several varieties of 'Solatro', comparing Dioscorides' descriptions with his own knowledge of the plants: 'Solatro Hortolano' on p. 1125 (*Solanum nigrum*); 'Solatro Halicacabo' on p. 1126 (*Physalis alkekengi*, **16**); 'Solatro Sonnifero' on p. 1127 (*Withania somnifera*); another 'Solano Sonnifero' on p. 1128 (*Scopolia carniolica*, **19**); 'Solatro Maggiore overo Herba Belladonna' on p. 1129 (*Atropa belladonna*, **17**); and 'Vesicaria' on p. 1130 (*Cardiospermum halicacabum*). Cesi identified the present specimen with the *Solanum nigrum* illustrated on p. 1125, and associated that plate also with the next three specimens (**16–18**, *Physalis alkekengi*, *Atropa belladonna* and *Solanum pseudocapsicum*).

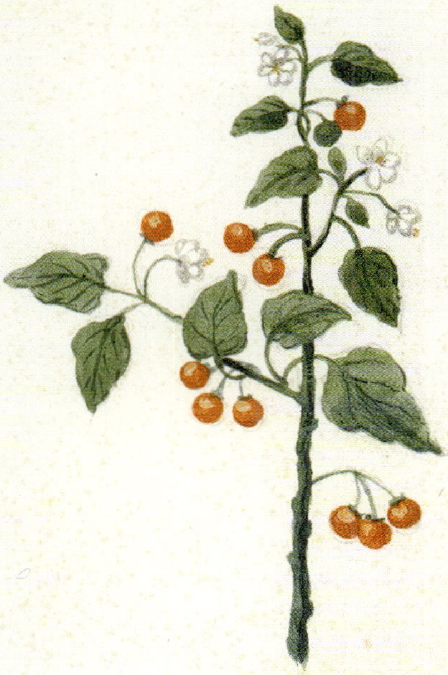

Di molti, e' diuersi,
~~[illegible]~~ sorte
sonno i, Solatri,

Solatro Hortolano. ha virtù di rifrescare: le sue fronde impiastrate con fiore di polenta giouano al fuoco sacro, e' al' ulcere serpigiose: sanano trite, e aplicate per se sole, le fistole lagrimali, e' i, dolori de la testa, conferiscono al ardore de lo stomaco: trite con sale, e fattone impiastro risoluano le postame che uengano dopo le orecchie. il succo mescolato con olio rosato. cerusa, e spiuma de argento, conferisce al fuoco sacro. all'ulcere corosiue: e incorporato con pane alle fistole lagrimali fassene utilmente linimento in su' l capo a' i fanciulli con olio rosato, per le infiamagione de li panicoli del ceruello. distilato nelle orecchie leua uia il dolore. aplicato disotto con lana. ristagna il flusso del mestruo. il succo mescolato con sterco giallo di gallina, che stia ne i, corbili, e impiastrato con tela. e' rimedio presentaneo delle fistole lagrimali 1125

16. Winter cherry or Chinese lantern, *Physalis alkekengi* L.

Erbario Miniato, fol. 16 (RL 27706)

Watermark: Fleur de lys 53

NUMBERING: *514*

ANNOTATION: *tre spetie de ~~S~~ Solatro, / questo alcuni lo chiamano / ~~A~~ halicacabo, e' altri Phisalida, / cioe vesciaria, a' la medesima / virtù che lortolano, ecetto che / no*[*n*] *si mangia ne i, cibi, il frutto beuto, giova al trabocco del fiele, / e' provoca lorina, 1125* ('Three species of *Solatro*. Some call this one *halicacabo*, and others *Phisalida*, that is *vesciaria*. This plant has the same properties as the garden *Solatro*, except that it cannot be eaten with food. The fruit when drunk is beneficial against excess bile [jaundice] and induces urination. 1125'). [From Mattioli 1568, p. 1124]

A perennial herbaceous species of the family Solanaceae, the winter cherry originally came from Asia and can now be found throughout southern and central Europe. It flourishes in damp, low-lying woodlands and in the undergrowth of higher plains, and is now widely cultivated as an ornamental plant. The winter cherry probably corresponds to the *halicacabos* of Dioscorides, a name that was rendered as *hab-kakeng* in medieval Arabic, and was subsequently modified into Italian common names such as *alkekengi*, *accatengi* and *chichingero*. According to the doctrine of signatures (see p. 38), the fruit resembled a vesicle containing a calculus, and was therefore used to treat kidney and gall-bladder stones; coincidentally, the plant does indeed have diuretic properties, because of an active substance in its calyx, stalk and leaves. In Asia the rhizomes are used to stimulate contractions during childbirth and as an expectorant to treat coughs.

This specimen has a glabrous stem with six leaves on long petioles. The leaves are ovate in shape, slightly lobed at the base, with entire, slightly wavy margins. There are two small white flowers on long peduncles (the artist has not drawn their calyxes, stamens or pistils), each springing from the axil of a leaf. To the right is an enlarged detail of the fruit, consisting of an orange-red calyx with five sepals that separate to reveal the bright red berry.

Cesi's annotation copies passages from Dioscorides' chapter on the 'Solatro Halicacabo' (p. 1124 in Mattioli's *Discorsi*), but mistakenly cites p. 1125, where a 'Solatro Hortolano' (*Solanum nigrum*) is depicted. The 'Solatro Halicacabo' (*Physalis alkekengi*) is illustrated on the following page, 1126 (see **15**). A fine drawing of this species was made by the unknown master 'ZS' at the beginning of the seventeenth century for the collection of the Botanic Garden of Pisa (Pisa, BU, MS 513, fol. 209).

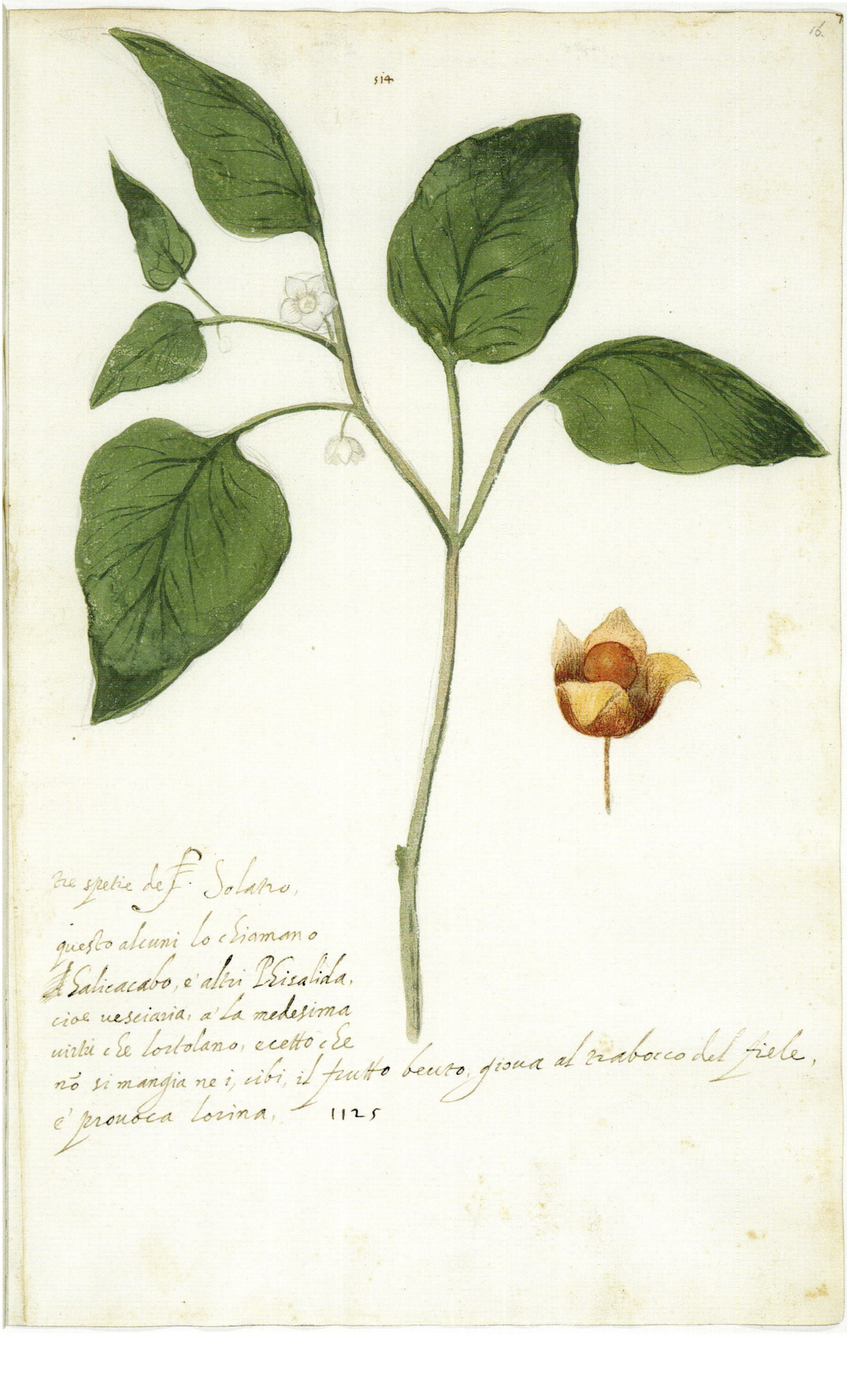
16.
514
tre spetie de Solano,
questo alcuni lo chiamano
Salicacabo, e' altri Phisalida,
cioe uesciaria, a' la medesima
uirtu che lortolano, ecetto che
nō si mangia ne i, cibi, il frutto beuto, gioua al trabocco del fiele,
e' prouoca lorina,
1125

17. Deadly nightshade or belladonna, *Atropa belladonna* L.

Erbario Miniato, fol. 17 (RL 27707)

Watermark: Eagle 18

NUMBERING: *515*

ANNOTATION: *Solatro sonifero. e' da alcuni halicacabo. 1125* ('Sleep-inducing *Solatro*, also called by some *halicacabo*. 1125'). [From Mattioli 1568, p. 1124]

Deadly nightshade or belladonna is a perennial bushy herb of the family Solanaceae. It can grow to a height of 1.5m and thrives in damp woodland, particularly beech, from sea level to an altitude of 1,400m. Though common in parts of Asia and central and southern Europe, it is rare in Italy. The eighteenth-century Swedish naturalist Carolus Linnaeus named this poisonous plant *Atropa belladonna* after one of the three Fates of Greek mythology, Atropos, who was responsible for cutting the thread of life. The leaves, flowers and berries contain the poisonous alkaloids atropine, hyoscine and hyoscyamine, used in therapeutic doses in the treatment of Parkinson's disease and to dilate the pupils during eye examinations. A preparation of belladonna was used as a cosmetic until the sixteenth century, applied to the eyes to dilate the pupils and make them more striking.

This drawing depicts the upper portion of a fruiting stem with six mature berries of a deep purplish-black. The calyx, which persists during fruition, is composed of five lobes fused at the base and along one-third of their length, opening to form a star-like frame around each berry. The large, alternate leaves are ovate in shape, tapering to sharp points, with smooth margins; the petioles are one-third as long as the leaves themselves.

As on **16** and **18**, Cesi's annotation mistakenly cites p. 1125 of the *Discorsi*, where a 'Solatro Hortolano' (*Solanum nigrum*) is depicted (see **15**). *Atropa belladonna* is illustrated on p. 1129, while the source of Cesi's annotation is Dioscorides' chapter on the 'Solatro sonnifero', p. 1124.

17.

515.

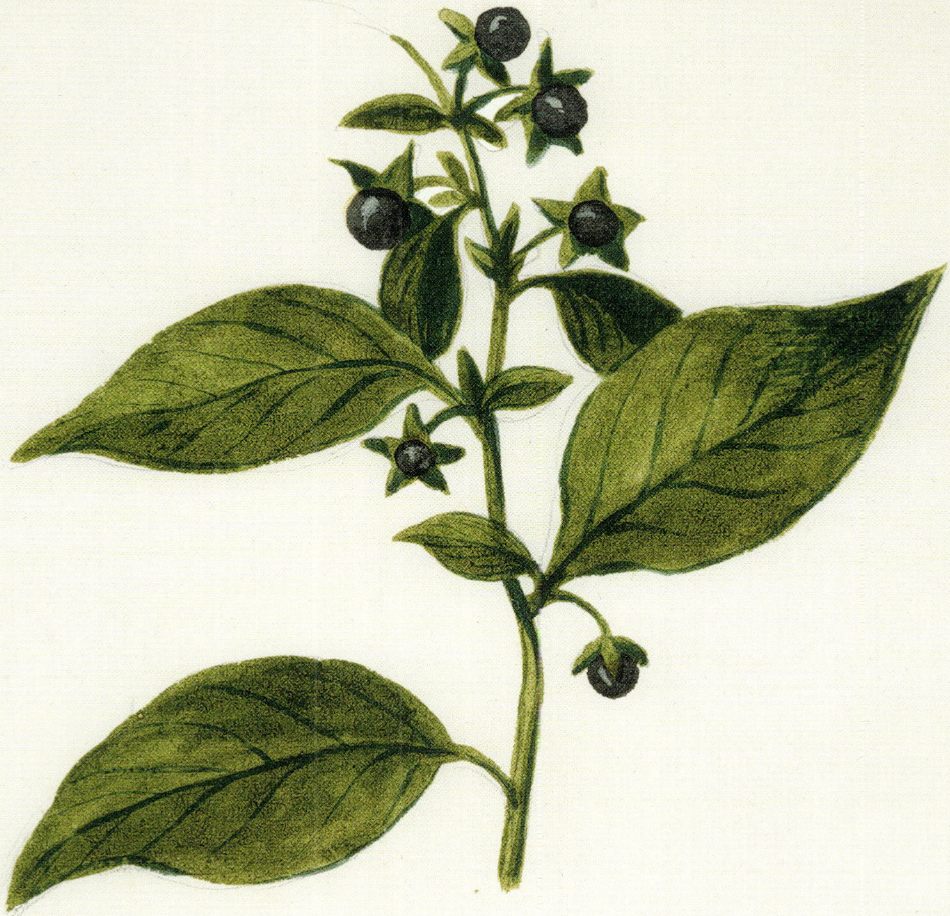

Solatro sonifero. è da alcuni Halicacabo. 1125.

18. Jerusalem cherry, *Solanum pseudocapsicum* L.

Erbario Miniato, fol. 18 (RL 27708)

Watermark: Eagle 14

NUMBERING: *516*

ANNOTATION: *Herba bella donna. Mangiato copiosamente, faccia / cosi lungamente dormire che amazzi. como essendo / intervenuto ad alcuni fanciulli. il quale no*[*n*] *conoscendo / il periculo. se le mangiareno. è spetie di solatro sonnifero. / 1125* ('*Herba bella donna* [lovely-woman herb]. Eaten in large quantities it makes one sleep for so long that one may die of it, as happened to some children who were ignorant of the danger and partook of it. It is a type of sleep-inducing *solatro*. 1125'). [From Mattioli 1568, p. 1131]

The Jerusalem cherry is a perennial shrub of the family Solanaceae, native to South America and growing to a height of 1m or more. Like many other members of the nightshade family, it contains toxic alkaloids, and its poisonous properties are noted in the inscription. Nonetheless, it is now a popular houseplant as it flowers during the winter months at northern latitudes.

The slender, tapering twig on the right carries three flowers on short pedicels, white with six reflexed petals (unlike the five-petalled flowers produced by most of the other members of the family Solanaceae). The stamens have yellow anthers that come together to form an erect spur. The fruiting branch on the left bears five crimson berries. The lanceolate leaves are dark green, becoming slightly yellower when the plant is in flower, with short petioles, entire margins and smooth surfaces through which the veins are clearly discernible.

The annotation mistakenly cites p. 1125 of the *Discorsi* (as on **16** and **17**), where a 'Solatro Hortolano' (*Solanum nigrum*) is depicted. The Jerusalem cherry was not among the 'Solatri' illustrated by Mattioli (see **15**), but as Cesi's annotation copies Mattioli's passage on the 'Herba bella donna' (p. 1131), he clearly identified the two specimens on this sheet as *Atropa belladonna*, illustrated on p. 1129 (see **17**).

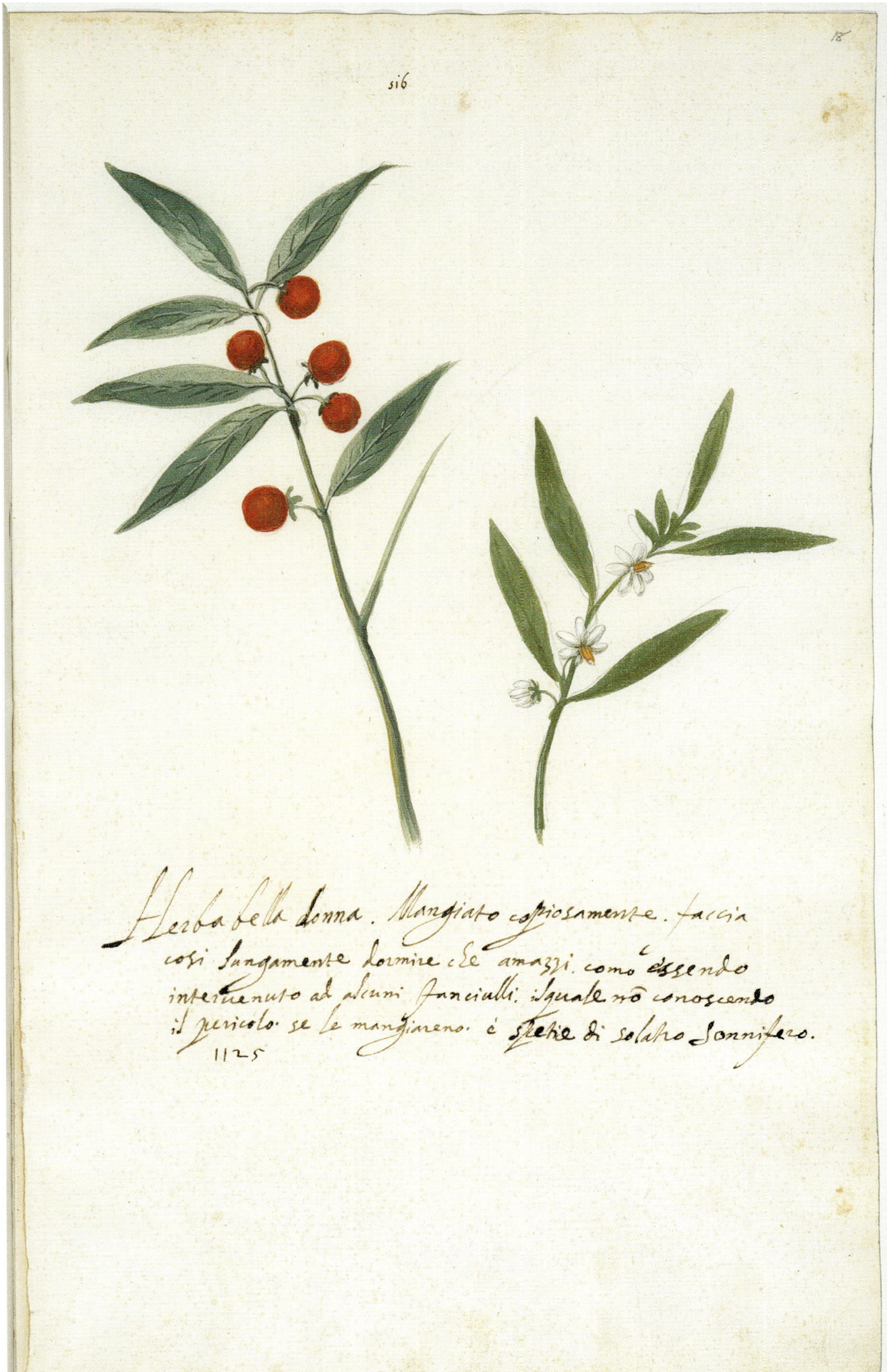
18
516
Herba bella donna. Mangiato copiosamente. faccia
così lungamente dormire che amazzi. como essendo
interuenuto ad alcuni fanciulli: i quale nō conoscendo
il pericolo se le mangiareno. è spetie di solatro Sonnifero.
1125

19. Scopolia, *Scopolia carniolica* Jacq. 1764

Erbario Miniato, fol. 19 (RL 27709)

NUMBERING: *517*

ANNOTATION: *Unaltro solatro Son*[*n*]*ifero, la sua virtu e' neilartri, fogli, nel grande. 1128* ('Another sleep-inducing *solatro*; its properties are found on the other sheets. In the large [edition of Mattioli], p. 1128'). [From Mattioli 1568, p. 1128]

The drawing shows a flowering stem of *Scopolia carniolica*, a perennial herbaceous species of the family Solanaceae, and similar to the deadly nightshade (**17**). It is native to the mountains of Europe, growing in broadleaved forests in the Alps, the Carpathian mountains and the Caucasus at altitudes from 500m to 1,500m. In Italy the plant is found only in the Carnic Alps. Linnaeus assigned this species to the genus *Hyoscyamus*, but because of differences in the structure of the flower, Nicolaus Joseph Jacquin renamed it in 1764 after the naturalist Antonio Scopoli, in whose *Flora Carniolica* (1760) it was described. The scopolia has many therapeutic properties and may be used as a substitute for deadly nightshade. The rhizome contains the alkaloids scopolamine and josciamine, both of which have been employed in the past as 'truth serums'.

The artist has depicted a single stem of the plant with three flowers in different stages of development – in bud, in full flower and wilting. The pedicel of each flower arises from the base of a leaf. The bell-shaped corolla is purplish-red, with a calyx that is divided into lobes for two-thirds of its length. The leaves are oval in shape with unbroken margins and tapered ends.

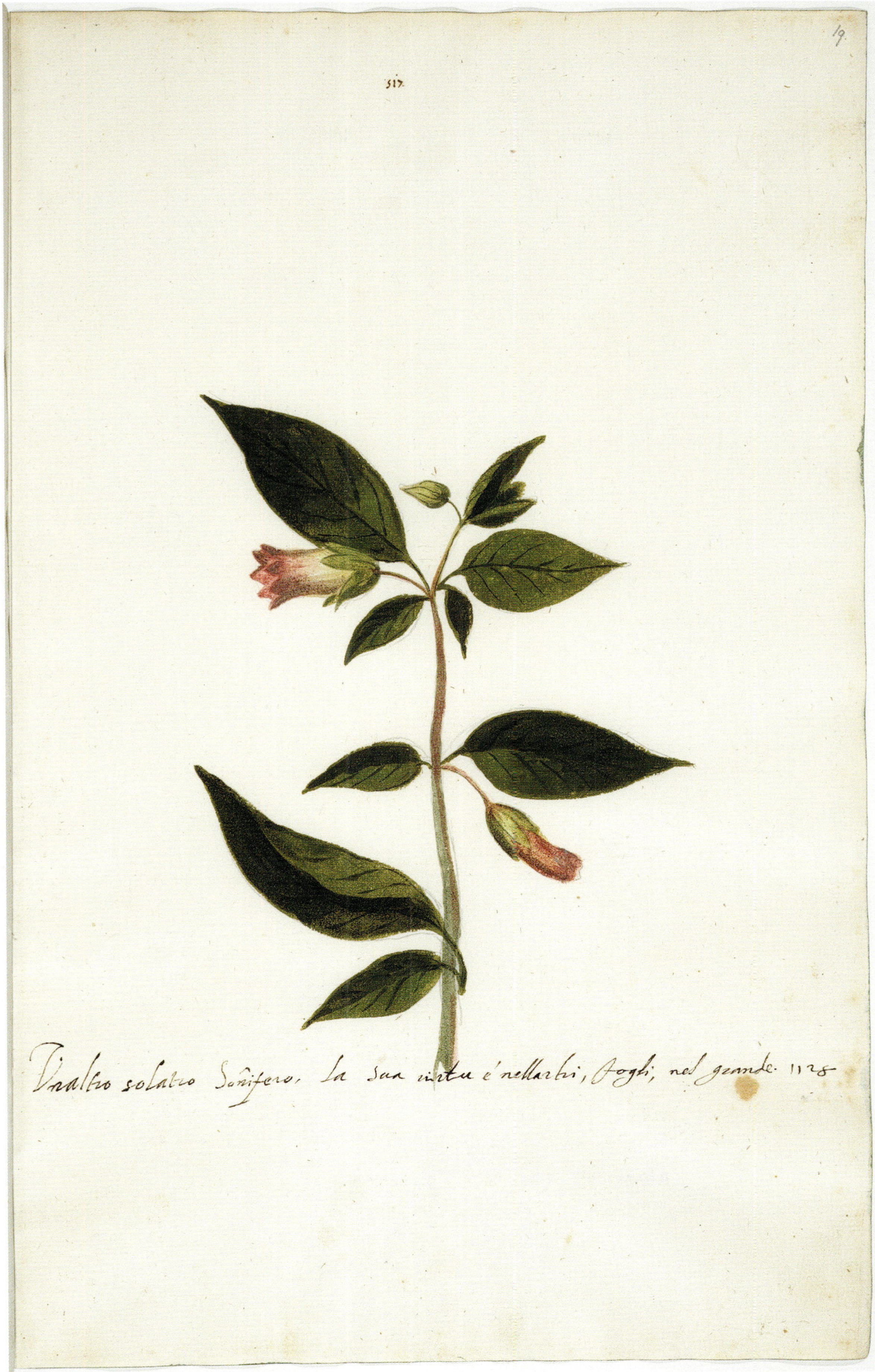
19
517
Vnaltro solatro Sonifero, la sua virtu è nellarbi, Fogli, nel grande. 1128

20. Autumn mandrake, *Mandragora officinarum* L.

Erbario Miniato, fol. 20 (RL 27710)

Upper right figure cut from another sheet, then inlaid (the fruit) and pasted (the stalk) on to the folio

NUMBERING: *518*

ANNOTATION: *Mandragola 1133; chiamano alcuni la Mandragola Antimello, e' / altri Circea. fa dormire. il succo beuto al peso / de doii oboli con vino melato purga p[er] il vomito. / metesi nelle medecine de gli ochii, aplicato di sotto / p[er] se solo tira i, mestuo. e' il parto. messo p[er] / soposta nel sedero fa dormire. Le fronde / fresche. risolvano tutte le durezze. posteme / scrofole, e' altri picoli tumori. La radice trita / e' impiastrata con aceto, medica il fuoco sacro. / mitiga li dolori de le gionture, quegli che ꝑ tro=/ ppo ~~li~~mangiano li suoi pomi e' anco li odo=/ rono. diventano muti, mangiando la radice. / fa impazire.* ('Mandrake, 1133. Some call the mandrake *Antimello* and others *Circea*. It induces sleep. The juice, drunk in the amount of two oboli with honey wine, purges by vomiting. Used in medicines for the eyes. Applied from below on its own it stimulates menstruation and childbirth. Used as a suppository it induces sleep. The fresh leaves cure all hardnesses, abscesses, scrofulas and other small tumours. The root ground and applied with vinegar treats holy fire [erysipelas]. It relieves pains in the joints. Those who eat too liberally of its berries, or even smell them, become mute. Eating the root induces madness.'). [From Mattioli 1568, pp. 1132–4]

The mandrake is a herbaceous perennial of the family Solanaceae, common in parts of southern Europe, including Sicily, but rare in the rest of Italy. It thrives in arid, stony terrain from sea level to an altitude of 600m.

The mandrake is characterized by a rosette of leaves above ground and a large rhizomatous root that may extend as far as 1m beneath the ground. The name *mandragola* is probably derived from the Persian *mardum-giâ* or 'herb of man', a name inspired by the supposed similarity of the root to the human body, in some cases complete with male or female sexual attributes. Dioscorides called the plant *antropomorphón*. During the Middle Ages merchants enhanced this resemblance by carving mandrake (or other) roots into miniature models of human beings (see Thompson 1934, pp. 122–7). The finest specimens were dressed in costly gowns and carefully conserved, and two mandrake roots in an ornate casket formed part of the natural history collection of the Emperor Charles V (1500–58). The scream of the plant on being uprooted was supposed to be fatal to any who heard it. Those wishing to procure the miraculous root were therefore advised to tie a dog to the plant, so that in the course of trying to get home it would pull up the mandrake and die from its scream while the human gatherer was safely out of earshot.

Aphrodisiac properties were also attributed to the root. Niccolò Machiavelli's satirical play on contemporary manners was entitled *La mandragola*, and in France up until the end of the nineteenth century it was the custom at country weddings to offer the bride and groom a cup of wine containing powdered mandrake root. In reality its medicinal properties are limited to the anaesthetic, antispasmodic and soporific effects of its alkaloids. The plant's sleep-inducing properties were supposedly used during the First Punic War by the Carthaginian general Hamilcar, who drugged the wine of the Syracusan army with mandrake and killed them in their sleep. Shakespeare has Iago say to Othello: 'Not poppy, nor mandragora, / Nor all the drowsy syrups of the world, / Shall ever medicine thee to that sweet sleep / Which thou owedst today' (*Othello*, III.iii).

Unlike most of the drawings in the *Erbario Miniato*, the artist has shown three details rather than a whole section of the plant. Dominating the page is an enlarged drawing of the basal leaf, oval with a blunt apex, undulating margins and strongly marked veins emerging from a thick, whitish central rib. The flower has a long peduncle, sharply toothed calyx and funnel-shaped corolla divided into five deep lobes. The petals are a very pale blue, flushed with pink at the margins, and marked by a delicate tracery

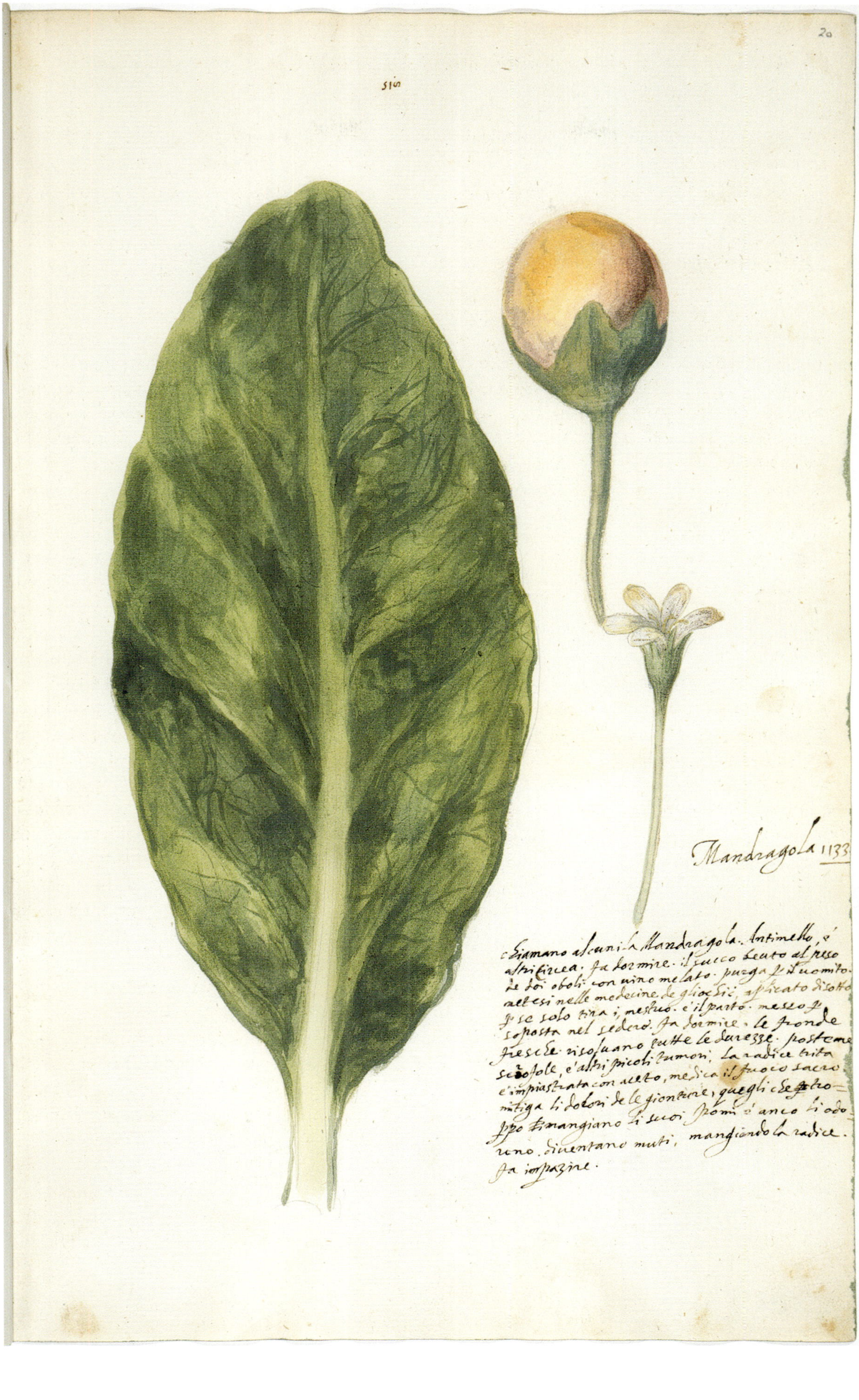
Mandragola 1133

of veins. Above the flower is an enlarged drawing of the plant's orange-coloured fruit with its enlarged, persistent calyx, a detail cut out from another sheet. Strangely, the root is not shown.

Mattioli's *Discorsi* illustrates two mandrake plants with their roots: a 'Mandragora Maschio' ('male mandrake', p. 1133) and a 'Mandragora Femina' ('female mandrake', p. 1134), both of which are identifiable as *Mandragora officinarum*.

21. Aubergine, *Solanum melongena* L.

Erbario Miniato, fol. 21 (RL 27711)

Watermark: Fleur de lys 49

NUMBERING: *519*

ANNOTATION: *Fior' di Melanzane; Maschio; femina; Melanzane, in lombardia e' in Toscana Petranciani, è spetie / di mandragola, overo p[er] piu proprio nome Mele insane, sonno / di natura loro. ventosi e' dure a' digirire, generano humori Malinconici, / huppilationi, Cancheri, lepra, dolore di testa, tristezze, opilatione di fegato / e' di milza. e' fanno cativo colore per tutto la persona, e' febre longhe, / 1135.* ('Aubergine flowers; male; female; aubergines, called in Lombardy and Tuscany *Petranciani*. They are a kind of mandrake, or to give them their proper name, *Mele insane* [unhealthy apples]. They are by nature gaseous and difficult to digest. They generate melancholy humours, occlusions, cancers, leprosy, headache, sadness, obstructions of the liver and spleen, and lend an unhealthy colour to the whole person, and persistent fevers. 1135.'). [From Mattioli 1568, pp. 1135–6]

LITERATURE: Freedberg 2002, p. 204 (fig. 8.1)

The nightshade family (Solanaceae) includes many edible as well as poisonous species. This drawing shows two flowers and two fruits of the aubergine, one of the few nightshades to thrive in warm climates. It probably originated in south-east Asia (though it is not now known in the wild) and is cultivated in many parts of the world. The aubergine was not thought edible by the Greeks and Romans, and it first appeared on Italian tables in the fourteenth century, although it was still considered somewhat indigestible. It has, however, always been highly regarded in India, where the forms known in Europe may have originated. The young fruit contains significant levels of the poisonous alkaloid solanine (also present in the green parts of the aubergine's close relative, the potato), which is destroyed by heat when the aubergine is cooked.

The pale lilac, bell-shaped corolla of the flower is made up of five deeply incised and acutely pointed lobes. The calyx, which remains attached to the mature fruit, is also bell-shaped with five deeply incised teeth. The peduncle is twice as long as the calyx, and both are sparsely covered with spinules. The fruit may vary in shape from subspherical to oval, as shown in these two specimens, and may range in colour from dark violet to white; a common name for the species – eggplant – is derived from a variety with a white, oval-shaped fruit similar to that illustrated on the next folio.

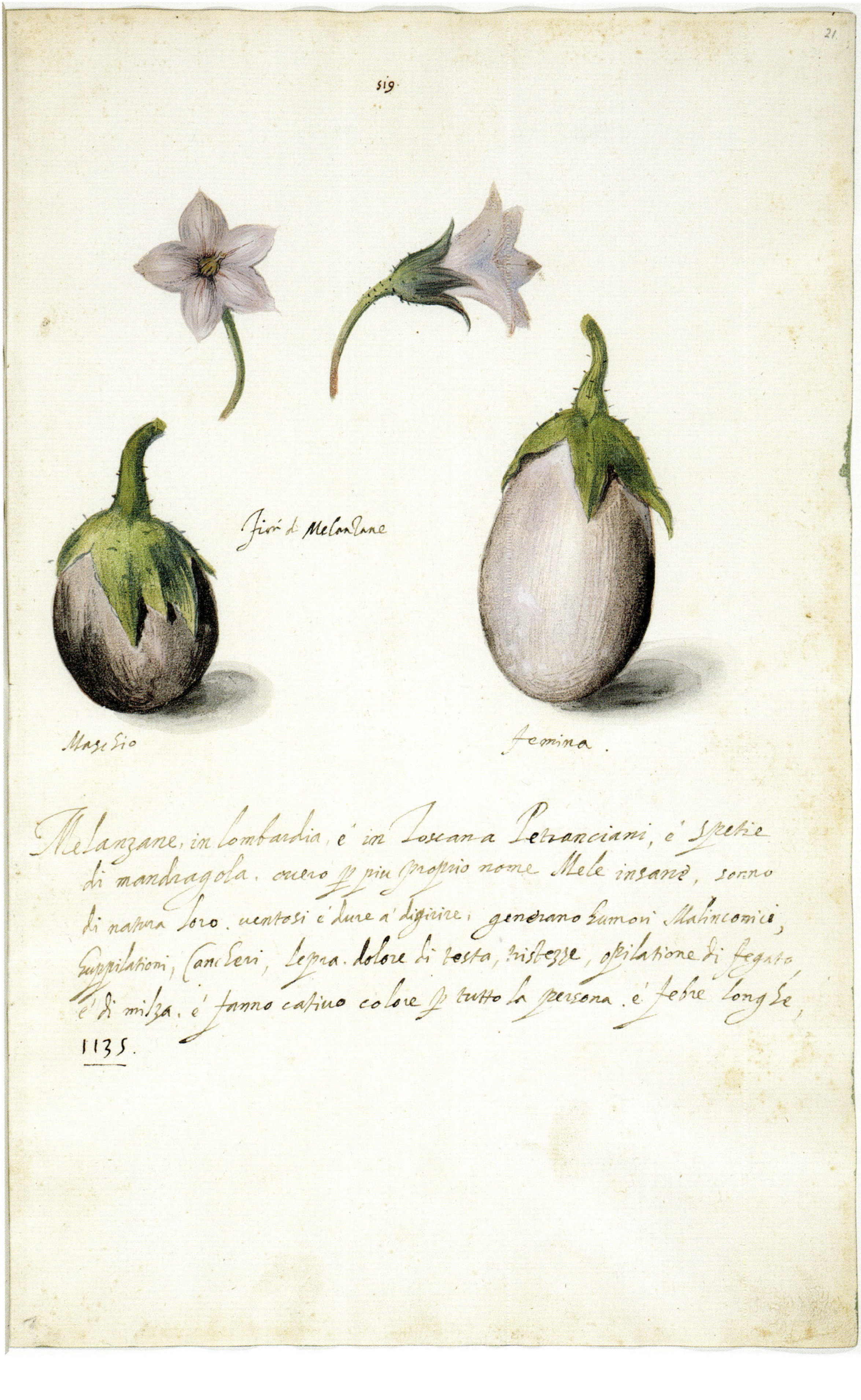
519
Fior di Melanzane
Maschio
femina.
Melanzane, in lombardia, è in Toscana Petranciani, è spetie
di mandragola. ouero per piu proprio nome Mele insane, sonno
di natura loro. uentosi è dure à digirire, generano humori Malinconici,
suppilationi, Cancheri, lepra. dolore di testa, tristezze, opilatione di fegato
è di milza. è fanno catiuo colore per tutto la persona. è febre longhe,
1135.

22. Aubergine, *Solanum melongena* L.

Erbario Miniato, fol. 22 (RL 27712)

NUMBERING: *520*

ANNOTATION: *Melinsani*

This sheet shows a stem of the aubergine (see **21**), the fruit white in colour and hanging, nearly ripe, from a long, robust peduncle. The erect, contorted and branched stem bears five pointed leaves with undulating, lobed margins and long petioles. An accidental splash of colour just below the fruit is masked with white lead.

At the beginning of the nineteenth century the agronomist, botanist and director of the botanical gardens of Modena and Bologna, Filippo Re (1762–1817), catalogued the cultivars of the aubergine, and the specimen here probably corresponds to his 'Petranciana bianca'.

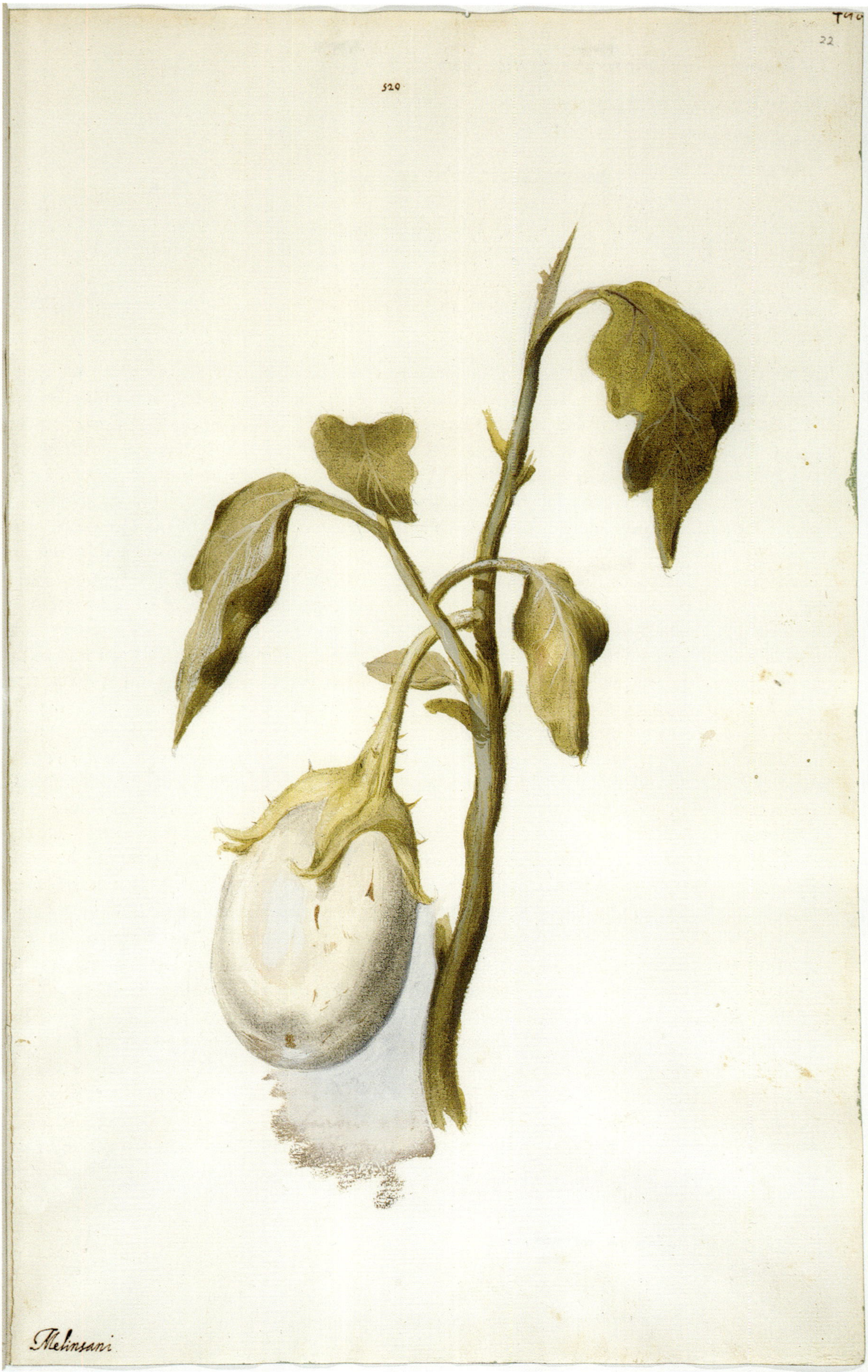
22
520
Melinsani

23. Tomato, *Lycopersicon esculentum* Mill.

Erbario Miniato, fol. 23 (RL 27713)

Watermark: Eagle 18

NUMBERING: *521*

ANNOTATION: *Pomi doro. sonno buoni da Mangiare como le meli insanie./ 1136. 56 se ritrovano di doi sorte. luna rossi e' laltri / gialli che rasembrano oro.* ('*Pomi d'oro* [golden apples]. They are good to eat like aubergines. [Page] 1136, [line] 56. There are two types, one red and the other yellow, resembling gold.'). [From Mattioli 1568, p. 1136]

LITERATURE: *Cassiano* cat. 1993, p. 200 (cat. 123); *Cassiano* cat. 1997, p. 31 (cat. 58); Freedberg 2002, pp. 204–5 (fig. 8.2)

The tomato is a herbaceous annual of the family Solanaceae. Native to the Americas, it was one of the most important food plants brought back to Europe following the Spanish conquest, and is now cultivated all over the world. Its English name is derived from the Nahuatl *tumatl* or *tumal*; Mattioli first recorded the name *pomodoro* or 'golden apple' in his chapter on the mandrake (where he also discusses the aubergine), but he did not illustrate the plant. The *Cinque libri di piante* by Pietro Antonio Michiel (1510–76) lists the tomato's names as 'Licopersicon Galeni oppure Pomodoro da volgari, oppure melongiana da Latini oppure poma amoris da alcuni et del Perù' (Venice, Biblioteca Marciana, MS Marc.It.II, 29, ch. 46.). The name *poma amoris* was found in English as 'love apple', a term that was current until the early nineteenth century.

Though the tomato was a staple food of the people of central and southern America, it was regarded as only an ornamental plant when it was introduced to Europe – in 1523 in Spain, in 1544 in Italy and later in the sixteenth century in England – and indeed the immature fruit, as well as the stem and leaves, are toxic because they contain solanine, the same alkaloid found in the potato and aubergine (see **21**). One of the first images of this plant appears in the 'Drake Manuscript' or *Histoire naturelle des Indes* of the late sixteenth century (New York, Morgan Library, MA 3900, fol. 7v); the inscription accompanying the drawing states that it was a 'Tomates – a delicious fruit which grows in the woods and can be eaten with fish or meat'. Of its medicinal properties the sixteenth-century French physician and botanist Jacques Daléchamps wrote that 'these apples, as indeed the entire plant, have a cooling faculty at least as great as that of the mandrake' (Daléchamps 1586, p. 628). The first Europeans to exploit the tomato as a food were the Italians – as demonstrated by the inscription on this folio. It was rarely eaten in northern Europe or England until the beginning of the nineteenth century, and its popularity grew with the development of the canning industry, the first large factory in Italy being opened by Francesco Cirio in 1875.

Shown here are the end of a fruiting branch, a smaller flowering branch and a single mature fruit. The branch in the centre of the drawing bears three fruits at various stages of ripening. The lower one hangs from a long, slightly bowed peduncle and has a persistent calyx; its fine red colour indicates that it is ripe. The two smaller fruits are green and immature. The branch ends in a pinnate leaf made up of five leaflets alternating with tiny lobes. The flowering branch has a thin hairy stem with three yellow flowers and an unopened bud, all on long peduncles. Each flower is composed of eight lanceolate petals that spread open completely and bend backwards slightly at their extremities when in full bloom. The calyx consists of eight to ten linear sepals which are longer than the petals. The androecium is erect and clearly visible.

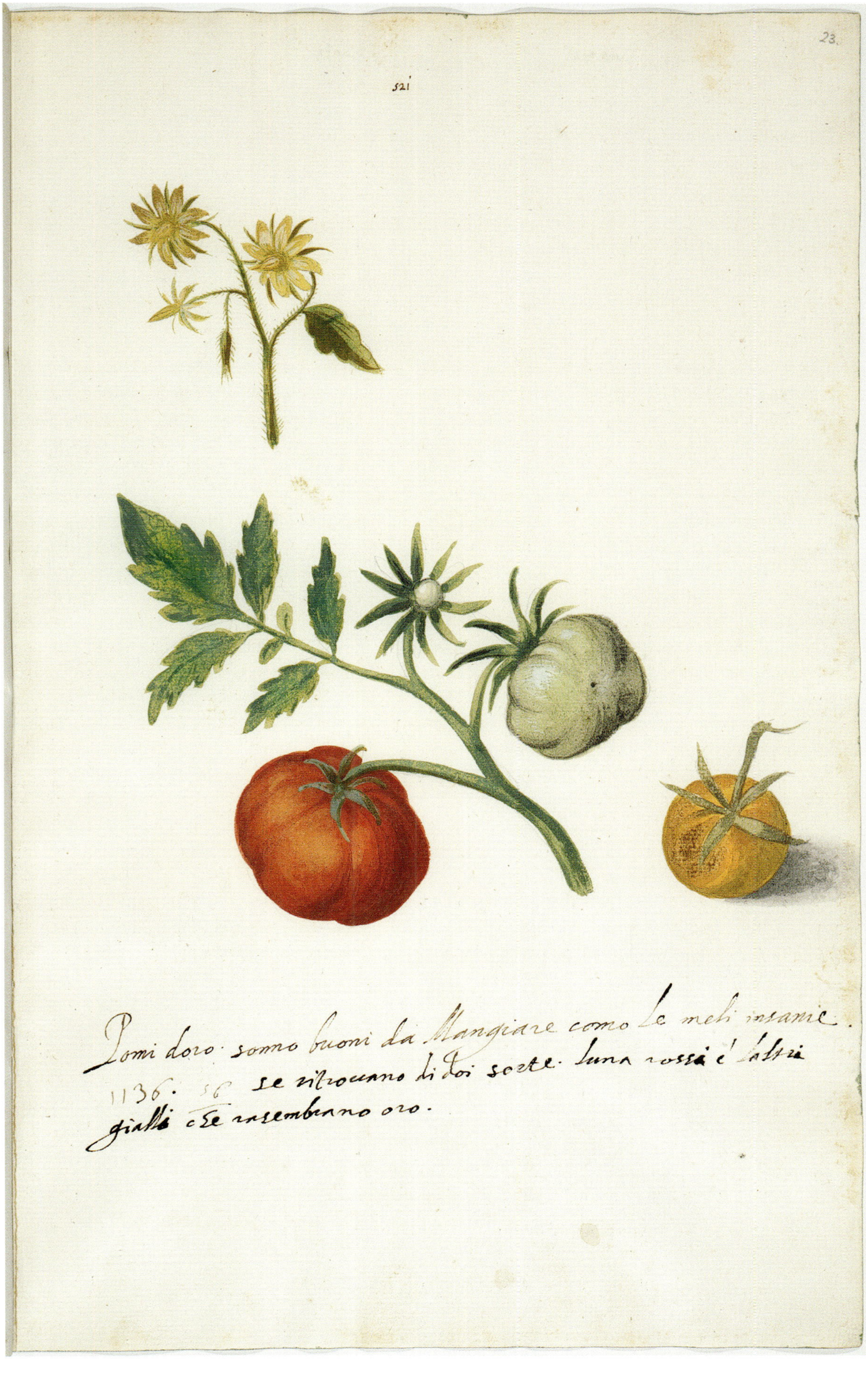
23.
521
Pomi doro· somno buoni da Mangiare como le meli insanie.
1136. 56 se ritrovano di doi sorte· luna rossa è laltra
gialli che rasembrano oro.

24. Leopard's bane, *Doronicum pardalianches* L.

Erbario Miniato, fol. 24 (RL 27714)

Left-hand figure and title inscription cut from another sheet and pasted on to the folio

Watermark: Fleur de lys 44

NUMBERING: *522*

ANNOTATION: *ACONITO PARDALIANCHE; Aconitum Pardalianches.* ~~*Dioscoridis.*~~ *Plinii / nel Eicones. 57980 / Aconito Pardalianche di* ~~*Dioscoride*~~ *Plinio. / nel Matthiolo. 1138* ('~~Dioscorides'~~ Pliny's *Aconitum Pardalianches.* In *Eicones* 57980. ~~Dioscorides'~~ Pliny's *Aconito Pardalianche.* In Mattioli 1138'). [From Mattioli 1568, p. 1138; Tabernaemontanus 1590, p. 580]

VERSO: offset of **26**

The leopard's bane, a herbaceous perennial of the family Asteraceae, is native to central and western Europe, growing in wooded areas and ravines. The plant is similar in structure to members of the genus *Arnica*, differing primarily in having alternate rather than opposite leaves. Its common name is derived from the Greek παρδαλιαγχές (*pardalianchés*), 'leopard-choking', a property which Aristotle, Dioscorides and Galen attributed to the aconite (monkshood), but which Linnaeus instead associated with this plant, for it was believed that it contained a poison so strong that it could kill leopards and other beasts if its roots or leaves were mixed with food and left in front of their dens. Nonetheless, an infusion of the roots was used as a mild tonic, and the plant was employed, like arnica, as a tincture to treat bruises and wounds. The origin of the genus name *Doronicum* is unclear; it was used for the first time by Tournefort and was later adopted by Linnaeus.

The folio shows two flowering stems of the plant; that on the left is erect, glabrous and branching, with three widely spaced, alternate, sessile leaves which closely envelop the stem. The leaves are heart-shaped with toothed margins, and taper to sharp points. The inflorescence consists of flower heads on long peduncles united in loose corymbs. The external petals of each flower are long and narrow with parallel margins, while the central petals are tubular. The enveloping bracts are linear and acute. The specimen on the right is similar, but the flower heads are completely open and the stem is hairy.

The annotation identifies the specimens as the 'Aconito Pardalianche di Plinio' illustrated by Mattioli on p. 1138 of his *Discorsi* and the 'Aconitum Pardalianches Plinij' found on p. 580 of Tabernaemontanus's *Eicones plantarum seu stirpium*. While the latter illustration corresponds to *Doronicum pardalianches*, Mattioli's woodcut corresponds to another species of leopard's bane, *Doronicum columnae*. *Doronicum pardalianches* is actually illustrated on the following pages of the *Discorsi*, pp. 1139 and 1140, labelled 'Aconito Pardalianche di Theophrasto' and 'Aconito Pardalianche Minore chiamato falsamente Doricnio'.

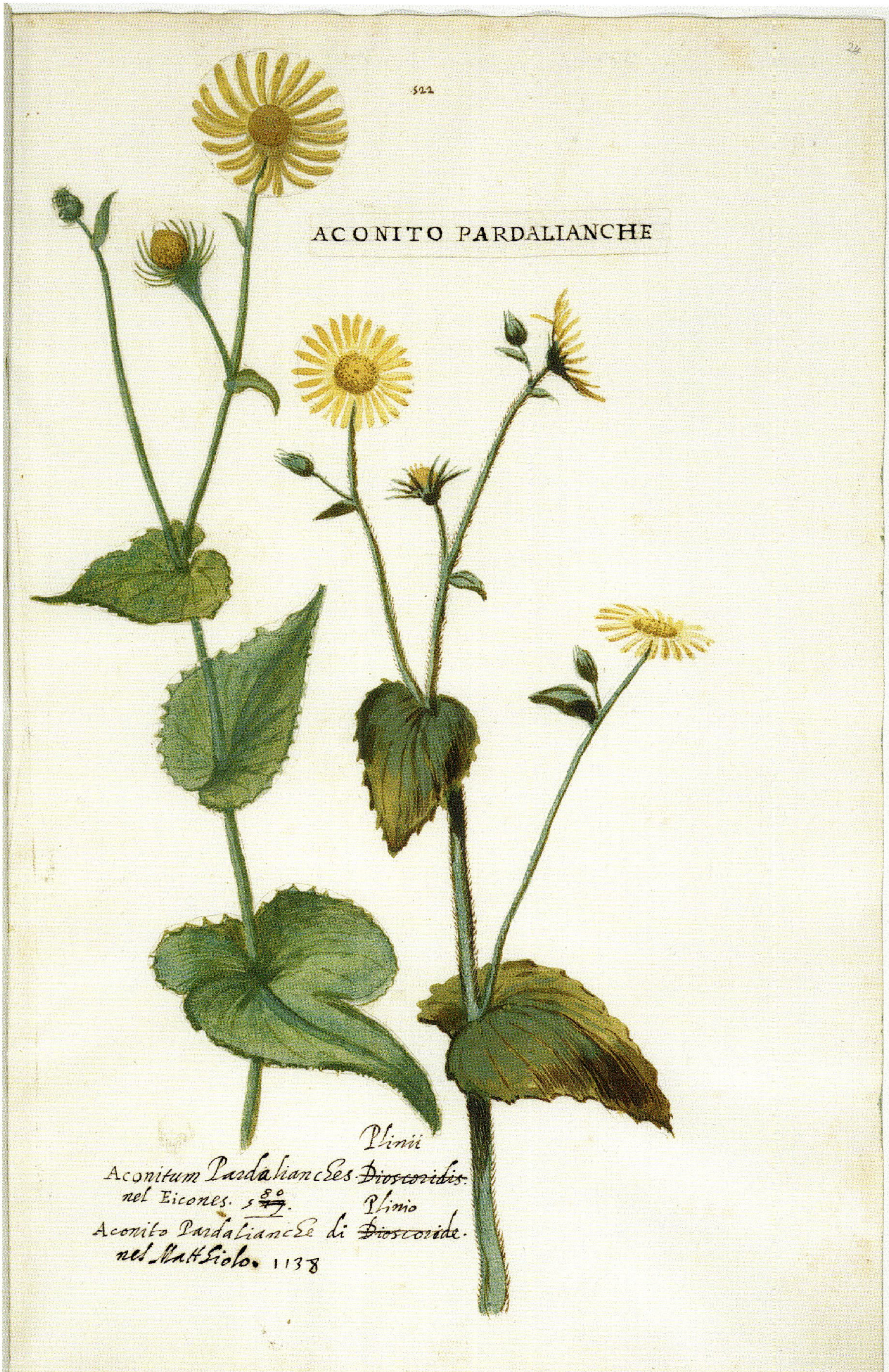
522
24
ACONITO PARDALIANCHE
Plinii
Aconitum Pardalianches ~~Dioscoridis.~~
nel Eicones. 580
Plinio
Aconito Pardalianche di ~~Dioscoride.~~
nel Matthiolo. 1138

25. Winter aconite, *Eranthis hyemalis* (L.) Salisb. 1807

Erbario Miniato, fol. 25 (RL 27715)

NUMBERING: *523*

ANNOTATION: *Aconito. 1139; Molti sonno le spetie de gli aconiti, la cui virtu, e' anco lor' / veleno si scrivera in unaltra sorte. perche questo credo che / sia del manco valeroso. / Fiorisce il mese de genaro e' febraro.* ('Aconite. 1139. There are many types of aconite, about whose properties and their poison too I will write elsewhere, because this one, I believe, is the least potent. It flowers during the months of January and February.')

This drawing shows a winter aconite in full bloom, complete with its roots, and two details, a flower still in bud and a specimen in fruit. This small herbaceous plant differs from most other members of the Ranunculaceae in consisting of a single flower growing out of a bright green, leafy collar (in which it resembles most closely the buttercup). The species is widespread in central Europe and parts of south-west Asia, and has become naturalized in temperate regions all over the world, thriving in wooded areas to an altitude of 1,000m.

This is one of the few plants in the *Erbario Miniato* that is shown with its root, a slightly tuberous rhizome with no scale leaves. The smooth, erect scape ends in a large yellow blossom which rises out of an enveloping bracteal leaf. The flower consists of six broad oval petals, at whose centre can be seen numerous yellow anthers and the ends of three green carpels. In the fruiting specimen the petals have dropped, and four follicles on short peduncles can be distinguished.

Cesi's annotation cites p. 1139 of the *Discorsi*, where, however, *Doronicum pardalianches* ('Aconito Paradalianche di Theophrasto', **24**) is illustrated. Mattioli applied the name 'Aconito' to many different plants from the families Asteraceae and Ranunculaceae, but he did not illustrate the winter aconite.

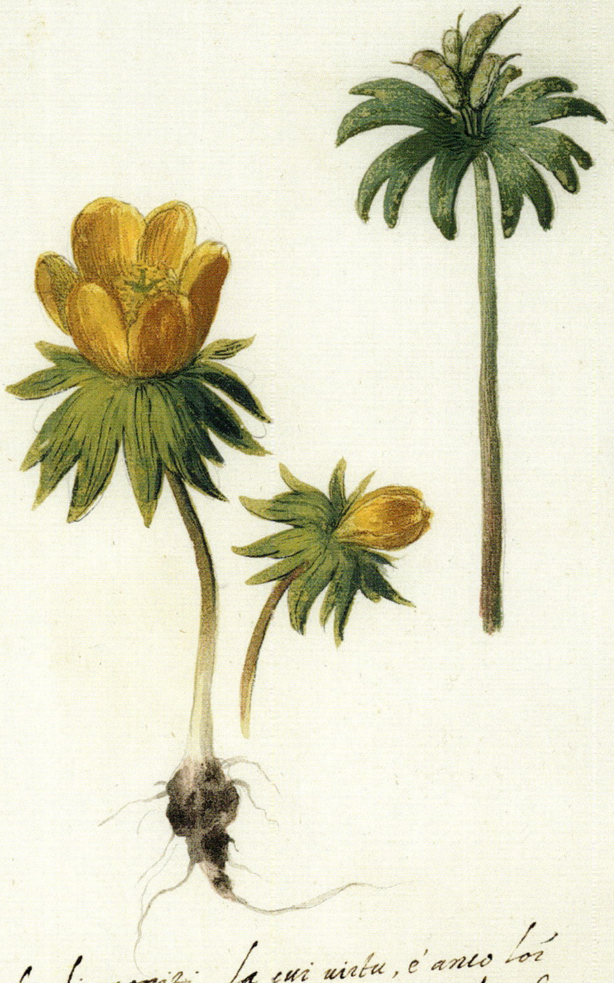

Aconito · 1139

Molti sonno le spetie de gli aconiti, la cui virtu, e ancho loro veleno si scrivera in un altra sorte. perche questo credo che sia del manco valeroso.

Fiorisce il mese de genaro è febraro.

26. Wolfsbane, *Aconitum lycoctonum* L. ssp. *vulparia* (Rchb.) Nyman

Erbario Miniato, fol. 26 (RL 27716)

Watermark: Eagle 15

NUMBERING: *524*

ANNOTATION: *Aconito Secondo. 1142.* ('Aconite of the second type. 1142.'). [From Mattioli 1568, p. 1142]

Wolfsbane is a herbaceous perennial of the buttercup family (Ranunculaceae), common to the forested mountain regions of Europe (see also **27**). It is a variable species that includes many intermediate hybrid subspecies, difficult to distinguish from one another. Like other species of the genus *Aconitum*, wolfsbane contains poisonous alkaloids which can be fatal in small doses, paralysing the central nervous system and causing death by cardiac and respiratory failure, and its common names in English, French and Italian (wolfsbane, *herbe au loup*, *erba di volpe*) stem from its supposed use as a poison for wolves. Nonetheless, the substance has occasionally been used to treat tonsillitis and glandular illnesses and to reduce fever.

In this specimen the stem is erect and glabrous with alternate, deeply lobed leaves, decreasing in size towards the apex. The stem terminates in a loosely branched panicle of white flowers tinged with pink. Each blossom consists of five petaloid sepals, with the large dorsal sepal assuming the shape of a hood; the smaller internal petals are not visible. The androecium is composed of numerous stamens whose dark anthers can be seen in the throat of the flower. Beneath this panicle are five immature clusters, each growing from the base of a leaf.

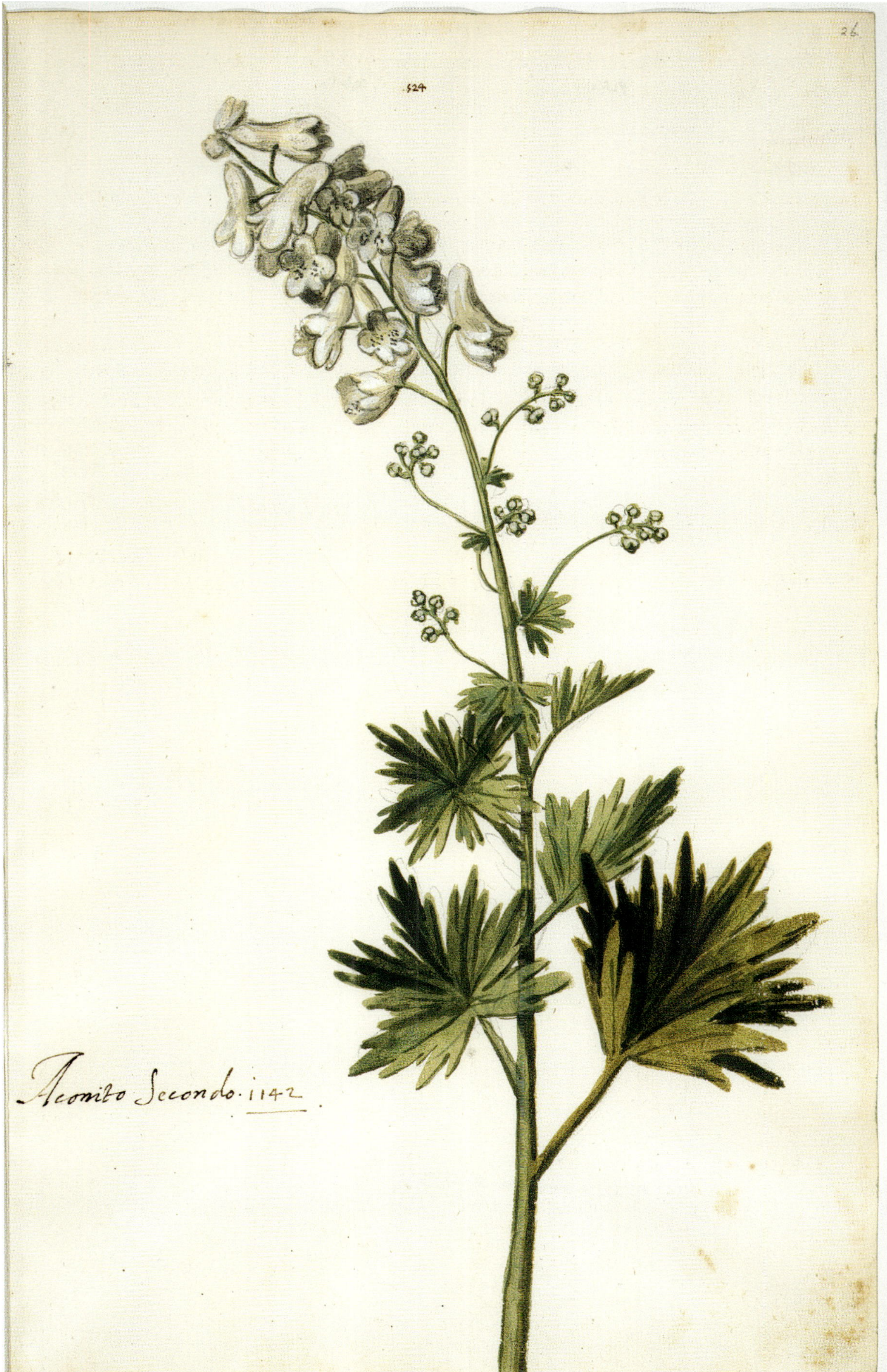
26
524
Aconito Secondo · 1142

27. Basal leaf of the wolfsbane, *Aconitum lycoctonum* L. ssp. *vulparia* (Rchb.) Nyman

Erbario Miniato, fol. 27 (RL 27717)

NUMBERING: *525*

ANNOTATION: *Aconito ~~4~~2 / 1144; Aconito. è di quattro spetie, cioe primo. secondo. terzo. e' quarto. / alchuni lo chiamano. Cinoctono, e alcuni. Licoctno, e' vulgarmente / Napello, questa foglia e' de la ~~tertia~~ seconda spetie. si adopra / p*[*er*] *amazare i lupi.* ('Aconite ~~4~~2. 1144. There are four types of Aconite, that is first, second, third and fourth. Some call it *Cinoctono*, and others *Licoctono*. It is popularly called *Napello*. This leaf belongs to the ~~third~~ second type. It is used to kill wolves.'). [From Mattioli 1568, pp. 1137, 1142–4]

This single leaf is probably of the wolfsbane (see **26**). The leaf is palmate with five deeply incised lobes and fringed edges. The petiole, which in the drawing appears to be incomplete, is longer than the leaf blade itself. The veins are strongly marked.

The cancelled number and word in the annotation suggest Cesi had difficulty identifying the plant with one of the many 'Aconiti' illustrated by Mattioli on pp. 1137–52. He seems originally to have identified this specimen with Mattioli's fourth 'Aconito', illustrated on p. 1144 ('Aconito IIII', actually *Delphinium fissum*), and secondly with Mattioli's third 'Aconito' ('Aconito III', p. 1143, actually *Ranunculus aconitifolius*) before finally settling on Mattioli's second 'Aconito' ('Aconito II', p. 1142), which indeed probably corresponds to *Aconitum lycoctonum* ssp. *vulparia* (see Fig. 13, p. 33).

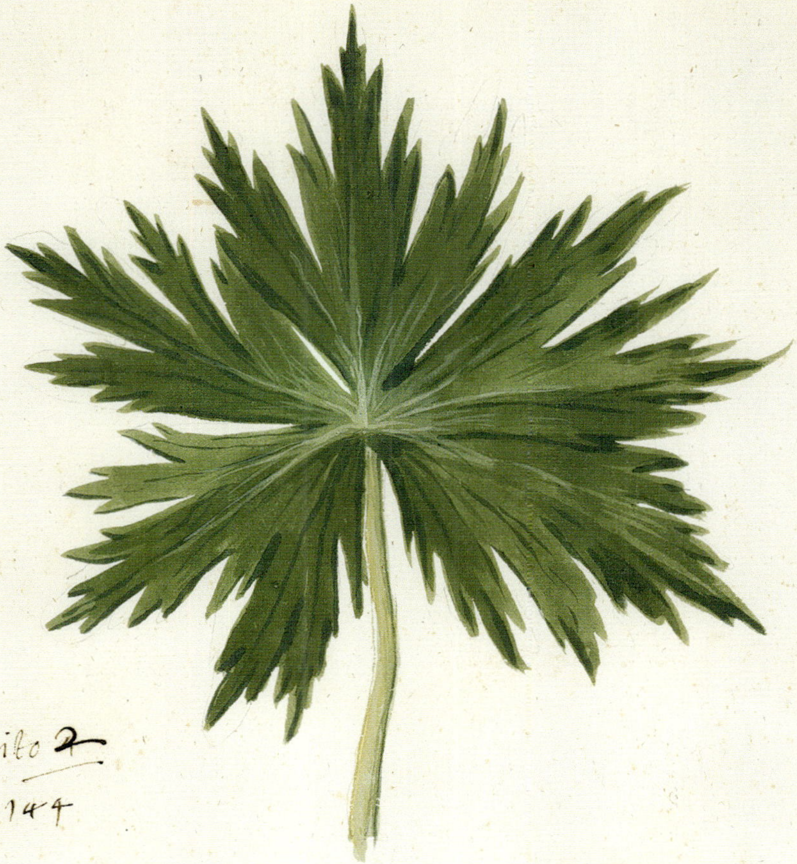

Aconito ~~2~~
1144

Aconito. e di quattro spetie, cioe primo. secondo. terzo. e quarto. alcuni lo chiamano. Cinoctono, e alcuni. Licoctno. e vulgarmente Napello, questa foglia e de la ~~terza~~ seconda spetie. si adopra ꝑ amazare i lupi.

28. Herb Paris, *Paris quadrifolia* L.

Erbario Miniato, fol. 28 (RL 27718)

NUMBERING: *526*

ANNOTATION: *Herba Paris. nel Matthiolo. 1150 / Aconitum Salutiferum. Herba Paris. nel Eicones. 720* ('Herb Paris. In Mattioli 1150; *Aconitum Salutiferum.* Herb Paris. In *Eicones* 720'). [From Mattioli 1568, p. 1150; Tabernaemontanus 1590, p. 720]

Herb Paris, or true-love, is a herbaceous perennial of the family Trilliaceae that can be found throughout Europe and Asia in damp forests, and is common to the mountains of northern and central Italy. It is mildly poisonous, and the berries when eaten can cause stomach-ache, headache and dizziness. The rhizome, leaves and berry contain compounds with emetic, purgative, narcotic and antispasmodic properties, and the name 'Aconitum Salutiferum' given in the annotation here (from Tabernaemontanus's *Eicones plantarum seu stirpium*) refers to its 'health-giving' properties. The etymology of 'Paris' is obscure, though it may stem from the Latin *paritas*, referring to the symmetrical arrangement of the parts.

The drawing shows a specimen of herb Paris in fruit. The elements of the plant are arranged in a series of concentric whorls; the erect stem bears four broad, oval leaves with a glaucous sheen. The floral tepals, which persist during fruiting, are arranged in two whorls, an outer verticil of ten linear elements and an inner one of four narrow, lanceolate elements. At the centre lies a tiny black berry. The lower part of the plant, including its creeping root, is not shown.

28

526

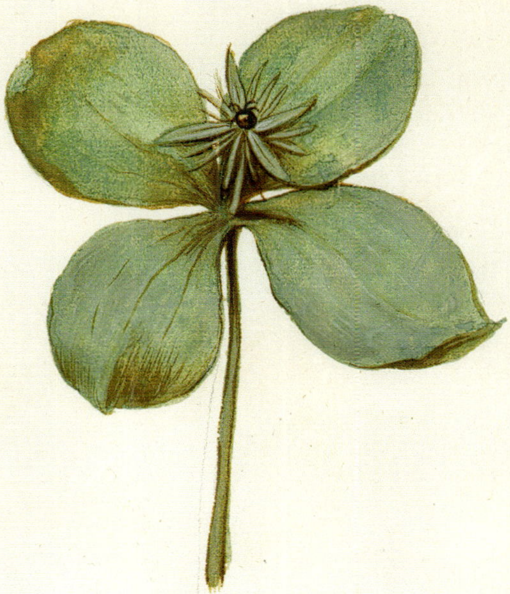

Herba Paris. nel Matthiolo. 1150

Aconitum Salutiferum. Herba Paris. nel Eicones. 120

29. Rocket larkspur, *Consolida ajacis* (L.) Schur

Erbario Miniato, fol. 29 (RL 27719)

Watermark: Eagle 18

NUMBERING: *527*

ANNOTATION: *NAPELLO 1151*. [From Mattioli 1568, p. 1151]

This drawing shows a flowering stem of rocket larkspur, a herbaceous annual of the family Ranunculaceae. Indigenous to western Europe, it has spread eastward to southern Europe and temperate regions of Asia, from sea level to an altitude of 600m. The larkspur has been cultivated as an ornamental garden plant since at least the sixteenth century, and there exist many varieties in a wide range of colours, as well as hybrids that have been developed by crossing the rocket larkspur with its cousin *Consolida orientalis* (see **237**). Its seeds contain an alkaloid which in powdered form can be used as an insecticide.

This specimen's erect pubescent stem bears two palmate leaves with profoundly incised, laciniate margins. The inflorescence consists of a raceme of small blossoms, each made up of three or four petals; their reproductive parts are not shown. The lower, more mature flowers are a deep cerulean blue while the younger flowers near the apex are lighter. The sepals resemble petals in form and are also coloured; the name of the species is derived from the spur-like shape of the uppermost sepal, which is almost purple.

Despite the inscription, this plant does not correspond to the 'Napello' illustrated by Mattioli on p. 1151, which is *Aconitum napellus* ssp. *tauricum*, a subspecies of common monkshood.

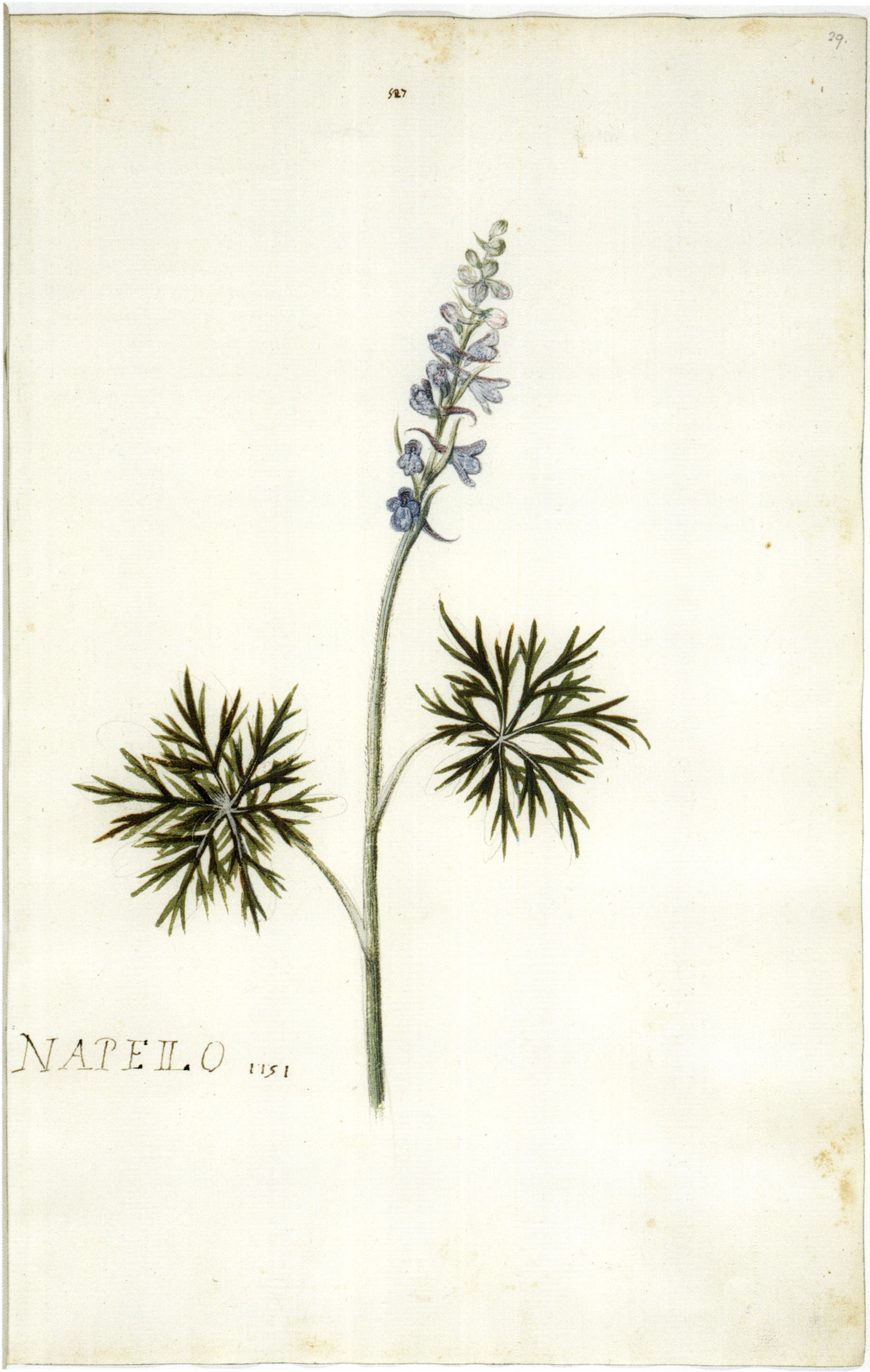
29.
527
NAPELLO 1151

30. Yew, *Taxus baccata* L.

Erbario Miniato, fol. 30 (RL 27720)

NUMBERING: *528*

ANNOTATION: *Tasso. overo Smilace, 1157* ('*Tasso* or *Smilace*, 1157'). [From Mattioli 1568, p. 1157]

The yew is a dioecious plant of the family Taxaceae (Gymnospermae) that may grow either as a shrub or as a tree with a straight trunk that can reach a height of 10m to 15m. Various subspecies are found in Europe, certain zones of northern Africa and North America, where it grows in cool, damp forests at altitudes of up to 1,600m. In Roman mythology the yew was sacred to Hecate, goddess of the Underworld, and the plant was a symbol of immortality as well as death because of its evergreen leaves and its longevity. A potent alkaloid in the leaves can cause asphyxiation and cardiac arrest. In the 1970s it was discovered that the bark and root of a related species, *Taxus brevifolia*, contain a substance that can inhibit the proliferation of cancer cells, but its use has been drastically reduced because of its side effects.

This illustration shows part of a branch of yew with two twigs bearing needle-like evergreen leaves and false fruit in various stages of maturation. Its 'fruit' actually consists of a large seed contained in a bright red, fleshy cup formed by the proliferation of the tissue at the base of the ovule during the growth of the seed, which at maturity protrudes slightly from the cup.

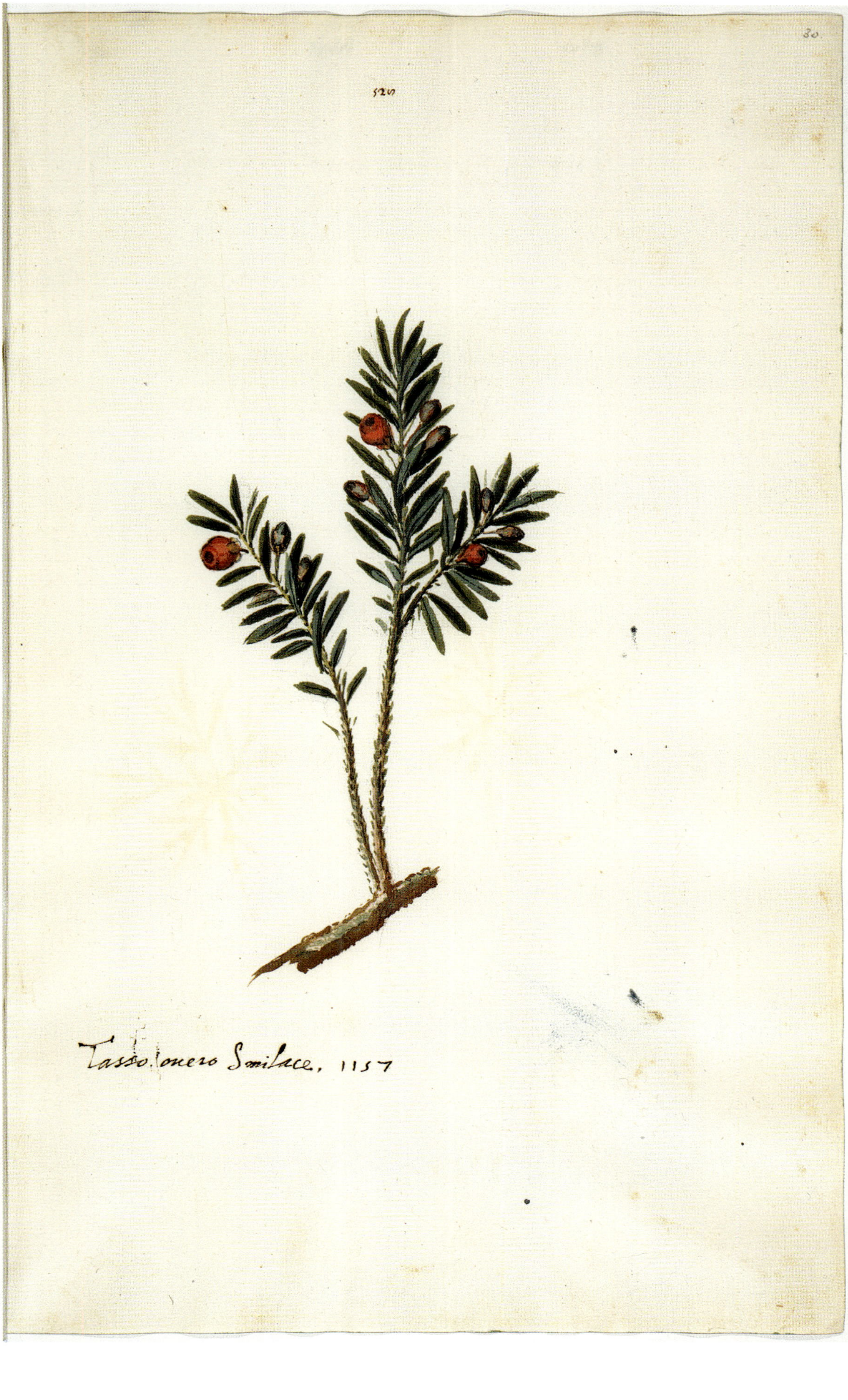
30.
520
Tasso, ouero Smilace. 1157

31. Silk vine, *Periploca graeca* L.

Erbario Miniato, fol. 31 (RL 27721)

NUMBERING: *529*

ANNOTATION: *~~Apucino~~.; Apocino, overo Brasica canina, le frondi incorporate / con grasso, e' con' pasta, e' fattene pane, amazza / i, cani, i' lupi, le volpi, e' le pantere, quando si danno / loro a' mangiare: 1159* ('~~Apucino~~; *Apocino* or *Brasica canina*. The leaves mixed into grease and dough to make bread kills dogs, wolves, foxes and panthers when it is given to them to eat. 1159'). [From Mattioli 1568, p. 1157]

The silk vine is a liana-type species of the family Asclepiadaceae that can be found in marshy coastal areas of Italy such as the Macchia Lucchese, the shores of Lake Massaciuccoli and the park of San Rossore near Pisa. The plant has been cultivated in European gardens since the end of the sixteenth century both for its medicinal properties and as an ornamental climbing plant, as indicated by its generic name, from the Greek περί (*peri*), 'around', and πλοκή (*ploke*), 'twisted'. Its bark, ground to a fine powder, has cardiokinetic properties, and its leaves were used as a purgative. The drawing shows the distal part of the plant in flower with two opposite pairs of leaves, and the detail of a single flower in a posterior view.

The annotation correctly cites p. 1159 of the *Discorsi*, where Mattioli's second 'Apocino' is illustrated, 'Apocino Serpeggiante'. The first 'Apocino', on p. 1158, illustrates *Cyonura erecta*, and the notes on the toxic qualities of the plant were copied from p. 1157. Mattioli wrote that he first came across this plant 'via the distinguished doctor M. Luca Ghini [the first *prefetto* of the Botanic Garden of Pisa], who recently sent me two specimens', one of which he called 'periploca repens' (creeping) and the other 'periploca non repens' (non-creeping).

31

529

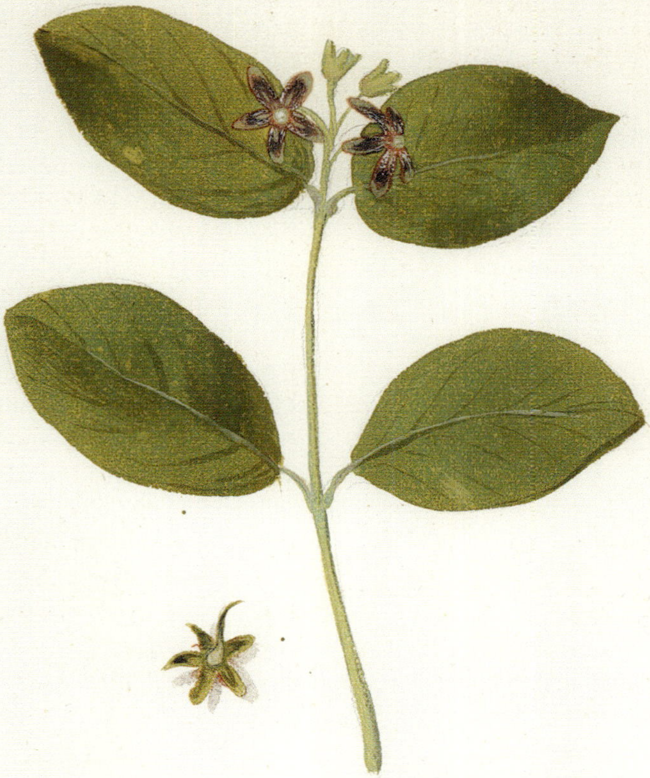

Apucino,

Apocino, overo Brasica canina, le frondi incorporate con grasso, e con pasta, e fattene pane, amazza i cani, i lupi, le volpi, e le pantere, quando si dano loro a mangiare: 1159

32. Oleander, *Nerium oleander* L.

Erbario Miniato, fol. 32 (RL 27722)

NUMBERING: *530*

ANNOTATION: *Chiamano il Nerio alcuni Rhododaphne, e' altri Rhododendo, sonno le / fronde e' i fiori veleno~~si~~ mortifero à i muli, à i cani, à gli asini, e' a molti / altri animali ~~quadupedi~~ quadrupedi, ma agli huomini sono salutifere / contra à i morsi dele serpi, le pecore e' le capere. muoino quando beuno / lacqua ove sieno stati infusione le dette frondi.* 1160 ('The *Nerio* is called by some *Rhododaphne* and by others *Rhododend*[*r*]*o*. The leaves and flowers are a deadly poison for mules, dogs and donkeys, and for many other quadrupeds, but are beneficial to humans against snake bites. Sheep and goats die when they drink of the water in which the leaves have been infused. 1160'). [From Mattioli 1568, pp. 1159–60]

The oleander is an ornamental evergreen of the family Apocynaceae, with a tall shrubby habit, sometimes attaining a height of 5m or more. The plant is native to the Mediterranean area; in southern Italy it grows along riverbanks and in the dry beds of mountain torrents. The Greeks had several names for the oleander, including *nerion* (from 'water', referring to the habitat of the plant) and *rhododendron*, 'plant with pink flowers'. During the Middle Ages the plant was known as *mazza di San Giuseppe* because, according to the Apocrypha, an oleander blossomed from the end of Joseph's staff during the Flight into Egypt.

The leaves contain cardiotonic substances similar to those present in the strophanthus (also of the Apocynaceae family), but which cannot be used for medical purposes because they contain the poison neriin. In countries from Italy to India the oleander has traditionally been considered a symbol of death. In Tuscany the dead were covered with flowering branches of oleander before burial, and in Venice it was believed that if the flower was brought into the house misfortune would befall the family. Pliny the Elder stated that the milky sap could kill serpents.

The drawing shows the lanceolate leaves with entire margins and a prominent central vein, and rose-coloured flowers arranged in wheel-shaped corollas (typical of the Apocynaceae) and united in terminal clusters. The pistils and stamens are not shown. To the left of the flowers is a fruit or seed vessel consisting of two long pods fused together, which at maturity will split to release seeds bearing a tuft of silky hairs. The drawing is unfinished, consisting only of the black chalk outline in the central part, and the leaves have only broad strokes of colour, lacking the fine detail of the fruit.

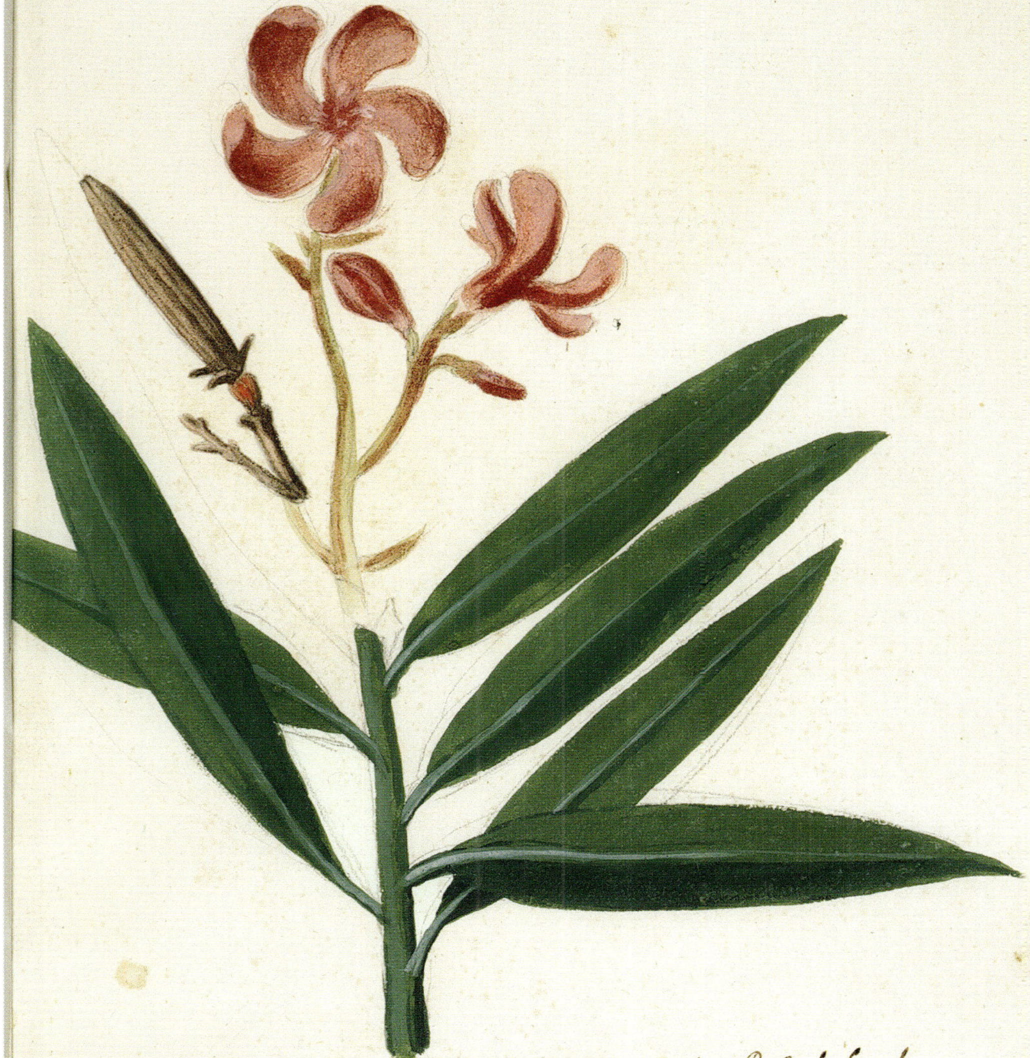

Chiamano il Nerio alcuni Rhododaphne, e' altri Rhododendro, sonno le
fronde e' i fiori veleno mortifero a' i muli, a' i cani, a' gli asini, e' a molti
altri animali ~~quadrupedi~~ quadrupedi, ma agli huomini sono salutifere
contra a' i morsi dele serpi, le pecore e' le capere. muoino quando beuno
lacqua oue sieno stati infusione le dette frondi. 1160

33. Caesar's mushroom, *Amanita caesarea* (Scop.: Fr.) Pers. 1801; honey fungus, *Armillaria mellea* (Vahl: Fr.) Kumm.; shaggy ink cap, *Coprinus comatus* (Müll.: Fr.) Pers. 1801

Erbario Miniato, fol. 33 (RL 27723)

NUMBERING: *531*

ANNOTATION: *boleti; La natura de i' fonghi e' umida e' veschiosa, ma questi Rossi. / sonno de i, buoni che si trovano, al paro de i, .1162. / Prunioli, dice uno autore;* ~~Nº 11~~ ('Boletes. The nature of fungi is moist and viscid, but these red ones are of the good kind that can be found, equal to the *Prunioli* according to one author. 1162. ~~Nº 11~~')

This folio depicts the young fruit-bodies of three edible species of mushrooms. The drawings at upper and lower centre illustrate the Caesar's mushroom, annotated 'boleti' (the name for *Amanita caesarea* used by ancient authors and still current in the seventeenth century; see also B.II.327–333). This is a large and fleshy mushroom with a bright red cap, yellow gills and stem, a hanging ring and a cup-like volva at the stem base. It is confined to southern Europe, usually associated with oak and chestnut trees, and is found between July and October. Here the cap has not fully expanded, the gills are still partially covered by the yellow partial veil and the basal volva is largely collapsed. The finely striated margin of the cap is well shown in the lower drawing.

Though it is one of the finest of the edible mushrooms, Caesar's mushroom is closely related to poisonous *Amanita* species, including the death cap, *Amanita phalloides*. It has been referred to repeatedly in literature through the ages, by authors including Cicero and Horace; according to Pliny the Elder, the Emperor Claudius was murdered by his wife Agrippina, who served him with a dish of this mushroom which had been soaked in juice extracted from the death cap.

The figure to the left probably represents a solitary young fruit-body of the honey fungus, a species depicted in detail in several succeeding folios (see **39**, **42**, **44**, **45**). To the right is a young fruit-body of the shaggy ink cap (see also B.II.565, 582). As the fungus matures, the tall cap (up to 150mm) develops tiers of white, curly scales and the gills autodigest, dissolving into a black inky liquid. This is a common grassland fungus, sometimes found growing in very large numbers, at any time of year.

The annotation is not copied from the chapter on fungi in Mattioli's *Discorsi* (pp. 1161–3) but cites the illustration on p. 1162, where different species of fungi are depicted.

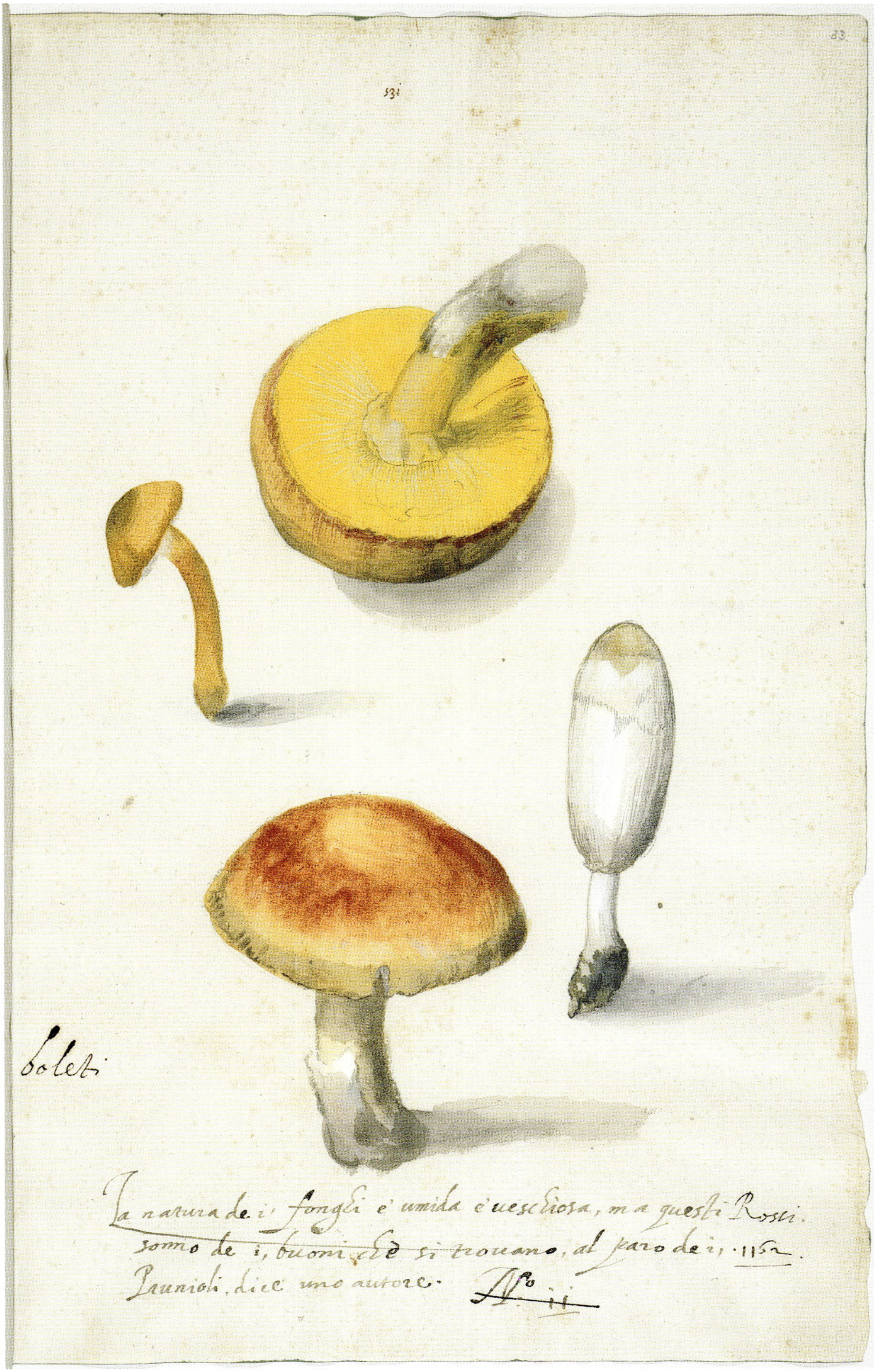
33.
531
boleti
La natura de i fongli è umida e uescciosa, ma questi Rosci.
sono de i, buoni chè si trouano, al paro de i, 1152.
Prunioli, dice uno autore.
No 11

34. [?] Cep, *Boletus edulis* Bull.: Fr.

Erbario Miniato, fol. 34 (RL 27724)

NUMBERING: *532*

ANNOTATION: *Fungho porcino, meglio dopo li prignoli, ma molto pericoloso / 1162*. ('*Porcino* fungus, the best after the *prignoli*, but very dangerous. 1162'). [From Mattioli 1568, p. 1161]

This folio claims to illustrate the most frequently eaten wild mushroom in Europe, *Boletus edulis* (see also B.II.159–161, 171–173, 178–180, 183, 218, 399, 404). In Italy it is still referred to as *porcino*, as in the inscription; in France it is a *cep*, and in England the French name is now commonly used, though the old name was penny bun. This is a large, robust mushroom, up to 300mm across, common in pine, oak and chestnut woods from June to November. The stem is thick and often swollen towards the base; here it is rather slender, reddish and lacks the fine whitish network pattern which typifies this species; in addition, the tube layer is shown as yellow rather than the cream of the cep. It is therefore possible that the artist has depicted not *Boletus edulis* but a related species such as the bay bolete, *Boletus badius*, or the red-cracked bolete, *Xerocomus chrysenteron*.

The inscription paraphrases a passage in Mattioli's *Discorsi* (p. 1162) and states that the *porcino* is 'best after the *prignoli*'. *Prugnolo* was the name used for some edible species of mushrooms with a floury, mealy smell, including the St George's mushroom, *Calocybe gambosa* (see **36**). Mattioli qualified his statement that in Tuscany the *prugnoli* held pride of place (*tengono il principato*) by adding that this was because they were 'extremely fragrant, most pleasant in taste and entirely harmless'. The note about *porcini* being 'very dangerous' must refer to the possibility of confusing them with one of the poisonous boletes such as *Boletus satanoides* or *Boletus satanas*; Mattioli wrote that despite the edibility of *porcini*, some were nevertheless extremely dangerous (though he adds that they could be distinguished by their colouring).

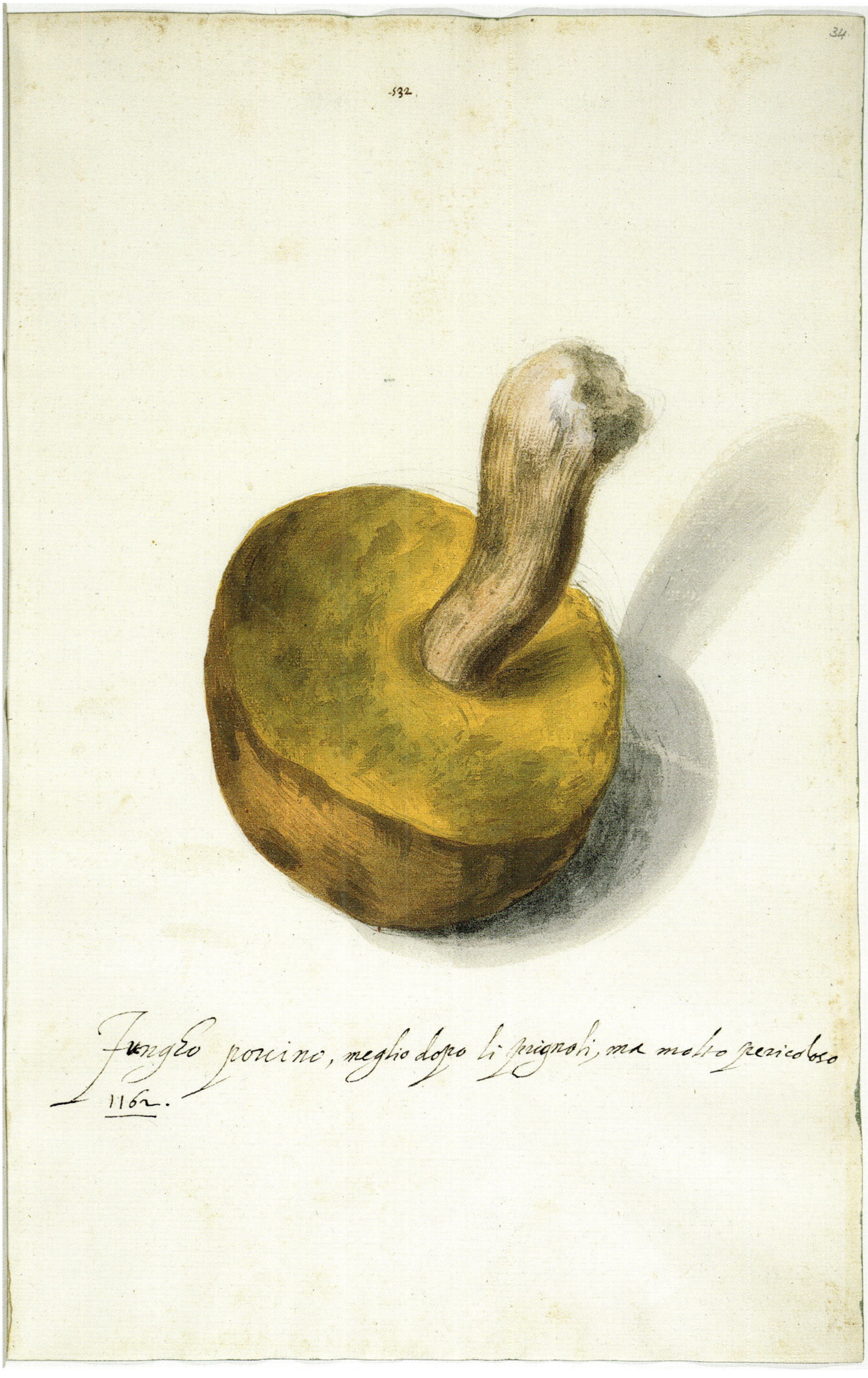
532
34
Fungho porcino, meglio dopo li prugnoli, ma molto pericoloso
1162.

35. Copper trumpet, *Omphalotus olearius* (DC: Fr.) Singer 1962; clustered coral fungus, *Ramaria botrytis* (Pers. 1801: Fr.) Ricken

Erbario Miniato, fol. 35 (RL 27725)

Watermark: Figure 54

NUMBERING: *533*

ANNOTATION: *Manine; Capreolini; Il nutrimento de i' Fonghi e' frigido e' flematico.* 1162.; ~~Nº 7~~ ('*Manine; Capreolini*; the nourishment of fungi is cold and phlegmatic. 1162. ~~Nº 7~~'). [From Mattioli 1568, p. 1163]

The copper trumpet, above, forms clusters on stumps and dead trunks, mainly of oak, elm and olive, from which it gets its specific epithet *olearius* and common Italian name *fungo dell'olivo* (see also B.II.135, 425–426, 524–525, 597). The orange-brown funnel-shaped caps have yellow-orange decurrent gills, and the shape and colour can lead to confusion with the edible and prized chanterelle, *Cantharellus cibarius* (see **43**). The copper trumpet, however, contains a toxic sesquiterpene called illudin S, similar to the muscarine which may be found in unrelated mushrooms such as fly agaric, *Amanita muscaria*, which causes headaches, sweating, nausea and vomiting. The mushroom is bioluminescent, and dead wood infected with the mycelium of the fungus is seen to glow in the dark.

Below is a portion of a fruit-body of the clustered coral fungus, called here 'Manine' ('little hands'), still a common name for this fungus in Italy (see also B.II.89–90). Fruit-bodies of *Ramaria* species are highly branched, forming cauliflower-like structures up to 150mm across. In *Ramaria botrytis* the main body is white, yellowing with age, and the many spiny tips are coloured wine-red or purple. It is an occasional species that grows on the ground in woodland, especially under beech trees. Though edible, the bitter reddish tips may cause gastrointestinal upsets.

The inscription is drawn from a passage in Mattioli's *Discorsi* (p. 1163) in which he relates Galen's words on the subject of 'boleti' (Caesar's mushroom: see **33**): 'their nourishment is cold and phlegmatic, and partaking of them too liberally generates bad humours; but among all other types of fungi these are the least harmful'.

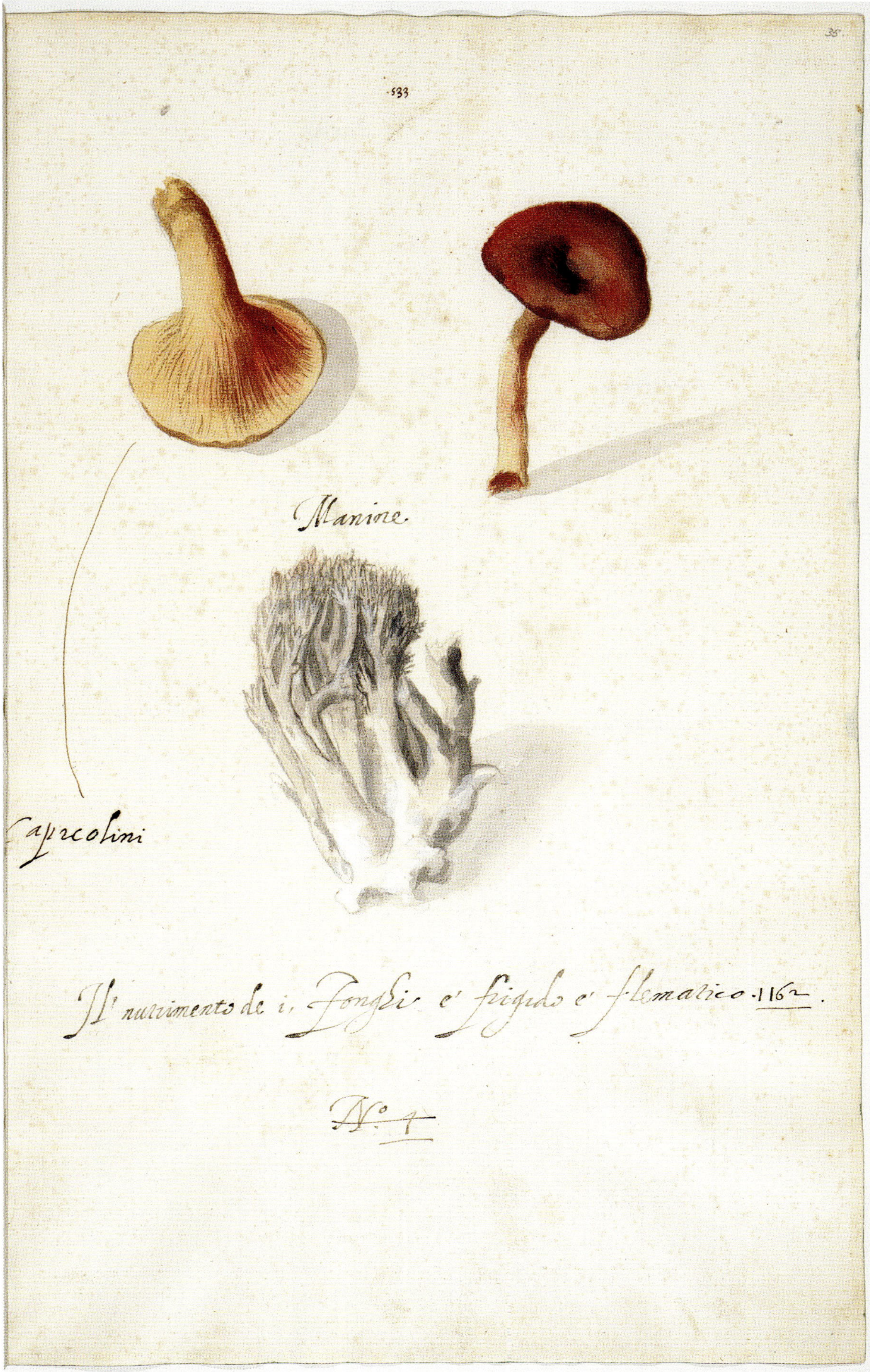
35.
533
Manine
Capreolini
Il nutrimento de i Fonghi e' frigido e' flematico .1162.
N.° 1

36. St George's mushroom, *Calocybe gambosa* (Fr.) Singer 1951

Erbario Miniato, fol. 36 (RL 27726)

Two sheets joined horizontally: upper sheet 151 x 275 mm; lower sheet 273 x 275 mm.
Watermark: Crown 5

NUMBERING: *534*

ANNOTATION: *Fonghi Prugnioli*

The ten figures represent young fruit-bodies of the St George's mushroom, called here 'Prugnioli', *prugnoli* being a name still used in Italy for this species (cf. **34**; see also B.II.291–295, 303–306). This common species is one of the few edible mushrooms to be found only in the spring, and it takes its English name from its appearance around St George's Day (23 April). The mushrooms often appear in large numbers and form 'fairy rings' in grassland, especially on calcareous ground. It is a large, fleshy mushroom, up to 130mm across, with short stems and crowded, narrow, pale gills, and a strong odour of meal or flour, which can be retained even on cooking. The margin of the cap is inrolled, as shown at upper left. The range of colours is shown in the contrast between the upper and lower halves of the sheet, executed at different times; the shadows indicated with light wash display the upper mushrooms as if lying on their sides (with the sheet turned to the right), and the lower mushrooms as if standing erect.

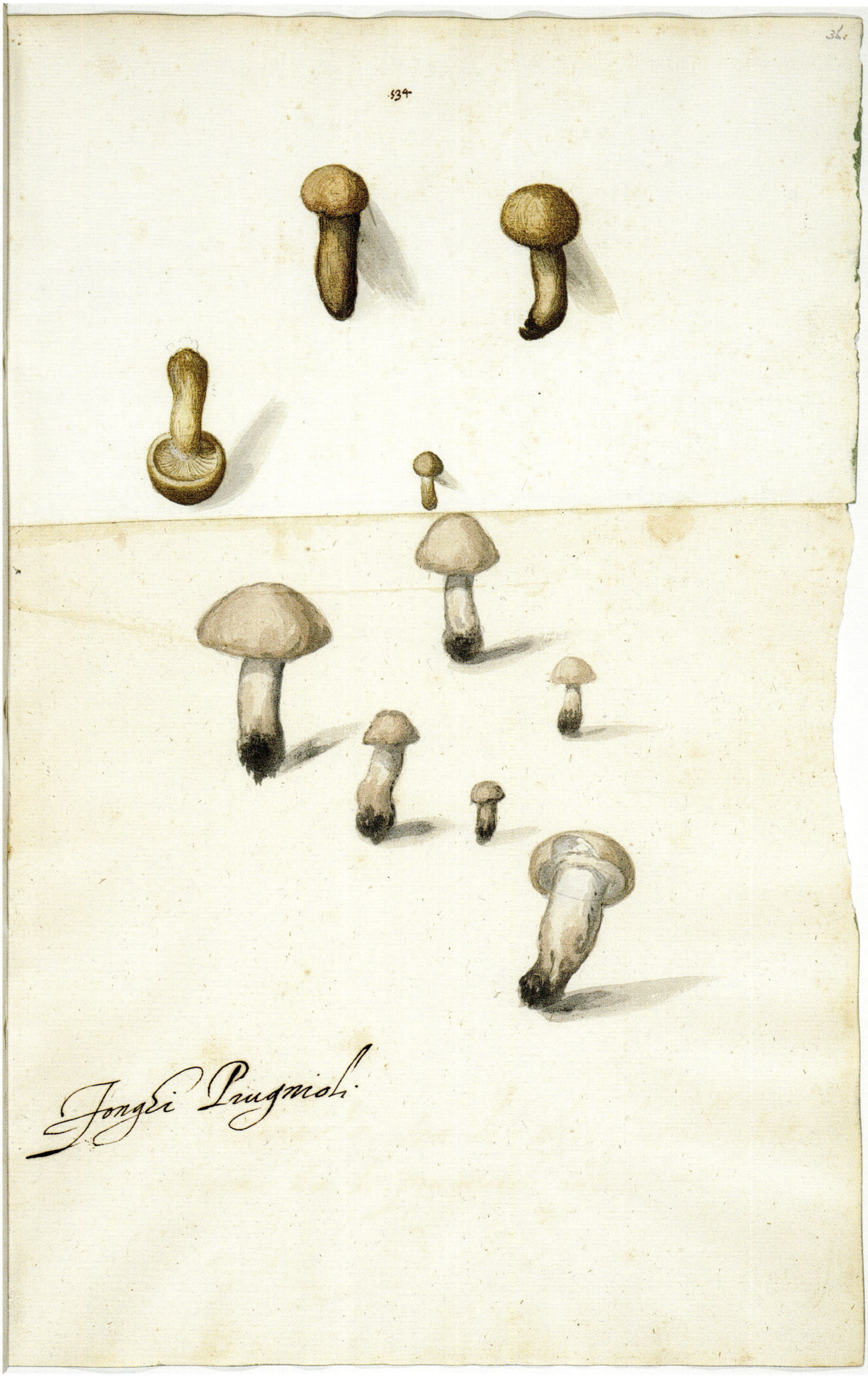
36.
534
Fongi Prugnoli

37. Black morel, *Morchella elata* Fr.: Fr.

Erbario Miniato, fol. 37 (RL 27727)

NUMBERING: *535*

ANNOTATION: *Fungo Spugnuolo, tra li altri funghi, pre= / fetissimo. da li prugnuoli inpuo'* ('*Spugnuolo* [spongy] fungus, the favourite amongst other fungi after the *prugnuoli*')

This drawing shows a fruit-body of the black morel, the most prized of the edible spring fungi, found in April and May, mostly in coniferous woodland but also common in apple orchards.

Morels belong to the Ascomycetes (which also include truffles and cup fungi). The hollow fruit-body comprises a conical head up to 60mm high, with deep polygonal cavities formed by deep ridges resulting in a spongy appearance, hence the name *spugnola* (still in use in Italy). The flesh is thin, whitish and brittle, with a strong smell. The stem is white to ochre in colour, with a smooth or scurfy surface, sometimes ribbed or wrinkled. The common morel (*Morchella esculenta*) is paler, with less distinct vertical ridges.

38. Wood urchin, *Hydnum repandum* L. 1754: Fr.

Erbario Miniato, fol. 38 (RL 27728)

Watermark: Anchor 29

NUMBERING: *536*

ANNOTATION: *Fonghi, Carpanelli*

The wood urchin is found throughout Europe from August to November, usually under birch, beech or oak, singly or in small groups (see also B.II.26, 583–584). The fungus is known in Italy as *carpinello*, probably from its association with the *carpino* or hornbeam, a tree that superficially resembles beech. It is edible and is widely sold commercially. The thick, firm flesh is white, occasionally discolouring reddish on bruising. The cap ranges from 50 to 170mm across, convex or depressed, and the margin is thick and persistently inrolled. The upper surface is initially velvety, becoming smooth and shiny when dry; the lower surface is crowded with fine brittle spines, 4–8mm long. The stocky stem is usually excentrically attached.

39. Honey fungus, *Armillaria mellea* (Vahl: Fr.) Kumm.

Erbario Miniato, fol. 39 (RL 27729)

NUMBERING: *537*

ANNOTATION: *Fonghi de olmo* ('Elm mushroom')

The honey fungus is a common caespitose species, with many fruit-bodies originating from a common base (see also **33**, **42**, **44**, **45**, and B.II.153, 422, 428–431, 588, 597). The fungus forms thick, black threads or rhizomorphs which attack the host tree and can cause its death. The Italian common name is usually *famigliola buona*, but in Umbria (where Cesi came from) it is known as *fungo dell'olmo*, as cited in the inscription.

The cap is initially subglobose in form, expanding to become convex with a slightly umbonate centre, and splitting at the margin. The fruit-body is honey-coloured, from which both the specific epithet and the English name are derived, though it may have green, olivaceous or reddish tints. The gills are decurrent, running down the stem almost as far as the attached ring. The caps are edible and good when young, but in older fruit-bodies the stems are tough and fibrous, tend to be bitter and can cause gastric upsets.

37

535

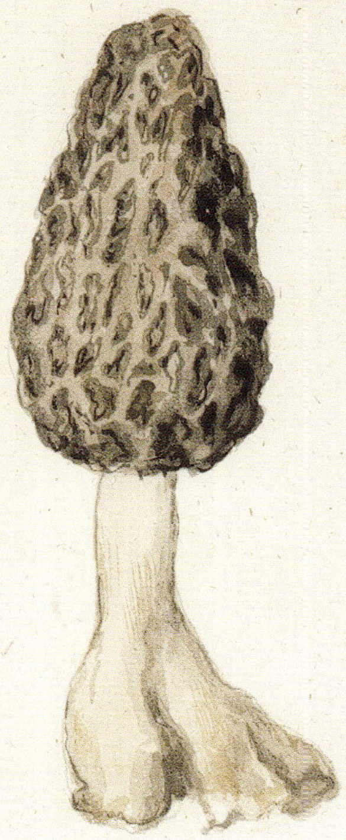

Fungo Spugnaolo, tra li altri funghi, pre=
fetissimo da li spugnuoli in spico

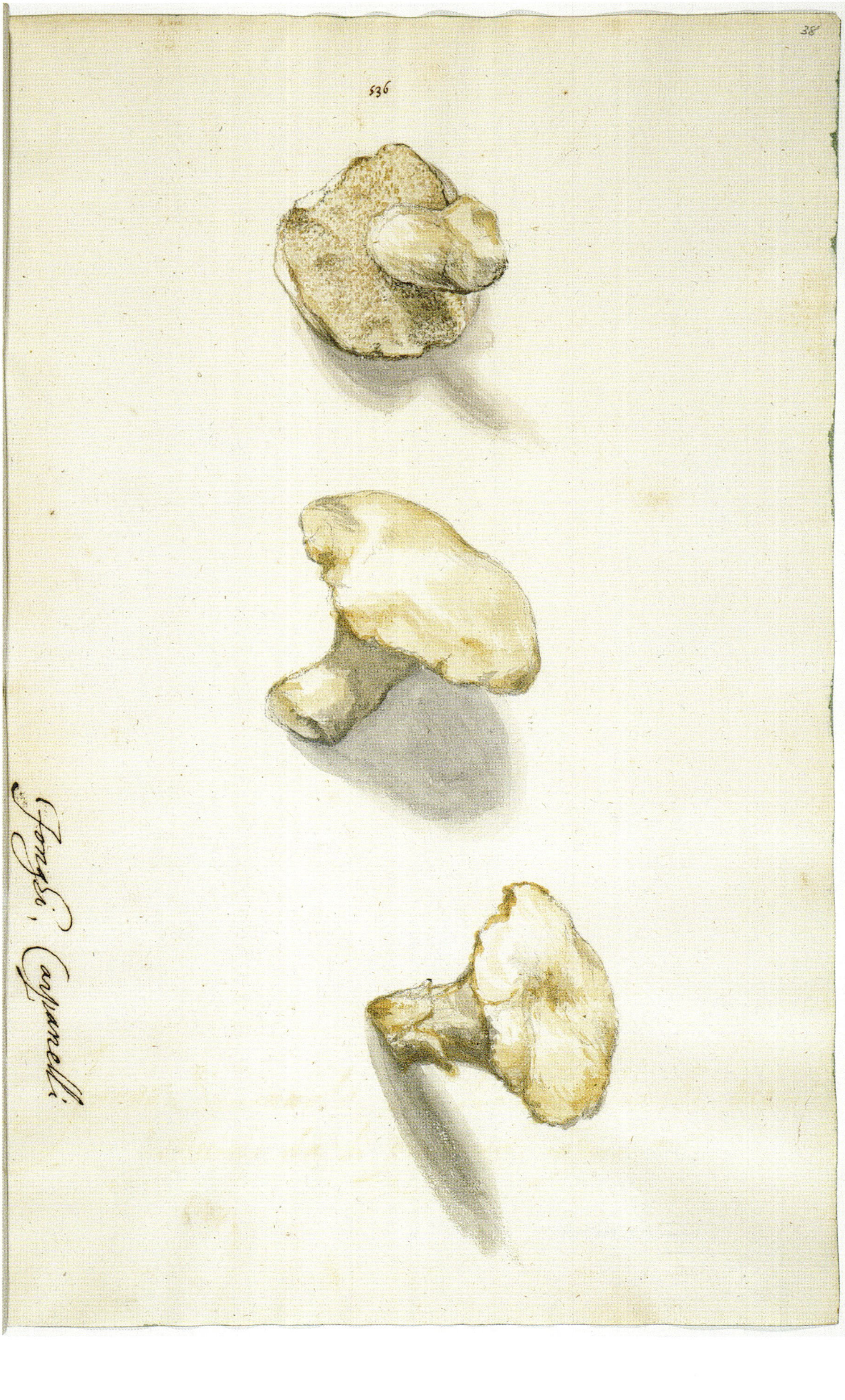
38
536
Fonghi, Campanelli

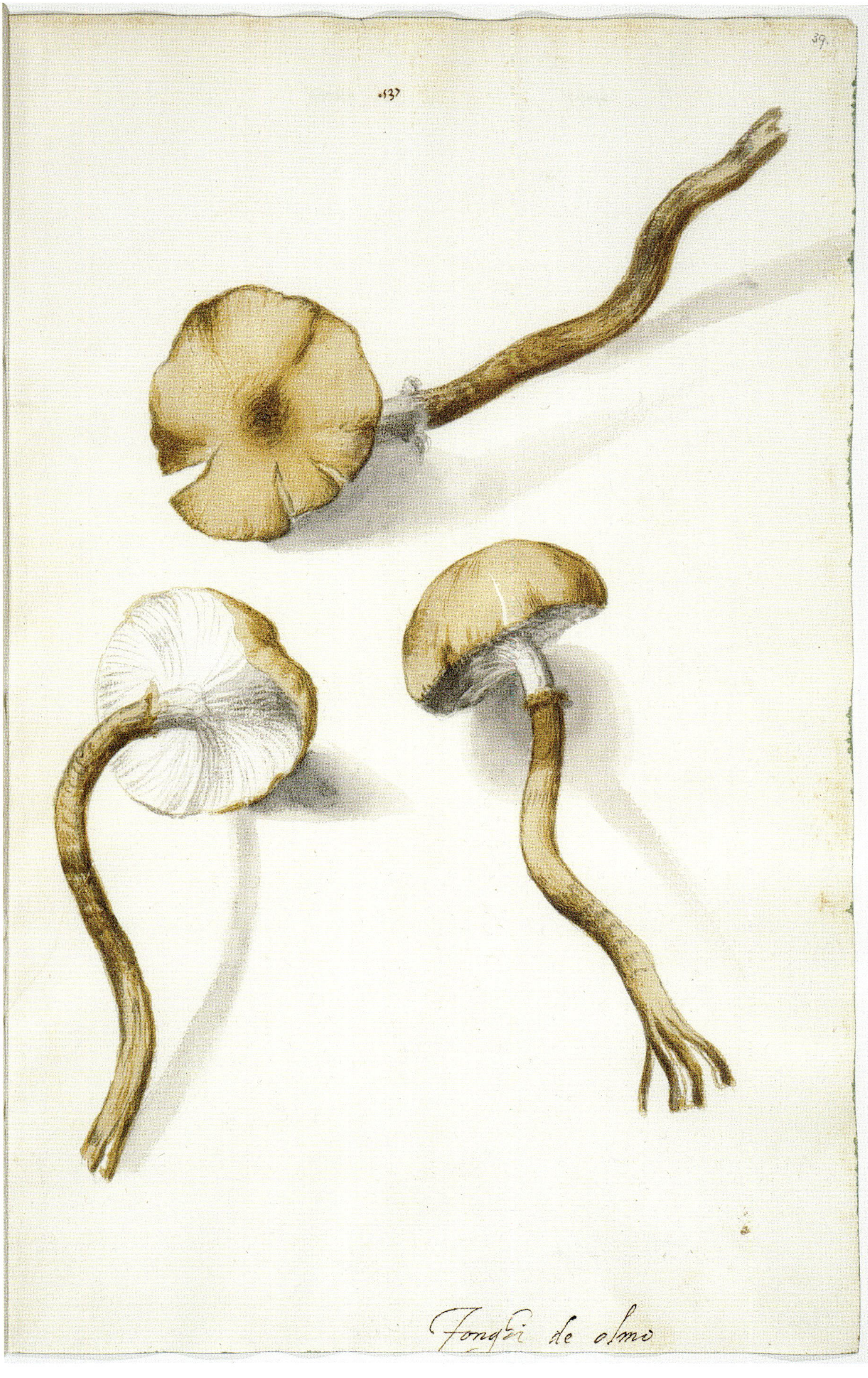
39.
537
Fonghi de olmo

40. Horse mushroom, *Agaricus arvensis* Schaeffer

Erbario Miniato, fol. 40 (RL 27730)

NUMBERING: *538*

ANNOTATION: *fonghi*

The yellow discoloration on the lower surface of the stem and towards the margin of the cap suggests that this is the horse mushroom, *Agaricus arvensis* (see also B.II.279, 287, 401, 406, 529). The cap is at first strongly rounded but becomes flattened and plate-like, up to 150mm across, smooth or with small scales towards the edge. The crowded gills are free from the top of the stem, at first grey then blackish-brown. The stem is smooth and initially white but discolours yellowish-brown; it normally has a white, hanging ring towards its top but this is easily removed and is not shown here. The flesh has a distinctive smell of bitter almonds. This is a species that grows in fields and pastures, common from August to October and forming large fairy rings. Though it is edible and good, care must be taken to avoid confusion with the poisonous yellow stainer, *Agaricus xanthoderma*.

41. Sterile base of the mosaic puffball, *Calvatia utriformis* (Bull.: Pers. 1801) Jaap

Erbario Miniato, fol. 41 (RL 27731)

Watermark: Fleur de lys 46

NUMBERING: *539*

ANNOTATION: *Spetie de fonghi, detto bessa de lupo* ('A type of mushroom called *bessa de lupo*')

This is the old and weathered basal remains of a puffball fruit-body. Once the spores have been released from a hole in the upper part, the fruit-body dries to a brown leathery cup-like base, which is commonly found in grassland, sometimes detached and blown about by the wind. *Vescia di lupo* ('wolf's fart') is the Italian common name for puffballs of the genus *Lycoperdon* (itself Greek for 'wolf's fart').

42. Honey fungus (cluster of young mushrooms), *Armillaria mellea* (Vahl: Fr.) Kumm.

Erbario Miniato, fol. 42 (RL 27732)

NUMBERING: *540*

ANNOTATION: *FONGHI*

This is a dense tuft of young honey fungus (see **39**), with the under-surface of the caps still concealed by the membranous partial veil. The darker stem bases are typical of the species. The form of the specimen is a clue to the origin of two of the popular Italian names for this species, *famigliola buona* or 'happy little family', for the mushroom always grows in clusters, and *chiodini*, 'little nails', from the shape of the young fruit-body.

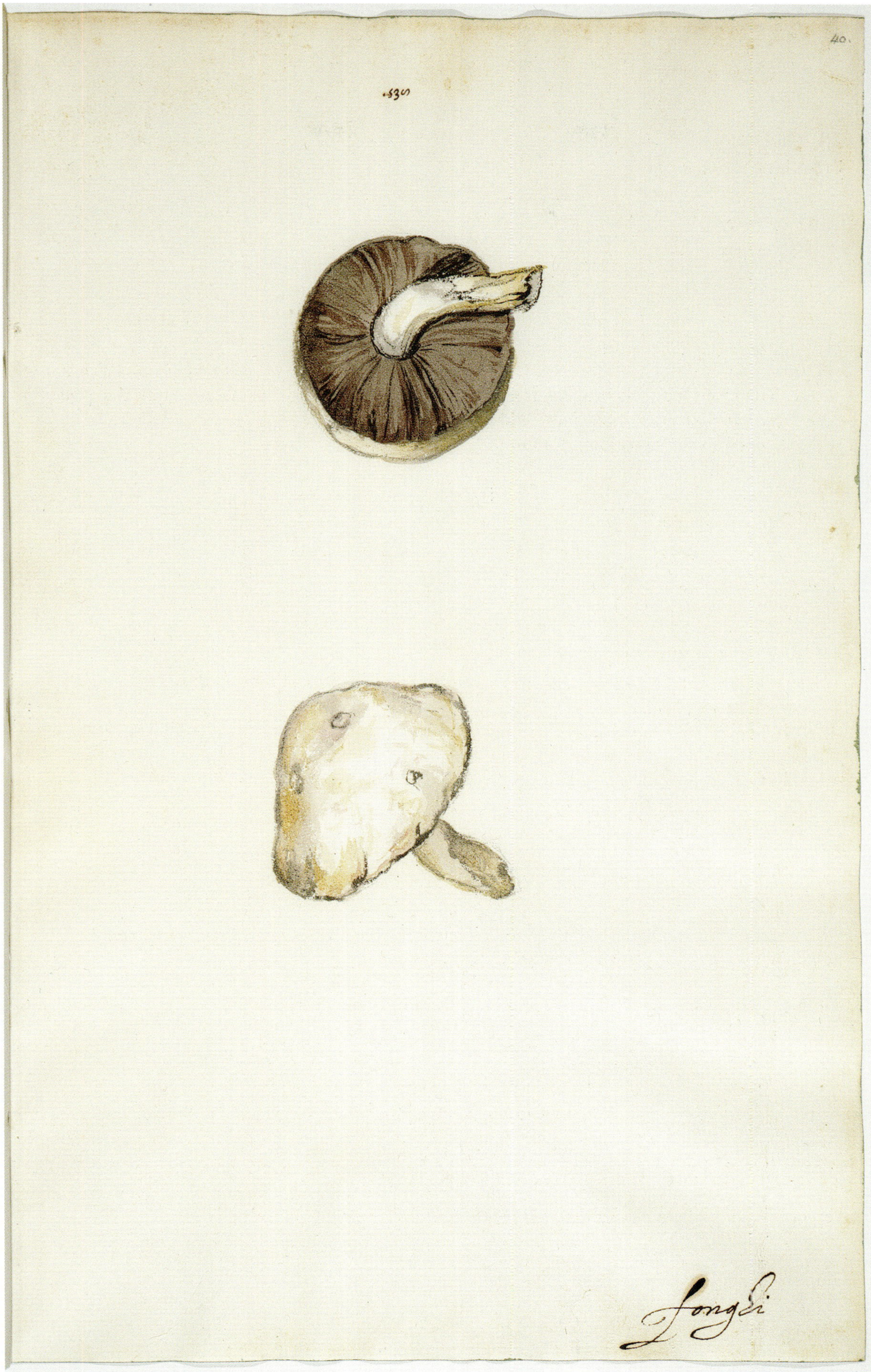
40.
Fonghi

41

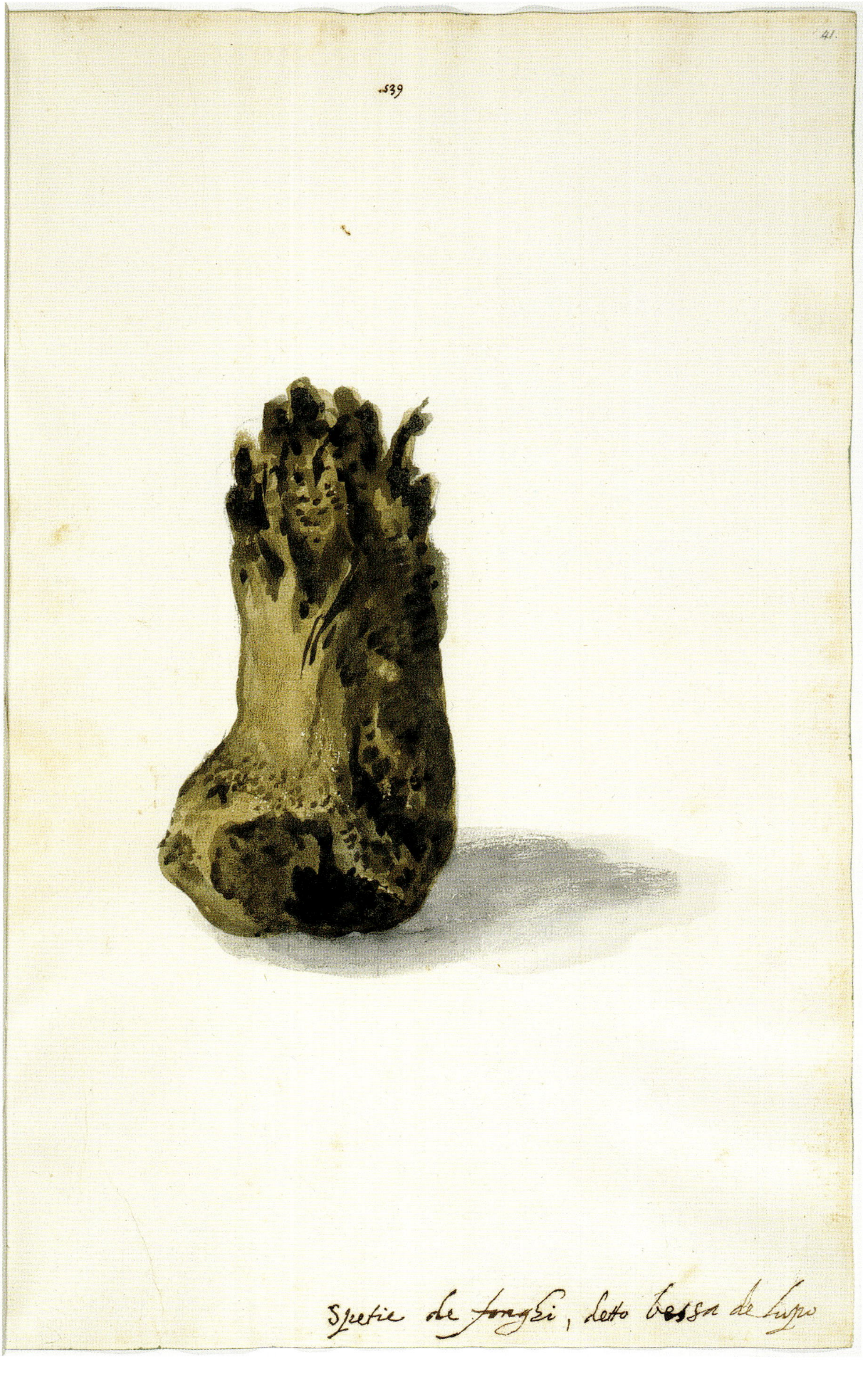

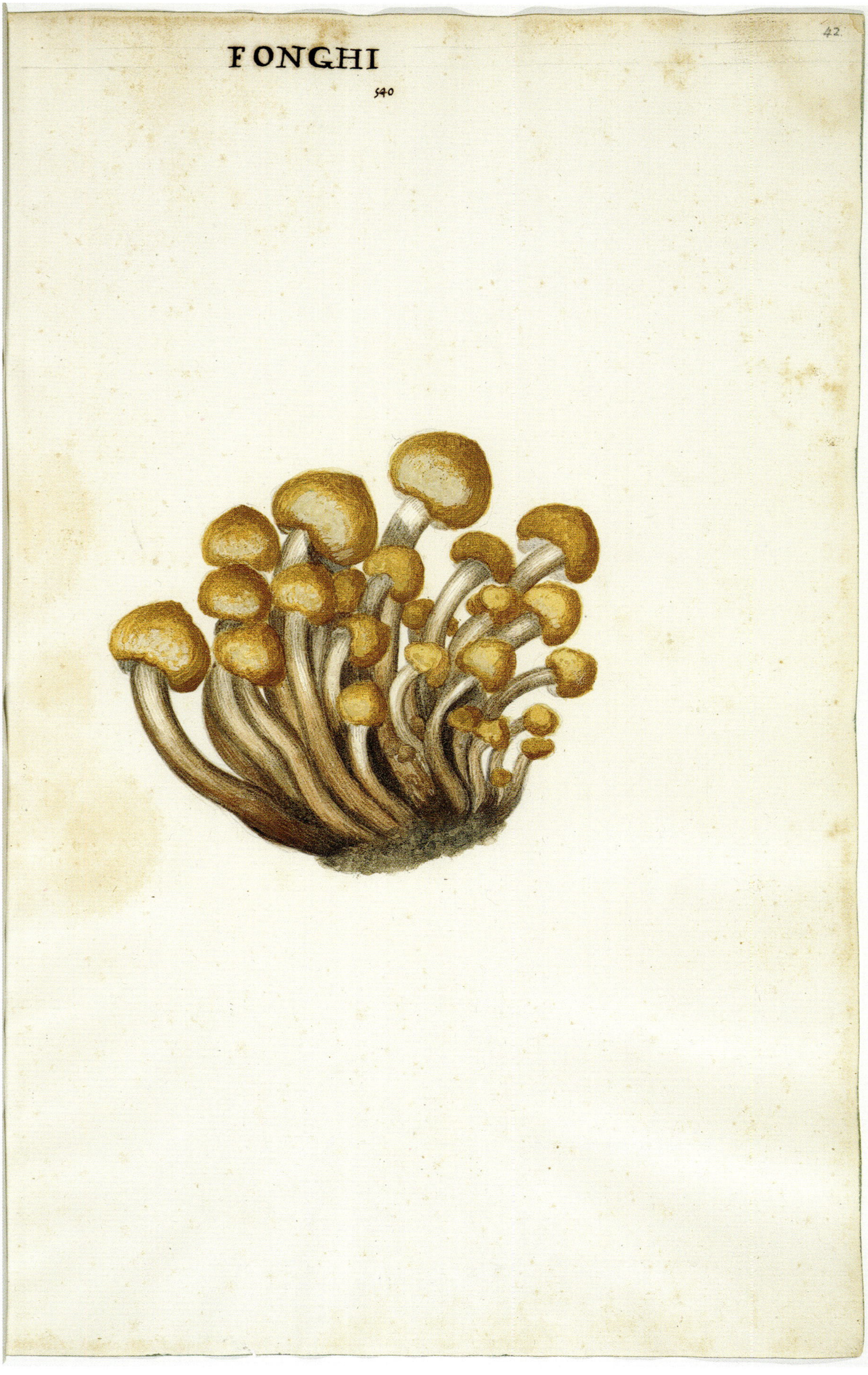
42
FONGHI
540

43. Chanterelle, *Cantharellus cibarius* Fr.

Erbario Miniato, fol. 43 (RL 27733)

NUMBERING: *541*

ANNOTATION: *FONGHI; Capreolini*

The chanterelle is one of the best known of the edible mushrooms (see also B.II.144–145, 400). It is found on the ground in moist woodland, both broadleaved and coniferous, forming associations with the roots of trees, especially oak, beech, birch, spruce and pine. The fleshy cap ranges from 30 to 140mm across, and is convex when young, becoming depressed or funnel-shaped, with a yellow to ochre surface, sometimes bruising brownish. On the underside of the cap are deeply decurrent ridges which resemble the gills of true mushrooms but are the result of wrinkling of the fertile surface as it grows. The stem is solid, as shown in the lower figure, more or less cylindrical and tapering below.

44. Honey fungus, *Armillaria mellea* (Vahl: Fr.) Kumm.

Erbario Miniato, fol. 44 (RL 27734)

NUMBERING: *542*

ANNOTATION: *Haltri fonghi* ('Other fungi')

Two mature fruit-bodies of the honey fungus (see **39**) are shown, with most of the stem torn away. In the upper figure the veil has partly broken away, although it still remains attached to one side of the cap margin. In the lower figure the veil has entirely separated from the cap and forms the characteristic ring attached to the stem.

45. Honey fungus, *Armillaria mellea* (Vahl: Fr.) Kumm.

Erbario Miniato, fol. 45 (RL 27735)

Watermark: Fleur de lys 46

NUMBERING: *543*

ANNOTATION: *Piu fonghi* ('More fungi')

In this old fruit-body of honey fungus, seen in two views, the cap has fully expanded, becoming flattened and almost depressed at the centre, and the margin has started to split. The surface of the cap has the small fibrous scales (*armillae*) which characterize the species and give it its generic name, but which usually flake off the mature fruit-body. The broken stem is clearly shown as longitudinally fibrous, especially at the broken base, and the ring has disappeared from the top of the stem.

43

sai

FONGHI

Caprecolini

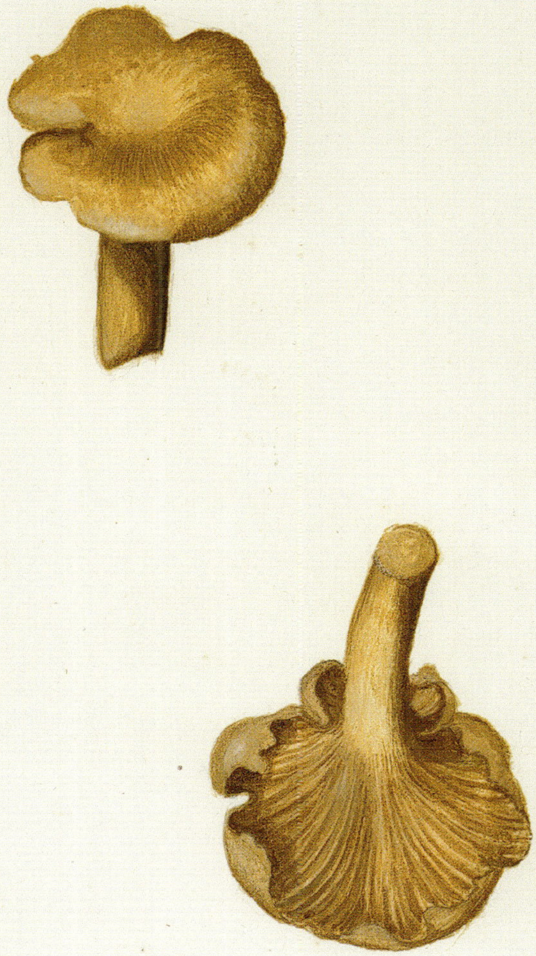

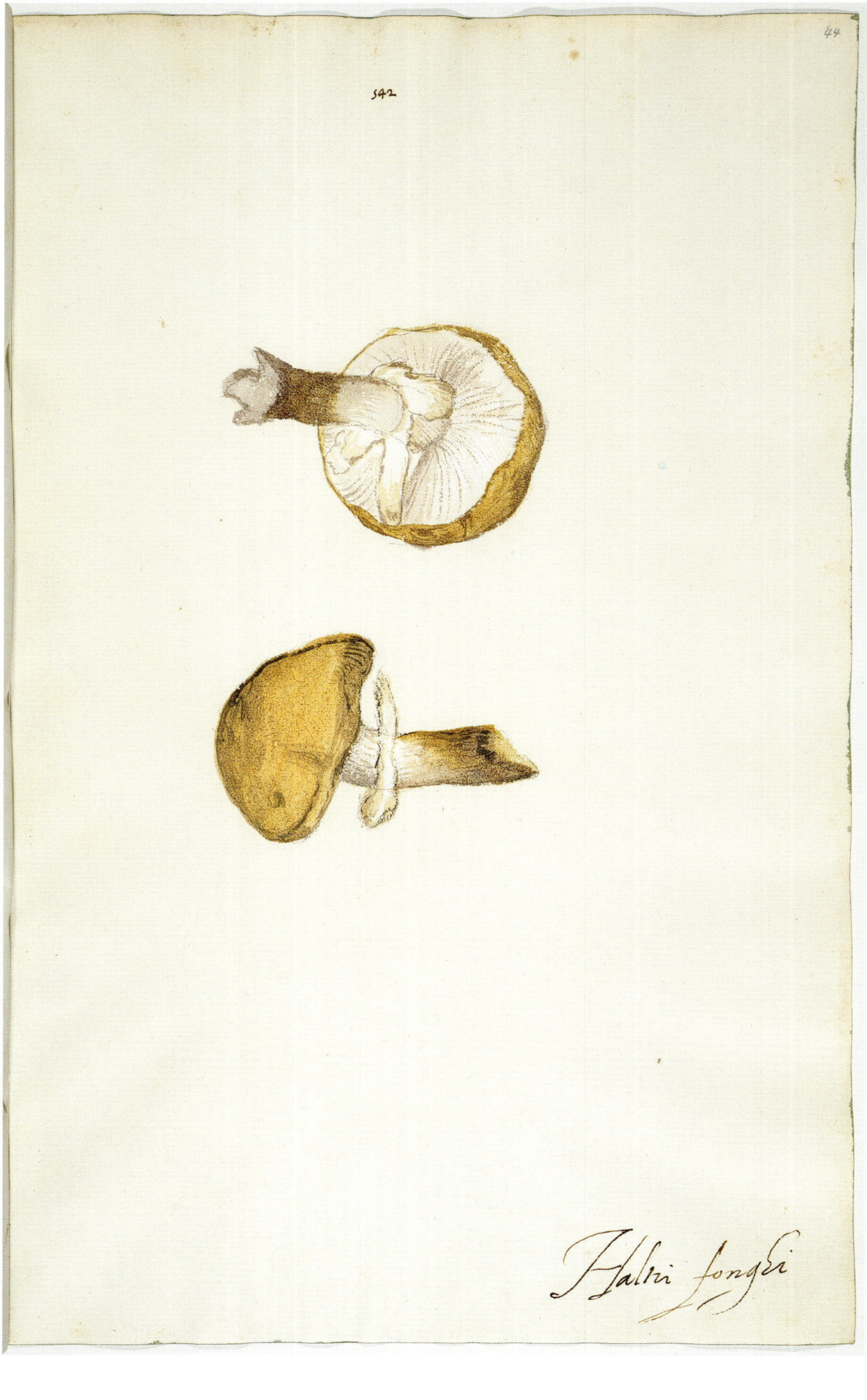
44
542
Altri fonghi

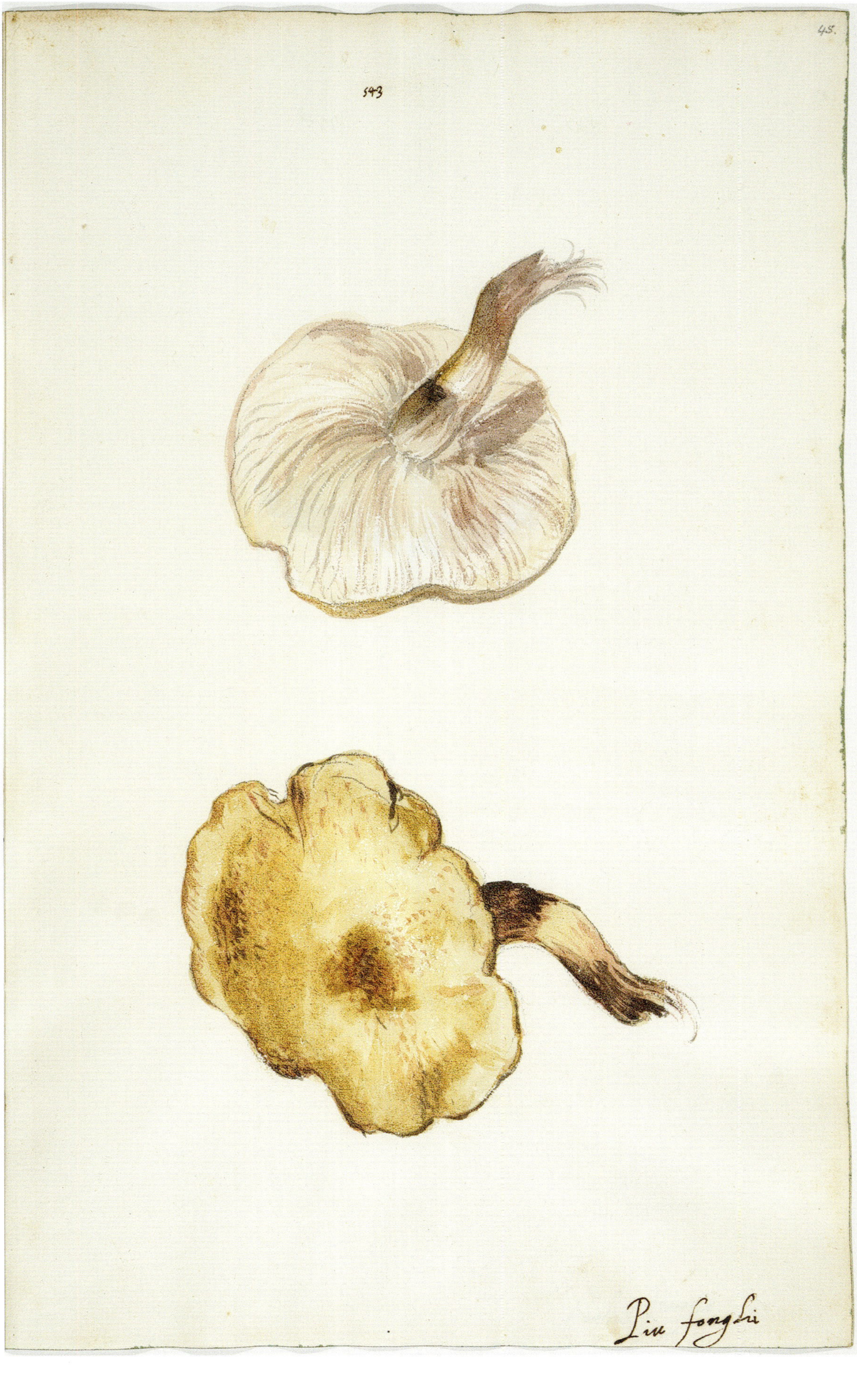
45.
543
Piu fonghi

46. Magpie ink cap, *Coprinus picaceus* (Bull.: Fr.) S.F. Gray

Erbario Miniato, fol. 46 (RL 27736)

Watermark: Bird 14

NUMBERING: *544*

ANNOTATION: *Unaltro fungo* ('Another fungus')

The magpie ink cap is one of the larger and more easily recognizable of the ink caps (see also B.II.475). In the young fruiting body the entire cap is covered by a white veil. As the cap expands, the veil breaks up, giving white patches contrasting with a black ground. The gills are initially white, but as the spores develop the gills darken, rapidly deliquescing as a result of autodigestion and dissolving to a black fluid. In the drawing the fruit-body is already in an advanced stage of autodigestion, the margin of the cap splitting and fragmenting.

47. Jew's ear fungus, *Auricularia auricula-judae* (Bull.: Fr.) Wettst. 1897

Erbario Miniato, fol. 47 (RL 27737)

Watermark: Fleur de lys 56

NUMBERING: *545*

ANNOTATION: *fonghi*

The folio depicts three young fruit-bodies of the Jew's ear fungus (see also B.II.80); two are joined at their base, for they usually grow in clusters with a lateral attachment to the substratum. This fungus grows on the branches of several species of tree, particularly elder and sycamore. Its name is probably a corruption of 'Judas's ear', from its association with the elder, traditionally the tree from which Judas hanged himself. This species has a tough, rubbery texture that can withstand frost, and can thus be found throughout the year. It is the best known of what are popularly called the jelly fungi, taxonomically a mixed group of species with gelatinous flesh.

48. Trooping crumble cap, *Coprinus disseminatus* (Pers. 1801: Fr.) S.F. Gray; [?] purple jelly drops, *Ascocoryne cylichnium* (Tul.) Korf

Erbario Miniato, fol. 48 (RL 27738)

NUMBERING: *546*

ANNOTATION: *Fonghi colti nelle muraglie de / matoni antiche; Fonghi che nascono / solo sopra a' doi o' tre / sorte de legno*. ('Fungi gathered from an old brick wall. Fungi that grow only on two or three types of wood.')

The left-hand figures show three fruit-bodies of the tiny trooping crumble cap, *Coprinus disseminatus*, normally found growing in large groups (troops) on rotting wood and old stumps (see also B.II.198–199, 461–462). This is another ink cap, though much smaller than the shaggy ink cap (**33**) or the magpie ink cap (**46**). The small fruiting bodies have very thin to membranous conical caps with grooved margins that rapidly autodigest.

The right-hand figure is more difficult to identify, but appears to be the same species as that illustrated on the following folios, possibly the purple jelly drops, *Ascocoryne cylichnium*.

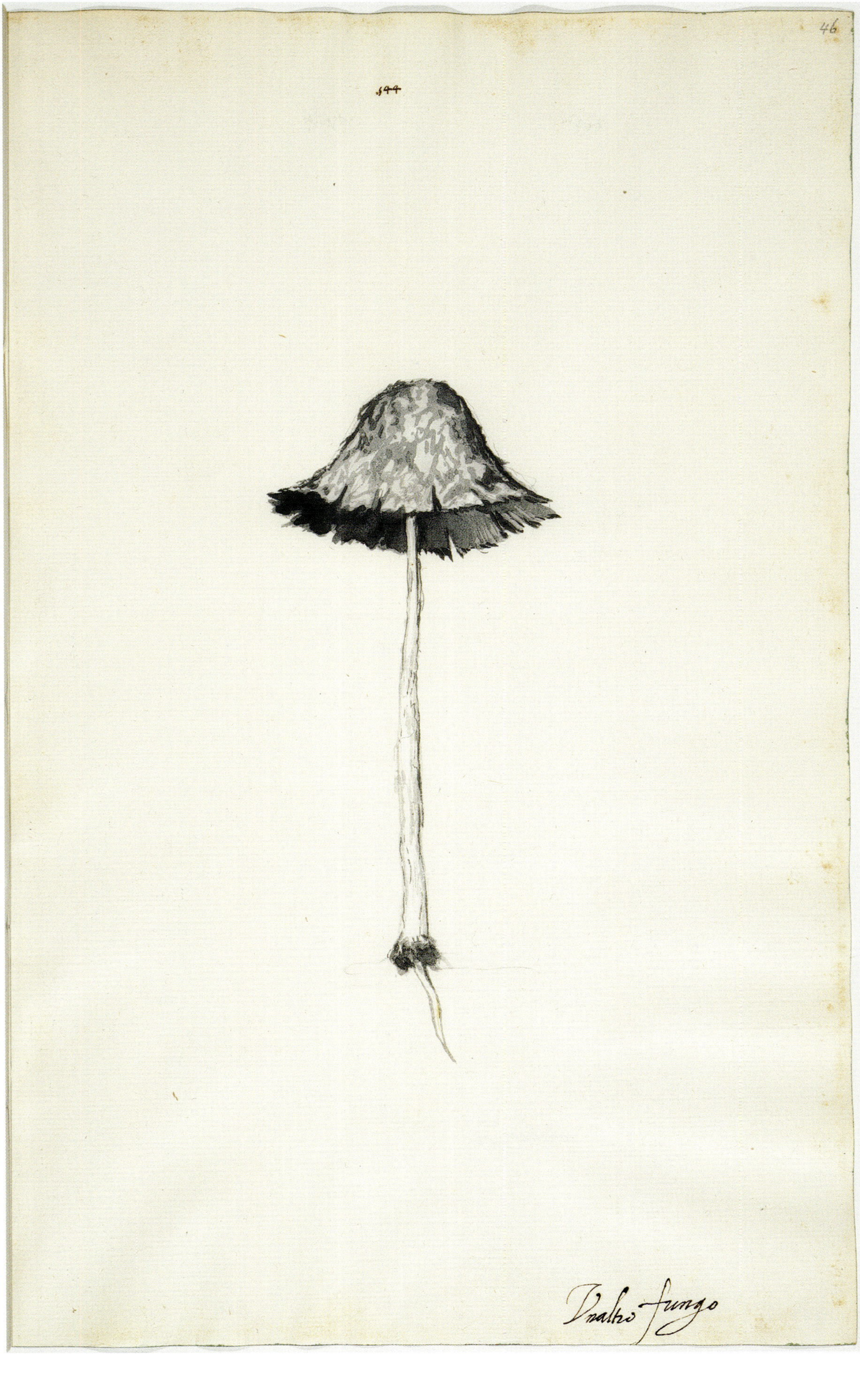
46
544
Vnaltro fungo

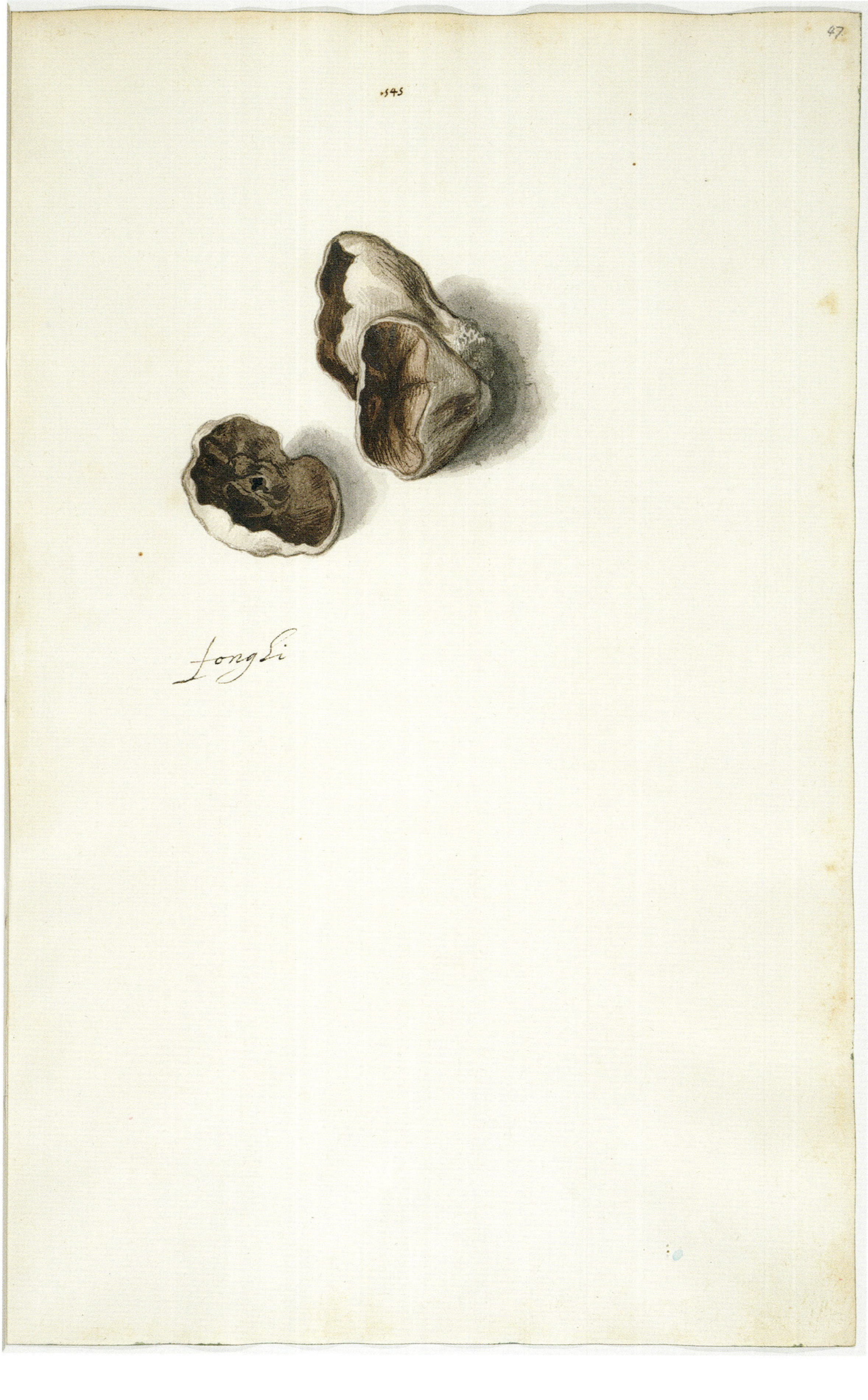
47
545
fonghi

48

546

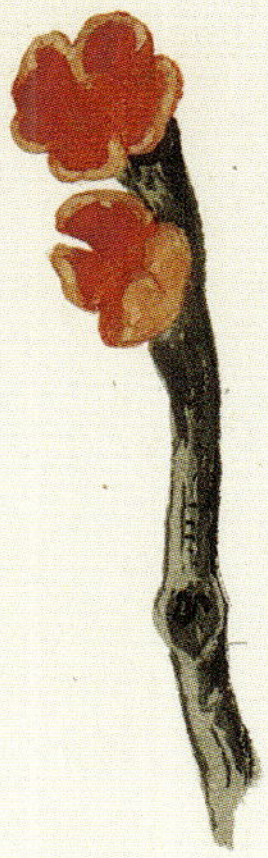

Fonghi che nascono
solo sopra a' doi ò tre
sorte de legno.

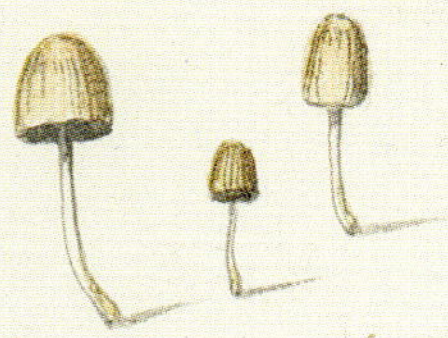

Fonghi colti nelle muraglie de
Cantoni antiche.

49. [?] Purple jelly drops, *Ascocoryne cylichnium* (Tul.) Korf

Erbario Miniato, fol. 49 (RL 27739)

Watermark: Lamb 6

NUMBERING: *547*

ANNOTATION: *Fonghi*

The fruit-body illustrated here is another specimen of the fungus shown on the preceding folio, possibly the purple jelly drops, *Ascocoryne cylichnium*. There are two common species of *Ascocoryne*, *A. cylichnium* and the smaller purple jelly disc, *A. sarcoides*. Both form superficial fruiting bodies with a short, central stem, but are sometimes sessile. The discs are concave, flat or pulvinate, and coloured various shades of reddish-purple. The outer surface is minutely scurfy. The clusters of fruit-bodies are commonly found on rotting stumps and fallen logs of a wide range of trees, especially beech, from August through to February. They are typically found in dense clusters, but are initiated as discrete, individual fruit-bodies.

50. [?] Purple jelly drops, *Ascocoryne cylichnium* (Tul.) Korf

Erbario Miniato, fol. 50 (RL 27740)

NUMBERING: *548*

ANNOTATION: *Fonghi*

Although the four figures are labelled as fungi, a firm identification has proved impossible. The proximity in the manuscript to **48** and **49** suggests that these may be young fruit-bodies of the same species, possibly the purple jelly drops, which have yet to expand and become plate-like. The dark spot in the upper figure probably indicates a central point of attachment, but the fruit-body has been separated from its substrate.

51. Red cage fungus, *Clathrus ruber* Mich.: Pers. 1801

Erbario Miniato, fol. 51 (RL 27741)

Watermark: Anchor 30

NUMBERING: *549*

ANNOTATION: *Fongo*

This is a young fruit-body of the red cage fungus, *Clathrus ruber*, common in the Mediterranean region on soil in deciduous woodland. The fruiting body is initiated as a white, gelatinous, egg-like structure, which bursts open to release a rapidly expanding red net-like structure, the receptaculum, which bears the spores on slimy patches on its inner surface. The smell is attractive to insects, to which the spores become attached and are thereby disseminated. Here the network has hardly expanded, and was probably removed from the ruptured 'egg' case.

Clusius illustrated this species on the last page of his *Fungorum in Pannoniis observatorum brevis historia*, an appendix to his 1601 *Rariorum plantarum historia*. This plate served as the model for a drawing of a fully expanded red cage fungus (B.II.99) made for Cesi as part of his later and much more extensive collection of mycological drawings (including six of *Clathrus ruber* in various stages of growth: B.II.95–100).

547
49.

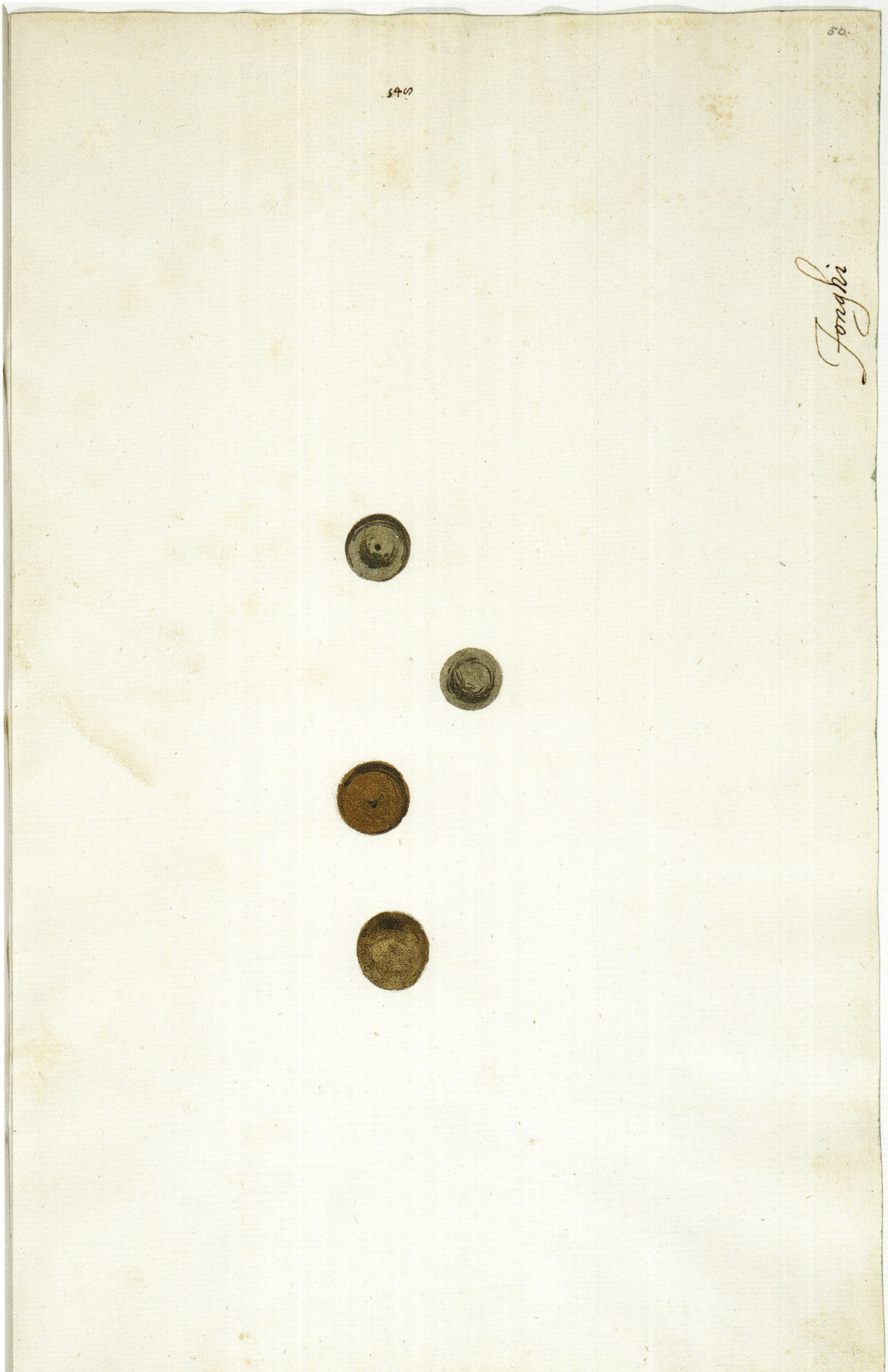
50.
Fonghi

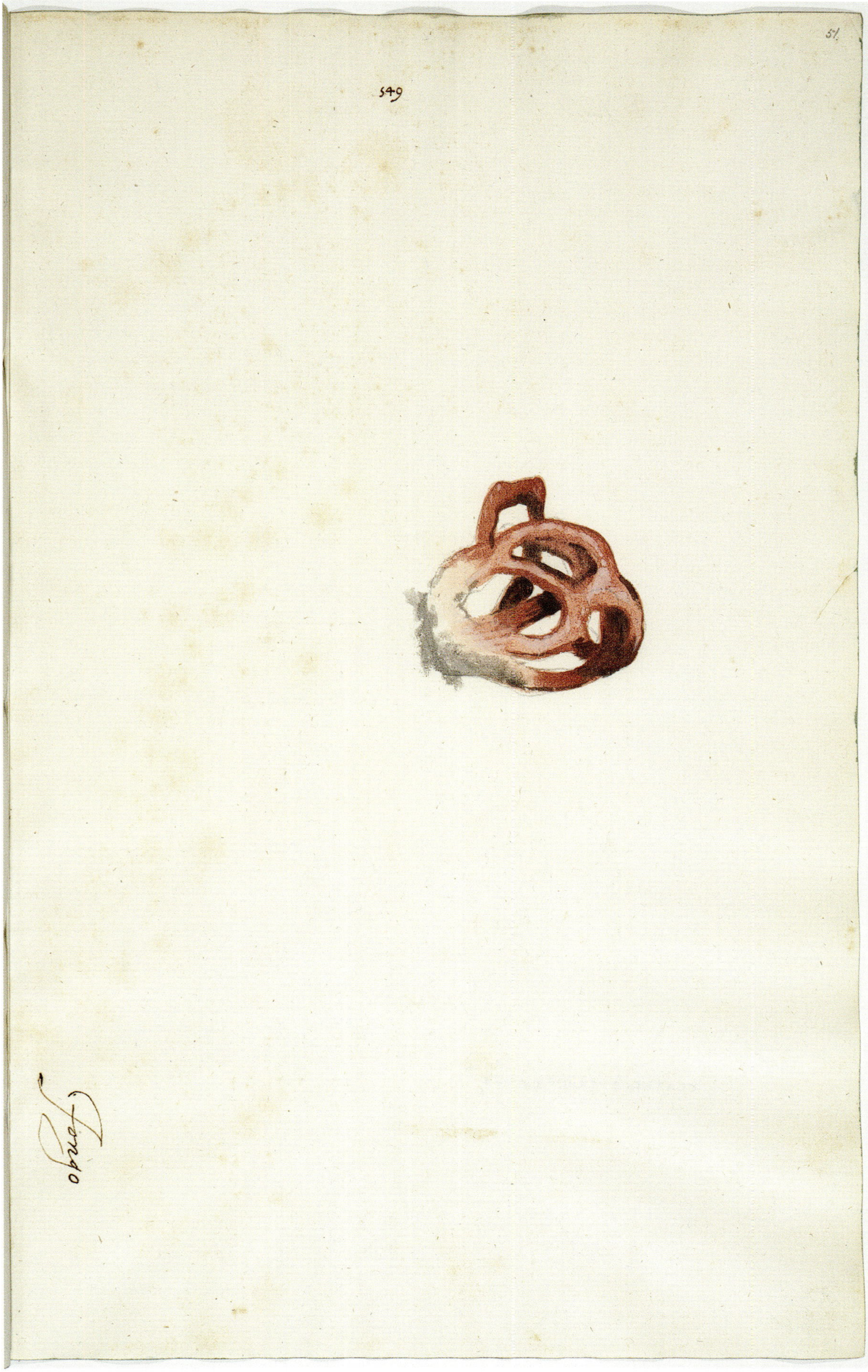
549
51.
Fongo

52. Autumn crocus or meadow saffron, *Colchicum autumnale* L.

Erbario Miniato, fol. 52 (RL 27742)

NUMBERING: *550*

ANNOTATION: *il Colchico, il quale chiamano alcuni Ephemero, e' altri bulbo salvatico, / mangiata la radice. amazza strangolando. como fanno i fonghi, / il latte di vacca e', otimo rimedio. à chi avesse mangiata la detta / radice.*; 1163 ('*Colchico*, called by some *Ephemero* and by others wild bulb. Like fungi, the root kills by choking if eaten. An excellent remedy for those who have eaten this root is cow's milk; 1163'). [From Mattioli 1568, p. 1163]

The autumn crocus or meadow saffron is a bulbous perennial of the family Liliaceae, native to most of central and southern Europe, growing in grassy spots and woodland clearings from sea level to 2,000m. It must have been known to the ancient Greeks for its name, *Kolchikion*, is derived from Colchis, a region on the eastern coast of the Black Sea (today Kolkhida in Georgia). The plant has been widely used by herbalists, and was included in the London pharmacopoeia as early as 1618. The corm and seeds contain the alkaloid colchicine (an important modern drug for the treatment of rheumatism, arthritis and gout), and were used to make emetics, diuretics and purgatives.

The plant has an oval bulb with a dark tunic which extends for half the length of the scape, forming a long collar. The pale pink flower with its six elongated oval tepals and yellow anthers is here shown twice – in full flower and then just before senescence (the scape has been partially effaced with touches of white lead). It may be distinguished from the saffron crocus (*Crocus sativus*) by the number of its stamens (three rather than six), and the unusual timing of its reproductive cycle, flowering briefly in late summer and autumn. Late the following spring a short stem appears, bearing the plant's fruit enveloped in leaves; due to this long quiescent period, the fruit of the crocus seems to appear before the flower.

Mattioli's *Discorsi* contains two illustrations of *Colchicum autumnale*. On p. 1164 is a plate showing two specimens of 'Colchico florido' with several flowers and the detail of a bulb, while on p. 1165 the 'Colchico senza fiori' shows the plant 'without flowers', as it appears during the summer.

62

550

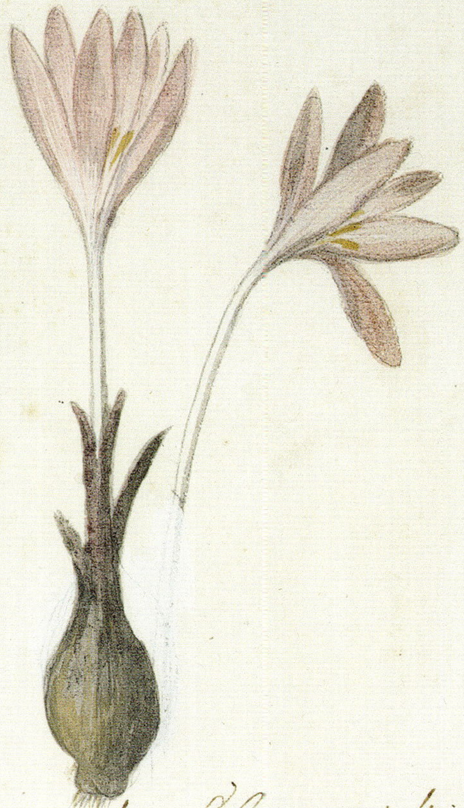

il Colchico, il quale chiamano alcuni Ephemero, e' altri bulbo saluatico,
mangiata la radice. amazza strangolando. como fanno i fonghi;
il latte di uacca è, otimo rimedio. a chi auesse mangiata la detta
radice. 1163

53. Common sternbergia, *Sternbergia lutea* (L.) Ker Gawl. ex Sprengel

Erbario Miniato, fol. 53 (RL 27743)

Watermark: Crown 5

NUMBERING: *551*

ANNOTATION: *COLCHICO OVERO NARCISSO AUTUNNALE* ('*Colchico* or autumn narcissus')

VERSO: black chalk sketch of the same specimen.

The common sternbergia (see also **125**), named after the naturalist Caspar von Sternberg (1761–1838), is a bulbous species of the family Amaryllidaceae (though some place it among the Liliaceae). Now cultivated as an ornamental, it is indigenous to Europe and western Asia, thriving in meadows and dry undergrowth from sea level to 1,200m, though it has been designated a protected species in Italy. Like many members of the family Amaryllidaceae it is poisonous.

This specimen has five leaves that vary in length depending upon their age and end in either rounded or subacute tips. The flower is shown growing out of a persistent, light green bract. Its six narrow, pointed, ovate-lanceolate petals are bright yellow in colour with a network of fine veins. Between the petals the flower's long style and five of its six anthers can be seen. The underground parts of the plant have been sketched in black chalk.

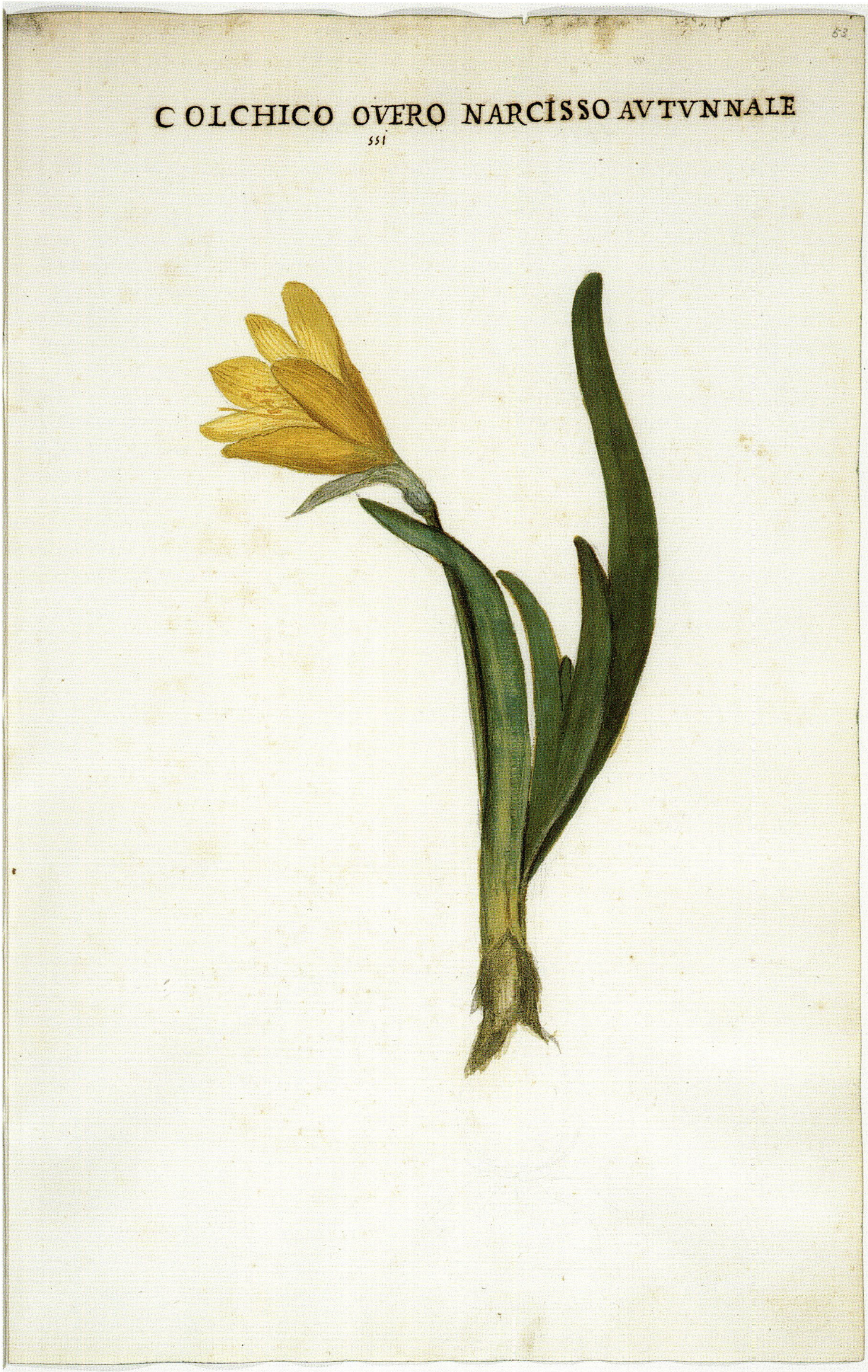
53
COLCHICO OVERO NARCISSO AVTVNNALE
551

54. Widow iris or snake's-head iris, *Hermodactylus tuberosus* (L.) Mill.

Erbario Miniato, fol. 54 (RL 27744)

NUMBERING: *552*

ANNOTATION: *HERMODATTILO VERO. 1167* ('True *hermodattilo*. 1167'). [From Mattioli 1568, p. 1167]

The drawing shows the widow iris or snake's-head iris, a rhizomatous species of the family Iridaceae. It is widespread in the Mediterranean, growing in poor soil on uncultivated land and in olive groves, and is particularly common in southern Italy. The genus *Hermodactylus* consists of this single species and can be differentiated from the true iris only by its tuberous root system and the configuration of its ovary, a single chamber with no septa.

The characteristic root system of the plant is shown, consisting of five slender rhizomes and several fibrous roots. The five basal leaves are long and narrow, the three outermost ones taking up the entire right side of the page. Within the curve of the lowest leaf are sketched a cross-section and an oblique-section of the leaf to show the quadrangular structure typical of *Hermodactylus*. The flower is yellow except for the indigo-blue distal lobes of the outer petals. The segments of the innermost stamens are deeply forked. The capsule-like fruit is not shown, though Mattioli's illustration shows a specimen with its fruit rather than in flower.

The common name 'snake's-head' derives from the supposed resemblance of the flower to a serpent's open mouth, while the genus name *Hermodactylus*, 'finger of Mercury', is derived from the name given by Galen to the yellow saffron in his work *De simplicium medicamentorum facultatibus*, inspired by the formation of the rhizomes, which recall the fingers of a human hand.

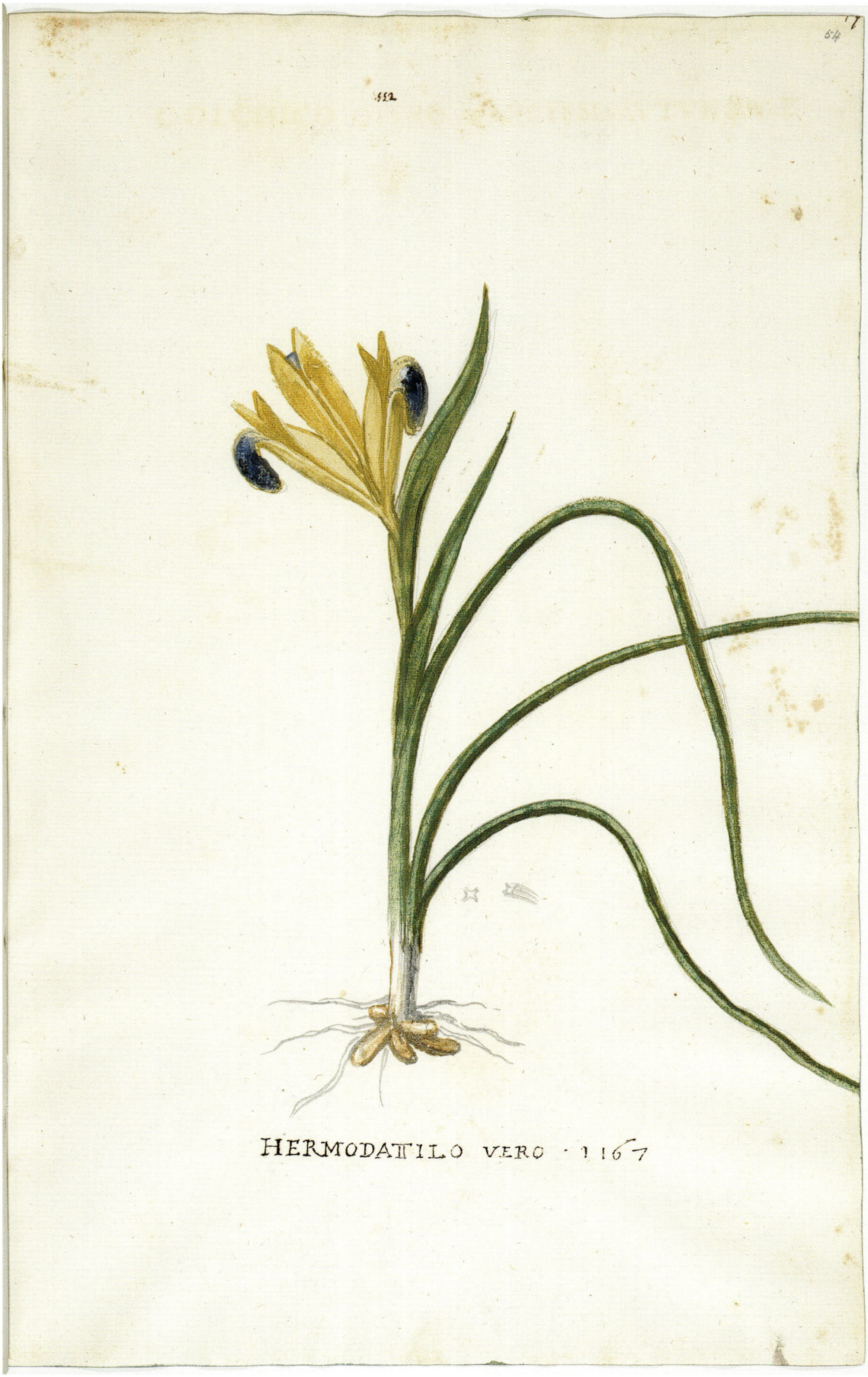
54
552
HERMODATTILO VERO · 1167

55. Pellitory-of-the-wall, *Parietaria diffusa* Mertens & Koch

Erbario Miniato, fol. 55 (RL 27745)

NUMBERING: *553*

ANNOTATION: *Parietaria; Vetriola; Helsine, le frondi hanno virtu de ingrosare, e' de infrigidire: / sanano impiastrati il fuoco sacro, le cotture del fuoco, le posteme / del sedere, il succo incorporato con cerusa, si mette utilmente in / su l'erisipele, e ulcere serpiginose, aplicate* [M: *applicasi*] *parimenti alle podagre / insieme con sevo di becco, overo con ciroto ligustrino, tolto ala / quantità d'un ciatho, cura la tosse vecchia, distilato nelle orecchie / con olio rosato ne cava il dolore, 1170* ('*Parietaria; Vetriola; Helsine*. The leaves have a thickening and cooling quality. They are applied to cure erysipelas, burns and anal warts. The juice mixed with wax is beneficial when applied to erysipelas and serpiginous ulcers. Together with goat's grease or a bandage made of privet, it is also applied to gout. Extracted in the amount of one cup it cures chronic coughs. Dropped in the ears with rose oil it relieves ear pain; 1170'). [From Mattioli 1568, p. 1171]

The pellitory-of-the-wall, a plant of the nettle family Urticaceae, is common throughout the Mediterranean from sea level to an altitude of 1,000m, on exposed cliffs and walls – hence the genus name *Parietaria*, from Latin *paries*, 'wall'. Its common name in Italian is *erba vetriola* ('vitreous plant') because, with its stiff stem and the hooked, mineralized hairs on the undersides of its leaves, it was used as a bottle brush. Like its better-known cousin *Parietaria officinalis* (the 'helsine' illustrated on p. 1170 of Mattioli's *Discorsi* and cited here, although the text is drawn from p. 1171), the pellitory has diuretic, sudorific, expectorant and purifying properties.

In the drawing the characteristic reddish, slightly tomentose (hairy) stem is clearly shown. The thirteen alternate leaves have short petioles and are oval in shape with unbroken margins, sharp tips and prominent veins. The flowers are clustered in glomerules at the base of the leaves. The pellitory is a gynomonoecious species, with monoclinous (hermaphrodite) flowers, with three deep lobes and four stamens, or pistillate (female) flowers, tubular with shallow lobes. The form of the flowers here cannot be clearly distinguished but appear to be hermaphrodite.

553

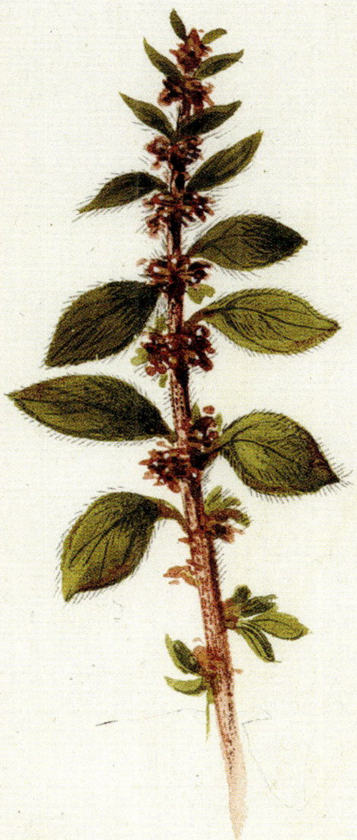

Parietaria,
Vetriola,

Helsine, Le frondi hanno virtu de ingrosare, e de infrigidire: sanano impiastrati il fuoco sacro, le cotture del fuoco, le posteme del sedere, il succo incorporato con cerusa, simette utilmente in su l' erisipele, e ulcere serpiginose, aplicate parimente alle podagre insieme con seuo di becco, ouero con ceroto ligustrino, tolto ala quantità d' un ciatho, cura la tosse vecchia, distilato nelle orecchie con olio rosato, ne caua il dolore, 1170

56. Common chickweed, *Stellaria media* (L.) Vill.

Erbario Miniato, fol. 56 (RL 27746)

NUMBERING: *554*

ANNOTATION: *Alsine. la quale chiamano alcuni Antillio, e' altri miosotta / in Toscana si chiama Centone. altri Pavarina, altri pizza / gallina, e' altri Centonice, à virtu de ristagnare. e' infrigidire. / impiastrasi con polenta à li infiamagioni de li occhi; al mio Matiolo grande. a' carte. 1171.* ('*Alsine*. Called by some *Antillio* and by others *miosotta*. In Tuscany it is called *Centone*, while others call it *Pavarina, pizza gallina* or *Centonice*. It has cooling and astringent qualities. It is applied with pearl barley to eye inflammations. On page 1171 of my large Mattioli.'). [From Mattioli 1568, p. 1171]

This common chickweed is a herbaceous species of the family Caryophyllaceae, found in temperate zones from sea level to an altitude of 1,600m. Here a slender, erect stem bears seven pairs of opposite leaves with entire margins, acute apices and dark veins. A characteristic line of fine downy hairs can be seen running between each node. At the axils of the lower leaves calyxes can be seen with immature capsules on long, slender peduncles. There are three white flowers at the apex of the stem, one still in bud, one in full bloom with its bipartite petals visible, and one which has begun to wilt. The star-like flowers of five forked petals give the genus name *Stellaria*.

56

554

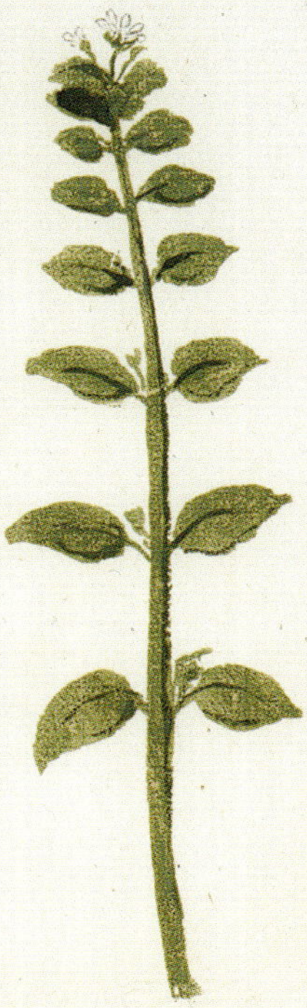

Alsine. la quale chiamano alcuni Antillio, è altri miosotta
intoscana si chiama Centone. altri Paparina. altri Spizza
gallina. è altri Centonice. à virtu de ristagnare. è infrigidire.
impiastrasi con polenta à li infiamagioni de li occhi;

al mio Matiolo grande. à carte 1171.

57. Houseleek, *Sempervivum tectorum* L.

Erbario Miniato, fol. 57 (RL 27747)

NUMBERING: *555*

ANNOTATION: *fiore de Semprevivo Magiore 1175* ('Flower of the greater *Semprevivo*. 1175'). [From Mattioli 1568, p. 1175]

This is a flowering scape of the common houseleek, *Sempervivum tectorum*, also called old-man-and-woman or hen-and-chickens (see also **58**). The succulent plant is a low-growing perennial of the Crassulaceae (stonecrop) family, native to the mountains of central and southern Europe, Morocco and western Asia, on cliffs and dry slopes at altitudes from 200m to 2,800m. It is cultivated as an ornamental, and many hybrid varieties exist.

The Italian name *semprevivo* and genus name *Sempervivum*, 'alive forever', are a tribute to the plant's hardiness. It supposedly offered protection against lightning: in Nordic countries it was sacred to Thor, the god of thunder (hence the German name *Donnersbart*, thunder-beard), and in various medieval herbals it is found as *herba saturna*. Charlemagne issued an edict that the plant be grown on the roofs of buildings in the Alps; it is known as *joubarbe des toits* (roof houseleek) in French, and the specific epithet assigned by Linnaeus, *tectorum*, means 'of the roofs'. In northern Italy, because of its similarity in form to the artichoke, the plant was also known as the 'wild' or 'mad' artichoke (*carciofo selvatico* or *matto*).

In the drawing the root system of the plant (considerably simplified by the artist) takes the form of a broadened portion of the stem from which emerge four small roots. The lower section of the stem is leafless, while the upper part is covered with overlapping, fleshy, pinkish-green scales. The numerous sessile flowers are arranged in a loose corymb; each pink flower is made up of many linear petals arranged like rays around the stamens and pistil, which cannot be clearly distinguished. The calyx is well developed with no apparent divisions.

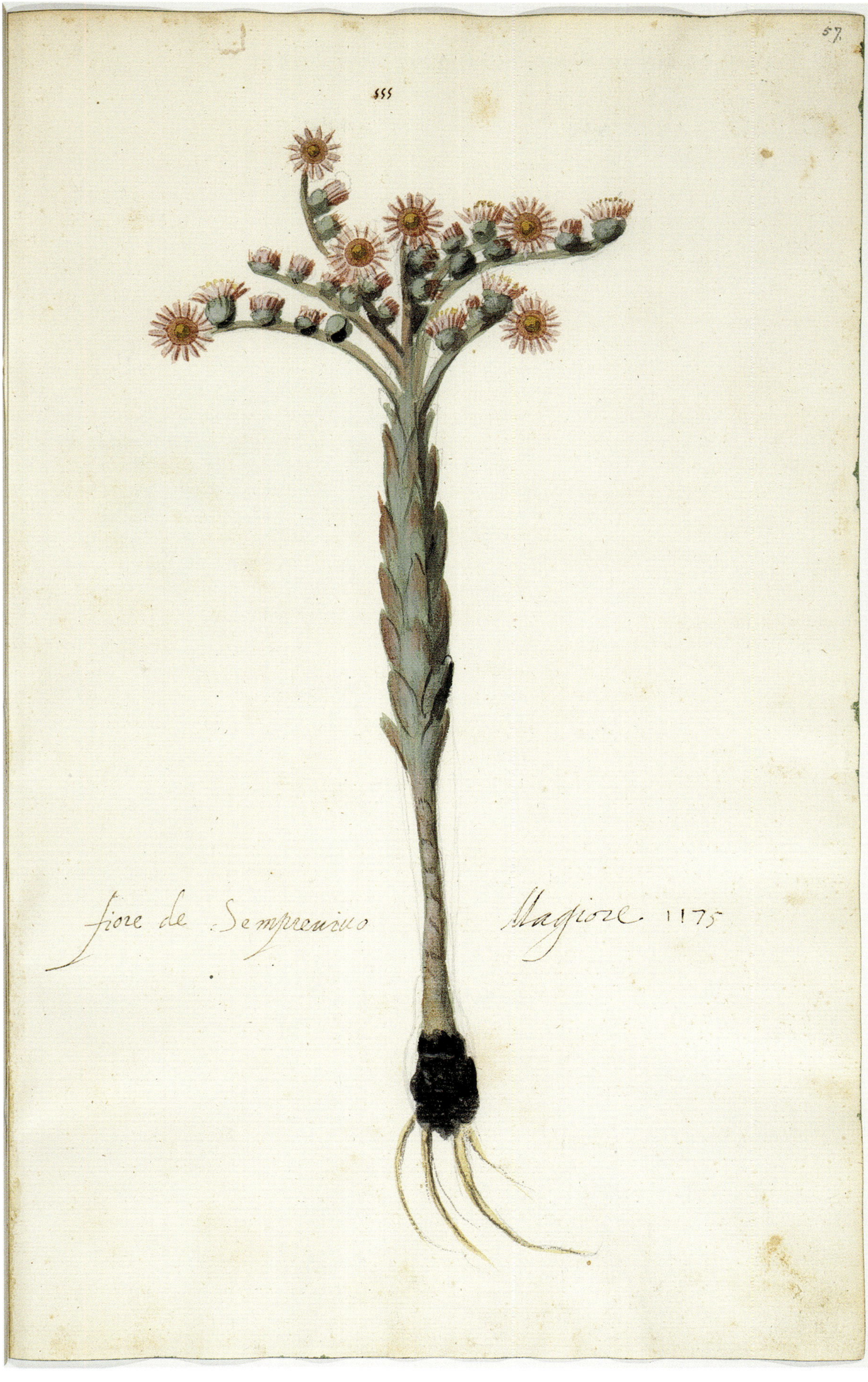
57
555
fiore de Sempreuiuo Magiore 1175

58. Rosette of a houseleek, *Sempervivum tectorum* L.

Erbario Miniato, fol. 58 (RL 27748)

Watermark: Fleur de lys 50

NUMBERING: *556*

ANNOTATION: *Semprevivo magiore. Ha virtu de infrigidire, e' di ristringere. / Le frondi medicano al fuoco Sacro, alle ulcere maligne, / e contumaci, e serpegiose, conferiscano ale infiamagione / de gli occhi, alle cotture del fuoco, alle podagre, tanto / aplicato p[er] se sole quanto insieme con polenta, / usasi infuso utilmente il succo insieme con polenta, / overo con olio rosato, ne i, dolori del capo, beuto / vale a' i, morsi de quegli ragni, che si chiamano palanghi* [M: *phalangi*], */ alla disentiera, e' altri flussi di corpo, beuto nel vino. caccia / i, vermi* [M: *vermini lunghi*] *del corpo, aplicato di sotto con lana, ristagna il flusso / delle donne, conferisce ungendosi, al defetto de li occhi, e' anco / prefettissimo. p[er] le hemoroide,* <u>*1175*</u> ('Greater *Semprevivo*. It has cooling and astringent properties. The leaves treat erysipelas and malign, persistent and serpiginous ulcers. Whether applied alone or with pearl barley, the leaves are effective against eye inflammations, burns and gout. Their infused juice, with pearl barley or rose oil, treats headaches. When drunk it is effective against the bites of those spiders called *p*[*h*]*alanghi*, against dysentery and other discharges of the body. Drunk in wine it eliminates worms from the body, applied below with wool it staunches women's menstrual flow. Rubbed on the eyes it cures eye defects, and it is also very effective for haemorrhoids. 1175'). [From Mattioli 1568, pp. 1174–5]

This drawing shows a basal rosette of the houseleek, *Sempervivum tectorum* (see **57**). The alternate leaves, thick and fleshy with curved tips ending in short points, are erect at the centre of the rosette, spreading more and more widely as they approach the circumference, and the outermost leaves are completely reflexed. A short stolon, or runner, with small roots is shown emerging from the base of the rosette.

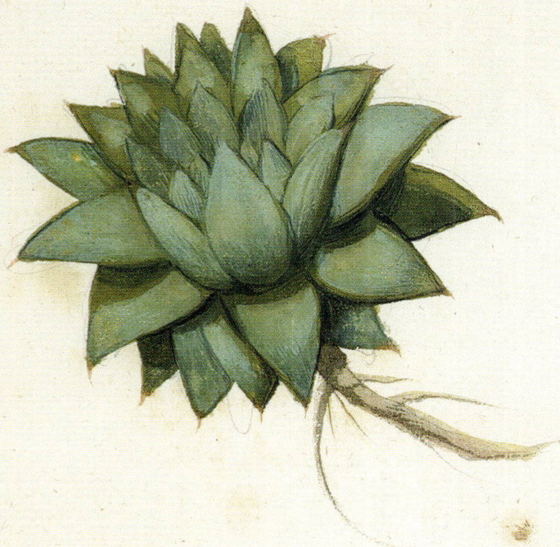

Sempreuiuo magiore. Ha uirtu de infrigidire, è di ristringere,
le frondi medicano al fuoco Sacro, alle ulcere maligne,
contumaci, e serpegiose. conferiscano ale infiamagione
de gli occhi, alle cotture del fuoco, alle podagre, tanto
aplicato p se sole quanto insieme con polenta,
usasi infuso utilmente il succo insieme con polenta,
ouero con olio rosato, ne i doloni del capo, beuto
uale à i morsi de quegli ragni, che si chiamano palanghi,
alla disenteria, e altri flussi di corpo, beuto nel uino. caccia
i uermi del corpo, aplicato disotto con lana, ristagna il flusso
delle donne. conferisce ungendosi, al defetto de li occhi, è anco
prefettissimo. p le Emoroide. 1175

59. Thick-leaved stonecrop, *Sedum dasyphyllum* L.; white stonecrop, *Sedum album* L.; yellow stonecrop, *Sedum* sp.; biting stonecrop, *Sedum acre* L.

Erbario Miniato, fol. 59 (RL 27749)

NUMBERING: *557*

ANNOTATION: *un altro sempre vivo.; sempre vivo. ~~minore~~ vermicola / detto da alcuni, barba / di Giove; Semprevivo Minore a' le Medesime virtu che il Magiore; .1175. Minimo; unaltro sempre vivo. minore, il quale chiamano / alcuni portulaca salvatica, altri telepio* [M: *telephio*], */ e' i latini, illecebra, a' virtu calida e acuta, e / ulcerativa. impiastrato con grascia risolve / le ~~srof~~ scrofole.* ('Another *semprevivo*; ~~lesser~~ *semprevivo*, called *vermicola* or Jupiter's beard by some; the lesser *Semprevivo* has the same properties as the greater one; 1175; *Minimo* [least]; another lesser *semprevivo*, called by some wild *portulaca*, by others *telep*[*h*]*io*, and by the Romans *illecebra*. It is sharp and has warming, ulcer-inducing qualities. Applied with grease it can heal scrofulas.'). [From Mattioli 1568, pp. 1175–7]

LITERATURE: *Quaderni Puteani* 1, pp. 63, 65 (fig. 44); Freedberg 2002, pp. 208 (fig. 8.8), 211–12

The genus *Sedum* forms part of the family Crassulaceae and includes about 600 species of succulent, low-growing rock plants common to southern and central Europe and the temperate areas of Asia and North Africa, where they grow at altitudes from sea level to 1,600m.

In this detailed drawing four species of stonecrop are shown. At upper left is a thick-leaved stonecrop, *Sedum dasyphyllum*, with four slender stems – two of which are in flower – growing out of a small taproot. The leaves are oval in shape, stemless and fleshy. The flowers are arranged in corymbs, one made up of five and the other of eight blossoms. The flowers on their short pedicels have pale pink corollas growing out of calyxes that are one-half the length of the blossoms. At upper centre is a white stonecrop, *Sedum album*, shown with its stolon and three stems bearing many elongated oval, fleshy leaves. To the upper right is some variety of yellow stonecrop, *Sedum* sp., with a large number of long, narrow, fleshy leaves; the flowering parts are not shown and a precise identification is not possible. Below is a biting stonecrop, *Sedum acre*, consisting of a slender, tapering taproot and an erect stem which branches from its base. The principal branch has two yellow flowers, each made up of five lanceolate petals.

The stonecrops, and the biting stonecrop in particular, were thought to have magical properties. The plant was placed in vases next to the pictures of relatives who had died, as it was believed that the length of time that it remained green after cutting (often as long as two months) would be subtracted from the period that the person spent in Purgatory. Farm animals were protected from sickness by placing a sprig on the doors of their stalls, and if grown on the roof of one's house it would shield the family from misfortune.

Mattioli discussed four types of 'Semprevivi', three of which had been described by Dioscorides: 'Semprevivo maggiore', 'minore', 'minimo' and 'arboreo'. The white stonecrop here, to which the inscription at centre seems to refer, corresponds to the second or 'lesser' Semprevivo of Dioscorides (p. 1175, illustrated by Mattioli on p. 1176), while the biting stonecrop below corresponds to Dioscorides' third type, 'Semprevivo minimo', illustrated by Mattioli on p. 1177.

557

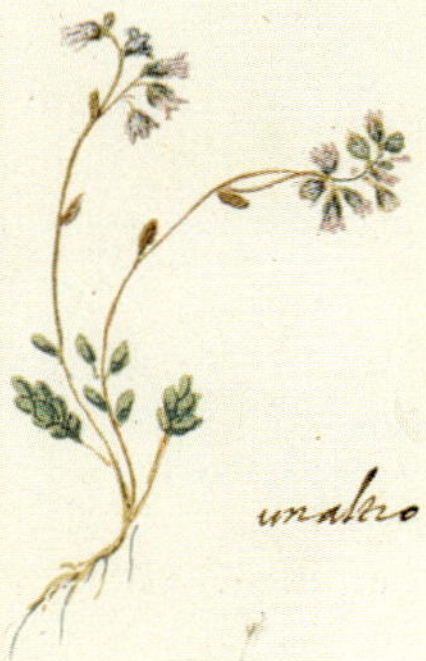

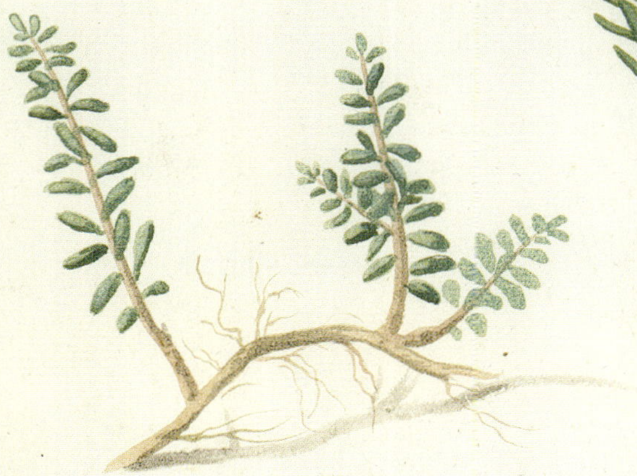

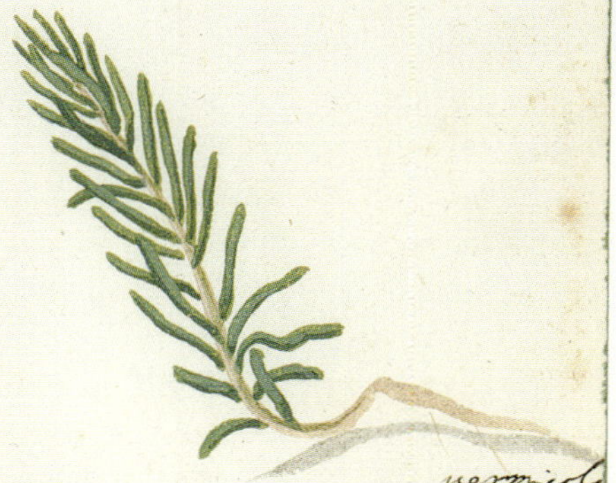

sempre uiuo. ~~minore~~ uermicola
detto da alcuni barba
di Gioue,

unaltro sempre uiuo.

Sempreuiuo Minore á le Medesime uirtu che il Magiore

. 1175 .

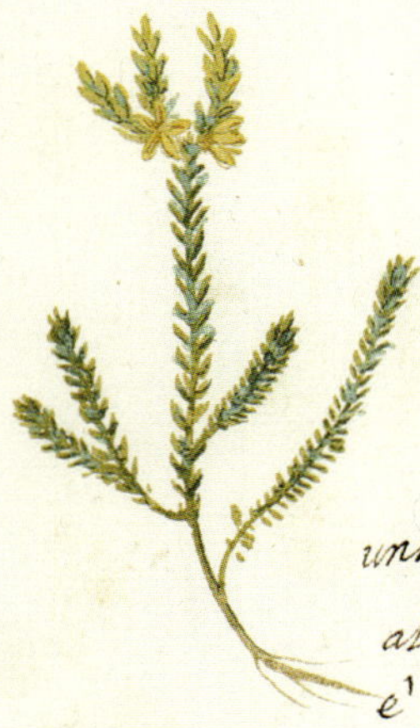

Minimo,

unaltro sempre uiuo. minore. il quale chiamano alcuni portulaca saluatica, altri telepio, è i latini, illecebra, á uirtu calida é acuta. e ulceratiua. impiastrato con grascia risolue le ~~[illegible]~~ scrofole,

60. Lifelong saxifrage, *Saxifraga paniculata* Mill.

Erbario Miniato, fol. 60 (RL 27750)

Watermark: Fleur de lys 46

NUMBERING: *558*

ANNOTATION: *Semprevivo Montano* ('Mountain *Semprevivo*')

This perennial of the family Saxifragaceae is common in the mountains of southern and central Europe, on cliffs and stony pastureland to an altitude of 3,000m. The plant has a short, fibrous root system. The basal leaves, arranged in a rosette, are linear with a truncated apex. The flowering scape is erect, slightly curved at the apex, and carries four closed buds and a flower in full anthesis arranged in a loose panicle. The blossom is made up of five white petals, bluntly oval in shape. The numerous golden stamens at its centre have been roughly sketched in. A distinguishing feature of many species of saxifrage is the row of pointed dimples that line the margins of the leaves. These are the plant's stomata, where water seeps out and dries to leave mineral deposits, indicated here with flecks of brown wash.

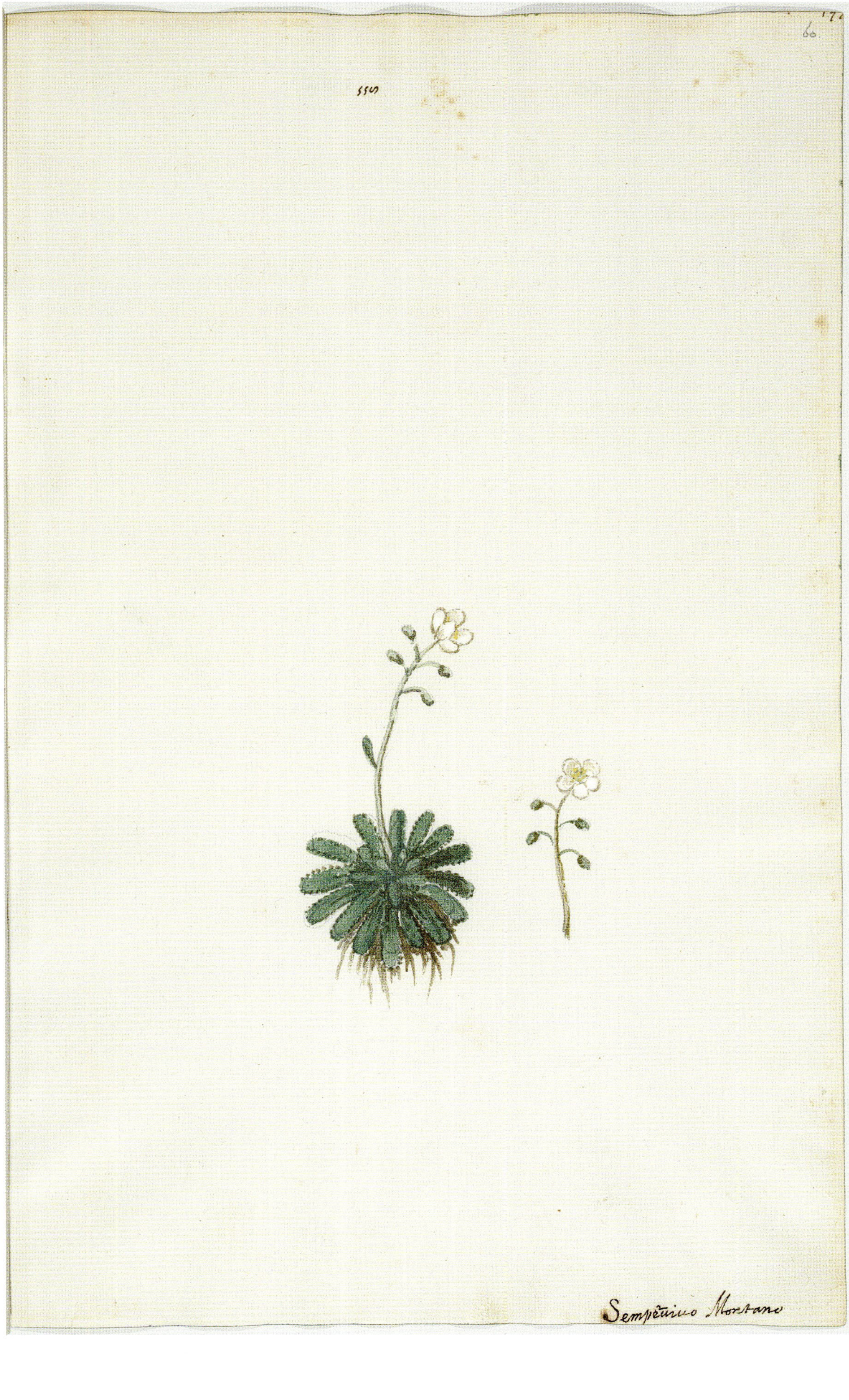

60

61. Navelwort, *Umbilicus rupestris* (Salisb. 1796) Dandy

Erbario Miniato, fol. 61 (RL 27751)

NUMBERING: *559*

ANNOTATION: *fiore de ombelico; Ombilico di Venere, il succo distillato, overo unto con vino, scuopre / le parti genitali, che sonno ricoperte di carne, e' giova parimente / al fuoco sacro, alle infiamagioni, alle scrofole, e alle bugancie, spe= / gne gli ardori dello stomaco. Le foglie mangiate insieme con la radice, / rompe le pietre, e' provoca lorina, dandosi con mele. agli hidropici; 1180.* ('Flower of the navel. Navel of Venus. The juice, administered in drops or anointed with wine, relieves the genital regions affected by blockages of the skin, and is equally beneficial against erysipelas, inflammations, scrofulas and chilblains. It extinguishes burning in the stomach. The leaves, eaten together with the root, break up kidney stones and induce urination in dropsy patients when administered with honey. 1180'). [From Mattioli 1568, pp. 1179–80]

LITERATURE: Freedberg 2002, pp. 213–14 (fig. 8.16)

The navelwort is a perennial of the family Crassulaceae, common throughout southern Europe on damp, shady cliffs and walls to an altitude of 1,200m. Here the artist has drawn the leaf in two views to show the deep green upper surface and yellowish-green lower surface, with its rounded form, scalloped edges and long, thick petiole. At upper right is the detail of a long raceme bearing many short-stemmed, greenish flowers with long, tubular corollas and toothed margins, each growing from the base of a bract.

The picturesque name recorded by Mattioli, 'Ombelico di Venere' or 'navel of Venus', was inspired by the rounded and gently curved form of the leaf with the veined depression at its centre. The genus *Umbilicus* was originally named *Cotyledon* by Linnaeus, from the Greek κοτυληδών, a cup-shaped hollow or cavity, used by Dioscorides and Pliny to refer to this species. The doctrine of signatures explains the many supposed properties of the plant: both Hippocrates and Dioscorides believed the plant had aphrodisiac properties and prescribed it as a remedy for barren women; because of the marked insertion point of the stem, the mature leaves were prescribed for problems of the hip and other joints, and the younger, crescent-shaped leaves for the kidneys.

61

559

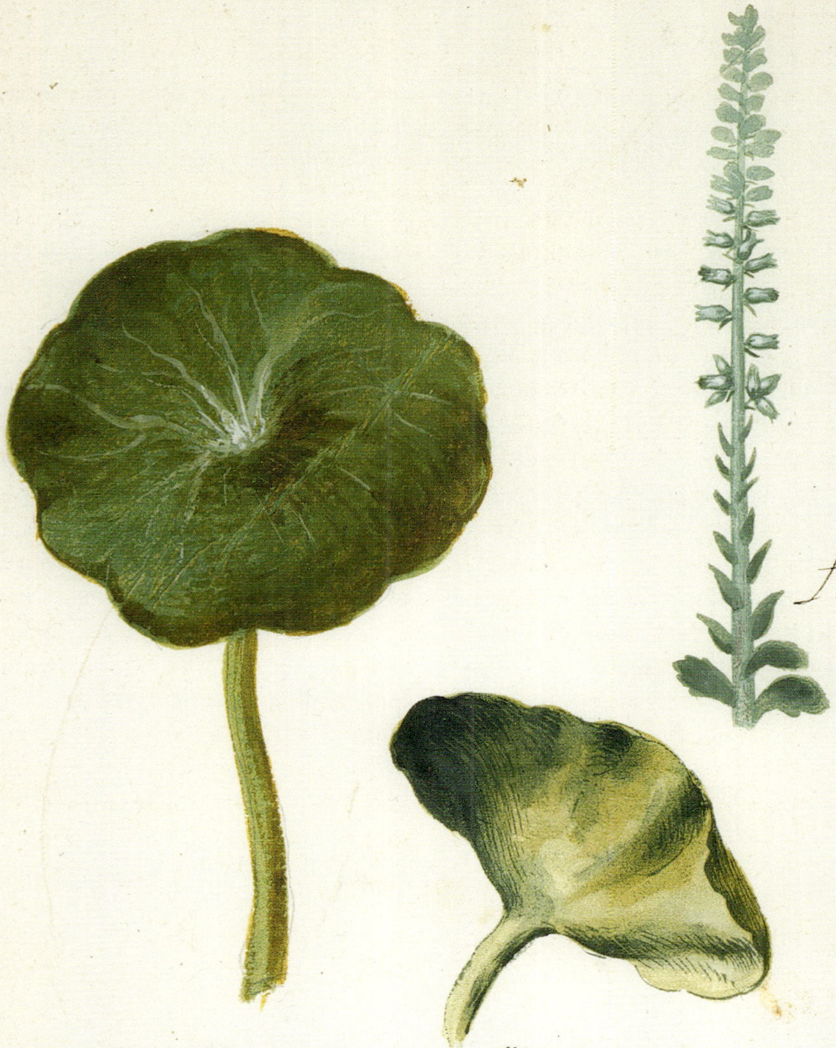

Ombelico di Venere. il succo distillato, ouero unto con uino. scuopre le parti genitali, che sono ricoperte di carne. è gioua parimente al fuoco sacro, alle infiamagioni, alle scrofole, e alle buganzie. ∴ spegne gli ardori dello stomaco. le foglie mangiato insieme con la radice, rompe le pietre, è prouoca l'orina, dandosi con mele. agli Eidropici.

1180.

62. Ivy-leaved toadflax, *Cymbalaria muralis* P. Gaertn.

Erbario Miniato, fol. 62 (RL 27752)

Watermark: Fleur de lys 54

NUMBERING: *560*

ANNOTATION: *Cimbalo, il Matiolo le scrive p*[*er*] *un altra sorte de / Ombelico di Venere. La sua virtu e' simil che / e il Sempre Vivo. veramente e' spetie de umbelico; 1182.* ('*Cimbalo*. Mattioli considers it another kind of Navel of Venus. Its properties are similar to those of the *semprevivo*. It is in truth a kind of *umbelico*; 1182.'). [From Mattioli 1568, pp. 1180, 1182]

The ivy-leaved toadflax, of the family Scrophulariaceae, is native to central and southern Europe and has become naturalized all over the world. It grows primarily on piles of rubble and on old walls. Here the artist has depicted an entire plant in the flowering stage. Its long, slender stem meanders across the page, indicating the prostrate habit of the vine. The heliotropic leaves (following the passage of the sun across the sky), on long, filiform petioles, are kidney-shaped when young and later develop six blunt, rounded lobes with palmate ribs. The three fully open blossoms are waxy white tinged with lilac. The corolla, growing out of a long pedicel, terminates in a short spur; the calyx is not shown.

Dioscorides described two types of 'Ombelico di Venere' (see **61**), illustrated by Mattioli on pp. 1180–1. A third type was introduced by Mattioli called 'Cimbalaria'; he believed it shared many of the properties of the 'Ombelico' and was therefore related to it. The *Erbario* seems to identify the present plant (as also **63**) with this third type, as the citation of Mattioli's p. 1182 would refer to the illustration of the 'Cimbalaria' – *Cymbalaria muralis* – on that page. The annotation, however, uses Dioscorides' name and description of the second type of 'Ombelico' (possibly *Saxifraga paniculata*).

560

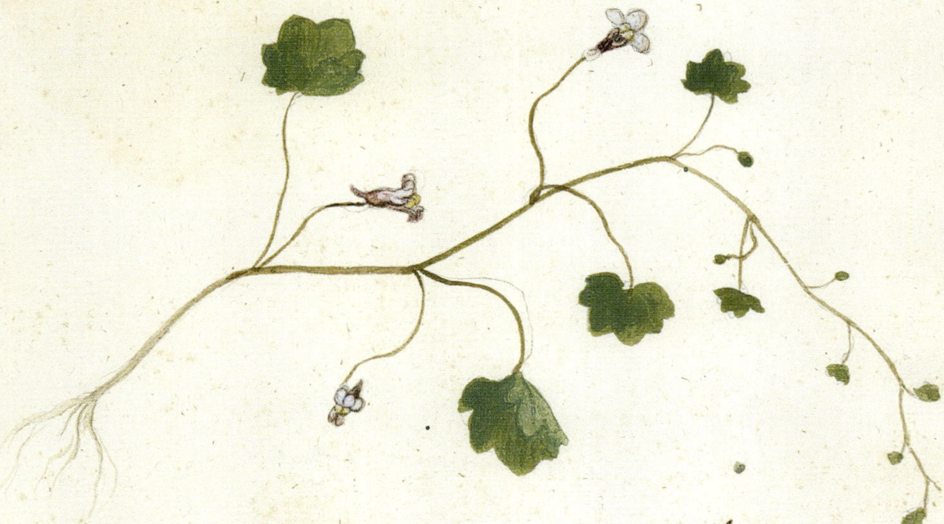

Cimbalo, il Matiolo lo scrive p[er] un'altra sorte de Ombelico di Venere. La sua virtu é simil alle e il Sempre Vivo. veramente é spetie de umbelico

1182.

63. Pale cymbalaria, *Cymbalaria pallida* (Ten.) Wettst. 1891

Erbario Miniato, fol. 63 (RL 27753)

Watermark: Eagle 19

NUMBERING: *561*

ANNOTATION: *CIMBALARIA*

The pale cymbalaria is a small creeping herbaceous species of the family Scrophulariaceae, common in the central region of the Apennine mountains, where it grows on the moraines of glaciers at altitudes of 1,500m to 2,000m. It is a pioneer species, capable of colonizing barren terrain and initiating an ecological succession, and can survive in loose, stony soil with very little water because of its robust, highly developed root system and long stolons.

The artist has carefully drawn the numerous short, closely bunched stems; the leaves, growing from the ends of long petioles, lobed with smooth margins; and the flowers, suspended from long, filiform pedicels, with pale pink corollas, darker near the base and almost pure white near the throat.

561

CIMBALARIA

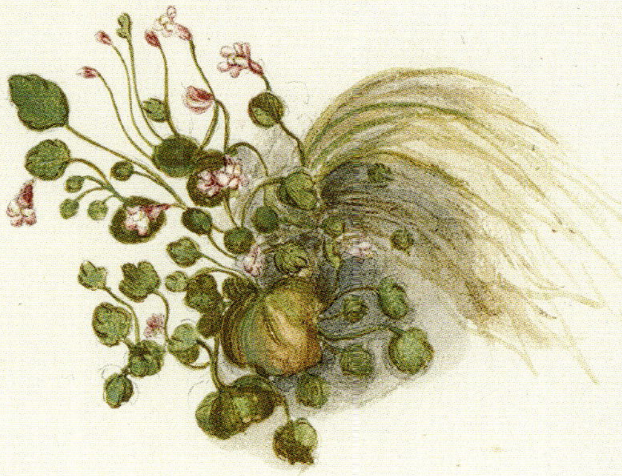

64. Roman nettle, *Urtica pilulifera* L.

Erbario Miniato, fol. 64 (RL 27754)

NUMBERING: *562*

ANNOTATION: *Ortica prima. 1183* ('Nettle of the first type. 1183'). [From Mattioli 1568, p. 1183]

The Roman nettle is a herbaceous annual of the Urticaceae family. It is indigenous to the Mediterranean and western Asia, although it is becoming increasingly rare, and may be found growing in abandoned fields from sea level to 1,200m.

The erect stem portrayed here bears opposite pairs of leaves, ovate in shape with saw-toothed margins and petioles a quarter to a third of the length of the leaves themselves. The female flowers of this monoecious plant are united in the spherical glomerules that distinguish the Roman nettle from other *Urtica* species, whose female flowers are usually more elongated. The male flowers are arranged in loose racemes; both male and female flowers grow on long pedicels from the base of the leaves. The stem, petioles and pedicels are covered with short hairs whose tips break off to release their irritating contents, primarily formic acid – hence the genus name *Urtica*, deriving from the Latin *urere*, 'to burn'.

64.

562

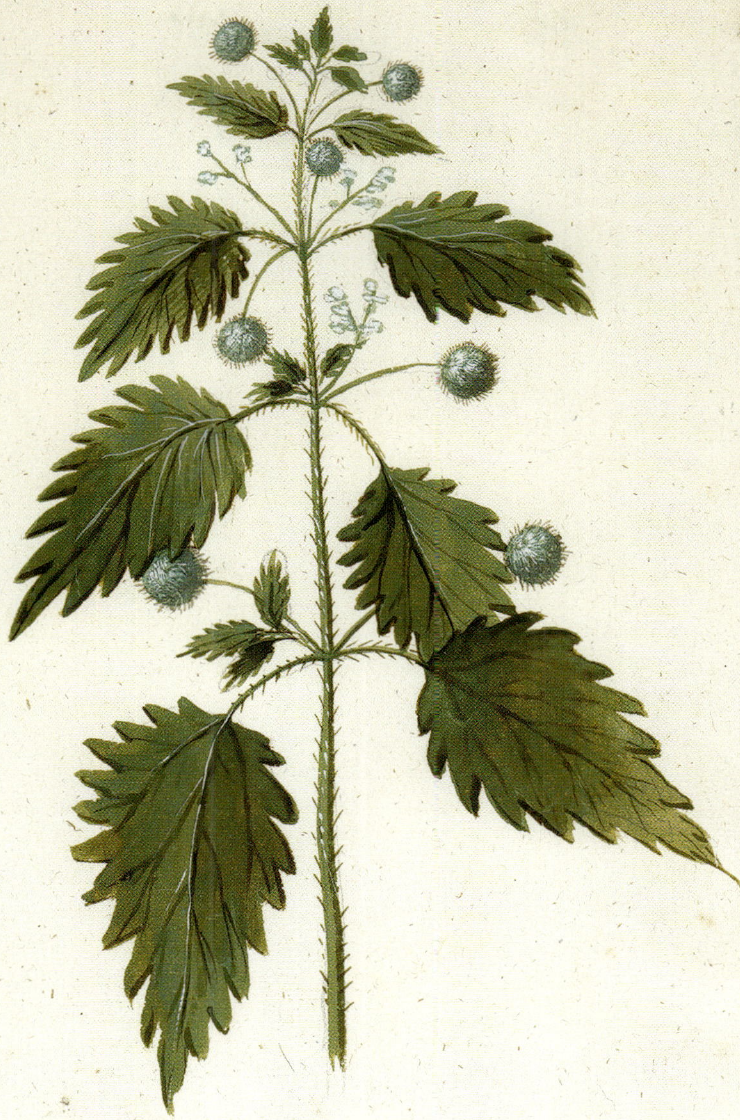

Ortica prima. 1183

65. Red dead-nettle, *Lamium purpureum* L.

Erbario Miniato, fol. 65 (RL 27755)

NUMBERING: *563*

ANNOTATION: [struck through: *Le fronde de l'ortica overo galiopsi, ~~prima~~ seconda e' seconta. inpiastrate con sale, giovano a' i morsi / de i cani, sanano le cancarene, i cancari, l'ulcere sordide. giovano aplicati / con cera. a'i difettosi di milza, il seme beuto con vino passo, muove a lusuria. / apre la bocca de la madrice: il succo gargarizato risolve le infiamagione / dell'ugola*]; *~~Galiopisi. 1187~~ Ortica seconda. 1184; ~~N°: 43~~* (['The leaves of the nettle or *galiopsi* of the ~~first~~ second type, applied with salt, cure dog bites, gangrene, cancers and sordid ulcers. Applied with wax they are beneficial to those with spleen problems. The seed drunk with unfermented wine inspires lust and releases the opening of the uterus. The juice when gargled heals inflammations of the uvula]; ~~*Galiopisi* 1187~~. Nettle of the second type. 1184; ~~No. 43~~'). [From Mattioli 1568, p. 1183–4, 1187]

The red dead-nettle is a herbaceous species of the family Lamiaceae, growing as a weed throughout Europe, North Africa, the temperate zones of Asia and (naturalized) in America, in fields and near abandoned habitations from sea level to an altitude of 1,500m. The leaves of *Lamium* are similar to those of the nettles, *Urtica* spp., heart-shaped at the base with indented margins and evenly covered with short, matted hairs, hence the various Italian names *falsa ortica* ('false nettle'), *ortica cieca* ('blind nettle') and *ortica morta* ('dead nettle'). The origin of the name *Lamium* is less clear. According to Pliny the Elder it was derived from the Greek λαιμός (*laimos*), 'throat' — inspired by the form of the flower, which appears to 'swallow up' the insects that come to gather its nectar — although it may equally have derived from the Greek λάμος (*lamos*), meaning 'bird's crop' or 'maw'.

Here the erect stem curves slightly at its apex and bears four clusters each of three to six purple flowers arranged in whorls, growing from the base of a pair of opposite leaves. The leaves, which decrease in size as they approach the apex, are triangular with toothed margins and very short petioles. The corolla of the red dead-nettle is bilabial, with dark anthers visible beneath the hood of the pronounced upper lip. At the foot of the stem are the details of two flowers, one in profile with the lips carefully delineated, the other in a three-quarter view; the calyxes are not depicted.

The annotator of the *Erbario* seems to have been uncertain whether the plant should be identified with Mattioli's 'Galiopsi' (*Lamium maculatum*, illustrated on p. 1187) or his 'Ortica seconda' (*Urtica dioica*, illustrated on p. 1184). He settled on 'Ortica seconda', but crossed out passages on medicinal usage from p. 1183 that applied to both plants.

65

563

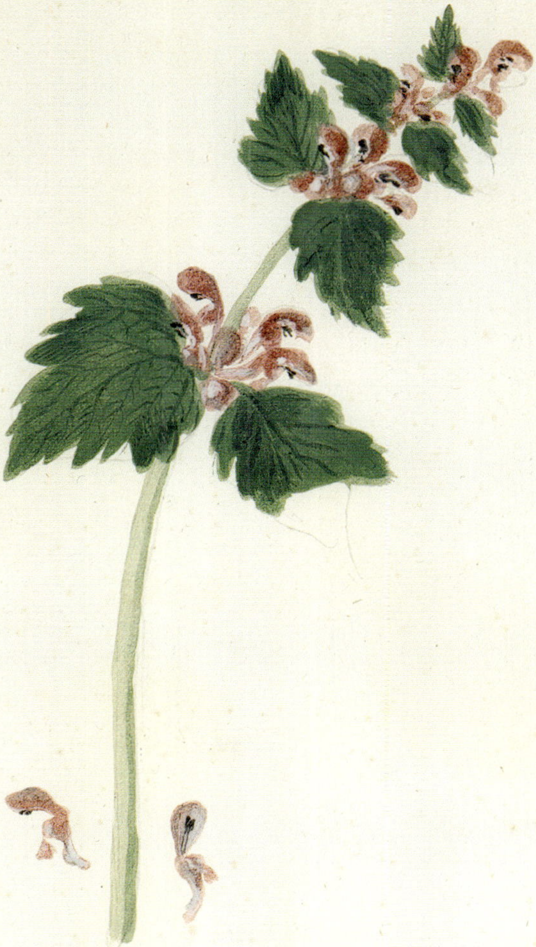

ouero galiopsi,

Le fronde de l'ortica ~~prima~~ e seconta seconda. impiastrate con sale, giouano a'i, morsi de i, cani, sanano le cancarene, i, cancari, l'ulcere sordide. giouano applicati con cera a'i, difettosi di milza, il seme beuto con vino passo, muoue a' lussuria. apre la bocca de la matrice. il succo gargarizato risolue le infiamagione dell'ugola.

~~Galiopisi. 1187~~ Ortica seconda. 1184

~~N.° 43.~~

66. Motherwort, *Leonurus cardiaca* L.

Erbario Miniato, fol. 66 (RL 27756)

Watermark: Fleur de lys 49

NUMBERING: *564*

ANNOTATION: *Cardiaca, e' calida, nel secondo, e' secca nel terzo ordine, / giova al batiquore, si loda p*[*er*] *lo spasimo, e' p*[*er*] *li paralitici, / apre le opilatione, causate da materie frigide, molifica / i nervi, e' asotiglia i grossi umori, provoca el orina, e' i, / mestui, mondifica il petto dalla flema, e' amazza, i ve= / rmi, la secca fatta impolvere, e data a' bere con vino / alle donne, che no*[*n*] *possono partorire, fa mirabile efetto,* 1186 ('*Cardiaca* of the second type is warm and of the third type dry. It relieves palpitations of the heart and is praised for the treatment of spasms and paralysis. It opens obstructions caused by cold matter, relaxes the nerves and lightens heavy humours. It induces urination and menstruation, clears the chest of phlegm and kills worms. The dried plant, ground to a powder and given to drink with wine to women who have difficulties giving birth, is marvellously effective. 1186'). [From Mattioli 1568, pp. 1186–7]

The motherwort is a herbaceous perennial of the family Lamiaceae, common throughout northern and central Europe (although very rare in Italy) and naturalized in North America, growing on uncultivated land and along roadsides and hedges, from sea level to 1,400m. It was employed as a tonic, a vermifuge against parasitic worms and a stimulant for the uterus and heart – hence the Italian common name *cardiaca* (also used by Mattioli), from καρδιά, 'heart'. The annotations are taken from Mattioli's commentary on Dioscorides' chapter on the nettle, as it had not been described by the latter.

This specimen has an erect, glabrous stem bearing seven pairs of opposite forked leaves with short petioles. The tiny flowers are clustered in verticils at the base of the leaves, their colours ranging from the yellowish-green of the buds still enveloped in their calyxes to the bright pink of the open corollas.

564

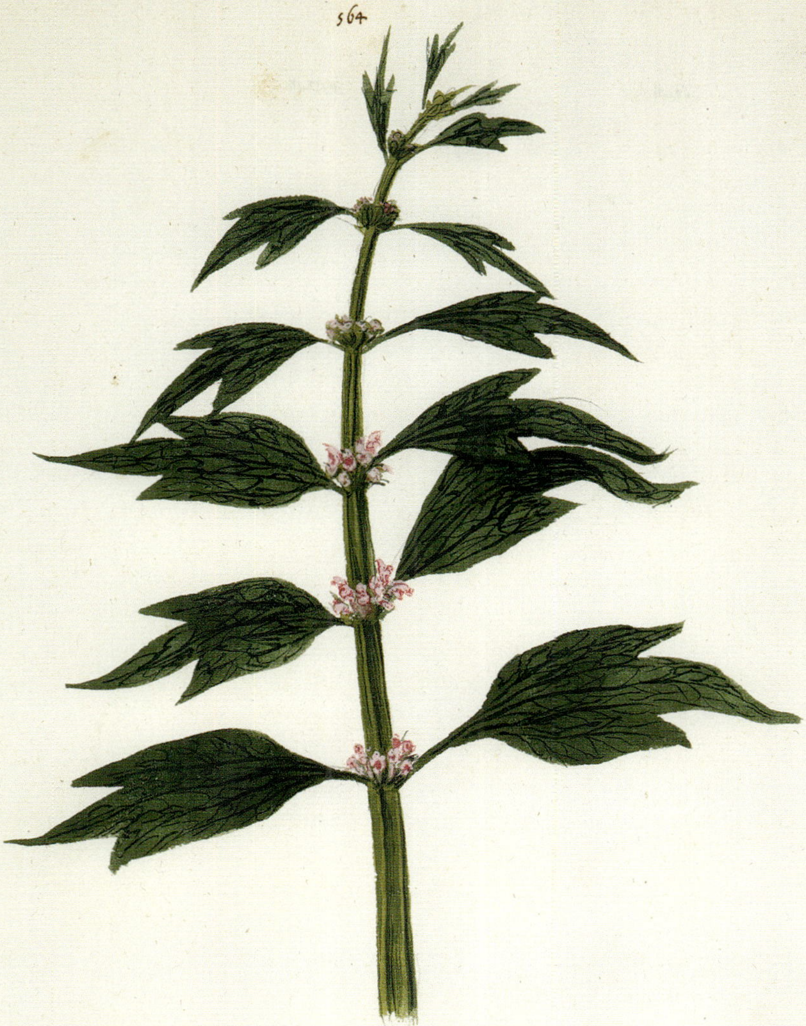

Cardiaca. e'calida. nel secondo, e'secca nel terzo ordine,
giotta al batiquore. si loda p lo spasimo, e'p li paralitici,
apre le opilatione, causate da materie frigide, mollifica
i, nerui, e' asottiglia i, grossi umori, prouoca et orina, e' i,
mestrui, mondifica il petto dalla flema, e' amazza i, ue=
rmi, la secca fatta impoluere, e data à bere con uino
alle donne, che nō possono partorire, fa mirabile efetto, 1186

67. Figwort, *Scrophularia nodosa* L.

Erbario Miniato, fol. 67 (RL 27757)

NUMBERING: *565*

ANNOTATION: *La Scrofolaria, / ha virtu mirabile/ in risolvere le scrofole, / e' parimente le hemorroidi / nel quale uso si prende / nell'autuno la radice labe / vata, e netta dalla terra, / e' pestasi con boturo fresco / molto bene insieme, poscia / si mette serrata tra due catini / di terra all'humido nella cantina* p[*er*] / *15 giorni continui: e' di quindi / poscia togliendosi, si ffa liquefare / a' lento fuoco il boturo, e' cuolasi, e' / serbasi* p[*er*] *ungere il male, qua= / ndo se ne ha di bisogno. 1188;* N*°: 44* ('*Scrofolaria* has the marvellous property of resolving scrofulas as well as haemorrhoids. For this use one gathers the root in the autumn, washes it and cleans it of any soil, grinds it well with fresh butter, and then leaves it sealed between two clay jars in a damp cellar for fifteen consecutive days, after which it is removed and the butter melted over a low flame and strained. It is then conserved for anointing the affected areas when the need arises. 1188. No. 44'). [From Mattioli 1568, pp. 1188–9]

The figwort is a herbaceous perennial of the family Scrophulariaceae, a name deriving from scrofula, as several species were used to treat this skin disease. It is native to Europe and the temperate regions of Asia, and naturalized elsewhere, flourishing in damp forest glades and ravines, and along shorelines and riverbanks from sea level to 1,800m.

This erect, glabrous stem, curving at its apex, bears five closely spaced pairs of opposite leaves, acutely triangular in shape with toothed margins. A young branch springs from the base of one of the lower leaves, while dark purple flowers arranged in loose racemes grow from the points of attachment of all the other leaves. The tiny blossoms are only sketchily indicated, but at lower left the detail of two flowers clearly shows their bilateral, zygomorphic structure. At lower right is a detail of a dried stem bearing six pear-shaped capsules or fruit.

The annotations are drawn from Mattioli's discussion of the figwort ('Scrofolaria'), in his commentary on Dioscorides' chapter on the 'Galiopsi' (*Lamium maculatum*).

565

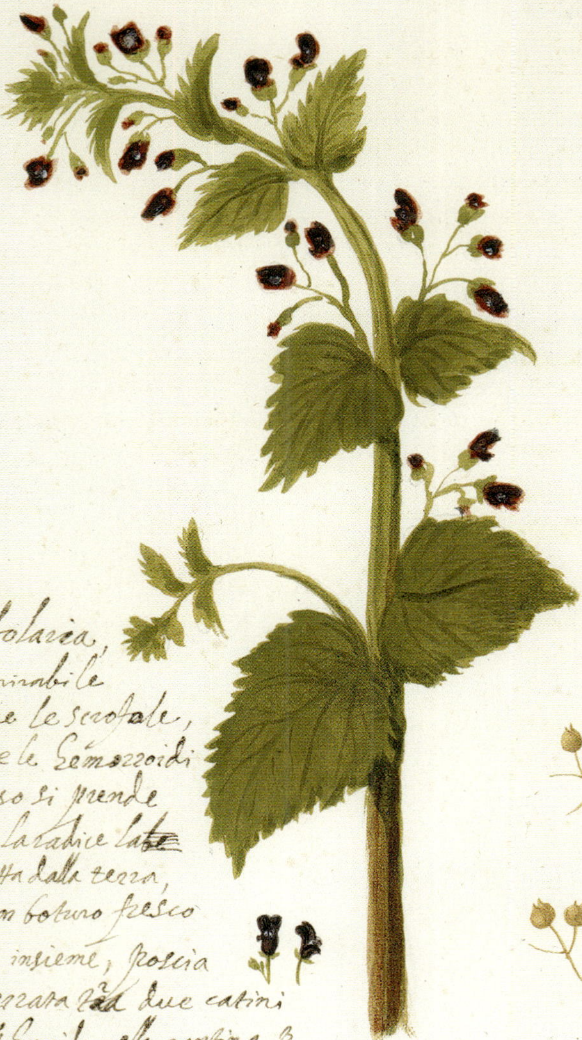

la Scrofolaria,
ha virtù mirabile
in risoluere le Scrofole,
e' parimente le Emorroidi
nel quale uso si prende
nell'autunno la radice lav
uata, e netta dalla terra,
e' pestasi con botiro fresco
molto bene insieme, poscia
si mette serrata tra due catini
di terra all'humido nella cantina per
15 giorni continui: e' di quindi
poscia togliendosi, si fa liquefare
a' lento fuoco il botiro, e colasi, e'
serbasi per ungere il male, qua=
ndo se ne ha di bisogno. 1188.

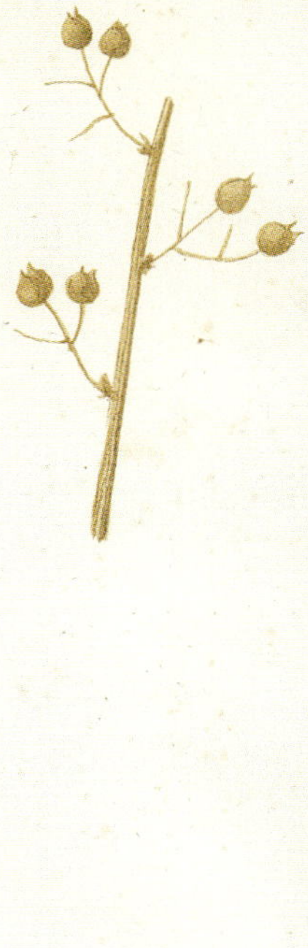

N.° 94

68. Lady's bedstraw, *Galium verum* L.

Erbario Miniato, fol. 68 (RL 27758)

NUMBERING: *566*

ANNOTATION: *Gallio. il fiore fa aprendere il latte. se impiastra su le cotture del / fuoco: ristagnano ⸗ i flussi del sangue. La radice provoca il coito.* ('*Gallio*. The flower curdles milk and is applied to burns. It staunches discharges of blood. The root acts as an aphrodisiac.'). [From Mattioli 1568, pp. 1189–90]

Lady's bedstraw is a herbaceous perennial of the family Rubiaceae, native to Asia and Europe where it grows in arid pastures, along paths and in forest clearings from sea level to 1,700m. The plant here has a slender stem and short branches with needle-shaped leaves growing from their verticils, and a large number of sulphur-yellow flower clusters at the apex.

The English common name lady's bedstraw (originally 'Our Lady's bedstraw') may be traced back to the legend that the manger in which the infant Jesus slept was lined with this flowering plant. The genus name *Galium* and the old Italian *gallio* are derived from *galion*, assigned by Dioscorides to a plant which was employed by shepherds in ancient Greece to curdle milk. Linnaeus assigned the specific epithet *verum* because it represented the 'true' plant used in Tuscany since at least the sixteenth century for the same purpose; its milk-curdling properties can be attributed to the presence of the enzyme phytokinase. Lady's bedstraw was also used to dye cloth, its roots imparting a reddish tint and the flowers bright orange.

The plant is described and illustrated (as 'Gallio') on pp. 1189 and 1190 of Mattioli's *Discorsi*, although the inscription on this sheet does not mention this fact.

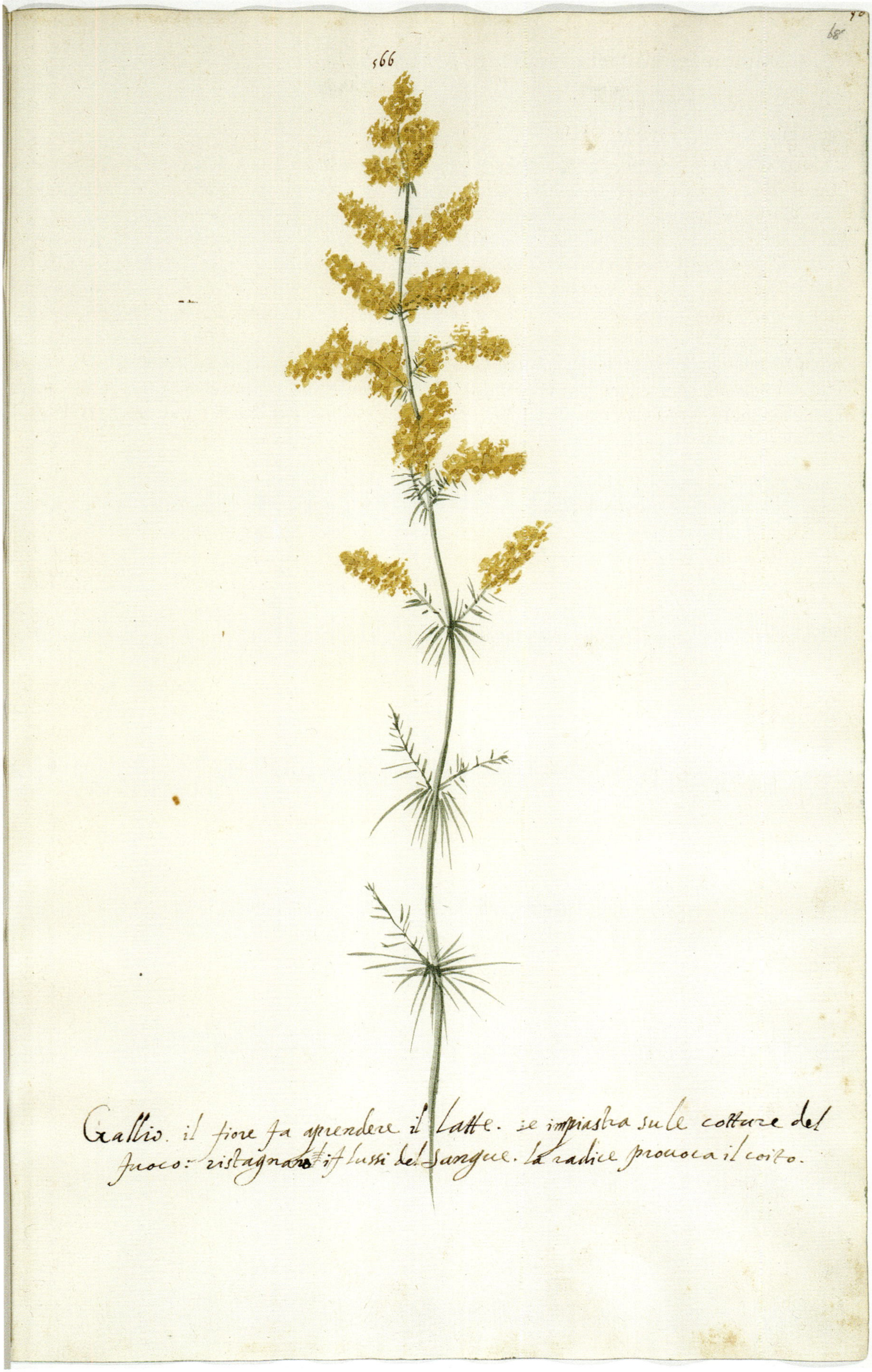
566
Gallio. il fiore fa aprendere il Latte. se impiastra sule cotture del
fuoco: ristagnano i flussi del Sangue. la radice prouoca il coito.

69. Common groundsel or ragwort, *Senecio vulgaris* L.

Erbario Miniato, fol. 69 (RL 27759)

NUMBERING: *567*

ANNOTATION: [struck through: *Il Crescione volgare. ha la medesima natura del vero sio. / mangiato tanto crudo quanto cotto. ł rompe le pietre / e' le fa orinare. provoca el orina, i, mestui, e' il parto.*]; *detto dal vulgo / Crescione; Senecio, overo Erigero, le fronde e' parimente i, fiori, hanno virtu de / infrigidire, sanano le infiamagione de li testicoli, e' del ł sedere, mescolate / con manna de incenso, medicano tutte le ferite. e particolarmente quelli de li / nervi. sa medesimo la piuma de li suoi fiori. cotto tutto il fusto. e' beuto con / vino passo. sana i, dolori cholerici, dello stomaco. 1191* ('[Common *Crescione*. Is of the same nature as the true sio. Eaten raw or cooked it breaks up kidney stones and these are then expelled by urination. It induces urination, menstruation and childbirth.] Commonly called *Crescione*; *Senecio* or *Erigero*. The leaves and similarly the flowers have a cooling quality, and heal inflammations of the testicles and anus. Mixed with frankincense they heal all wounds, particularly those of the nerves. The feather [pappus] of the flowers has the same effect. The whole stem can be cooked and drunk with unfermented wine, which relieves choleric pains of the stomach. 1191'). [From Mattioli 1568, pp. 512, 514, 1190–1]

The common groundsel or ragwort is a herbaceous plant of the family Asteraceae, indigenous to the Mediterranean and now distributed throughout the world, growing as a weed in inhabited areas and cultivated fields. It was used to prepare tonics and soothing lotions, and to promote menstruation and relieve menstrual cramps. It served as a surrogate for ergot (*Claviceps purpurea*) because, like all plants of this genus, it contains the active principle senecionine.

The specimen here has a narrow root surrounded by long filaments and an erect branching stem, reddish in colour and quite smooth. The leaves are lanceolate with short petioles and deeply indented margins, and vary in colour from deep green to yellow. Each parasol-shaped inflorescence is composed of three to five heads borne on peduncles as long as the heads themselves. The bracts are made up of slender, pointed scales. In one of the capitulums can be seen the white pappus, which Cesi describes as a 'feather'.

The annotation initially identified the plant as Mattioli's 'Crescione' on pp. 512–14 of the *Discorsi*, his name for the 'Sio volgare' and 'domestico' of Dioscorides (respectively *Nasturtium officinale* and *Cardamine pratensis*). That identification was correctly rejected in favour of the 'Senecio' (*Senecio vulgaris*) illustrated on p. 1191.

567

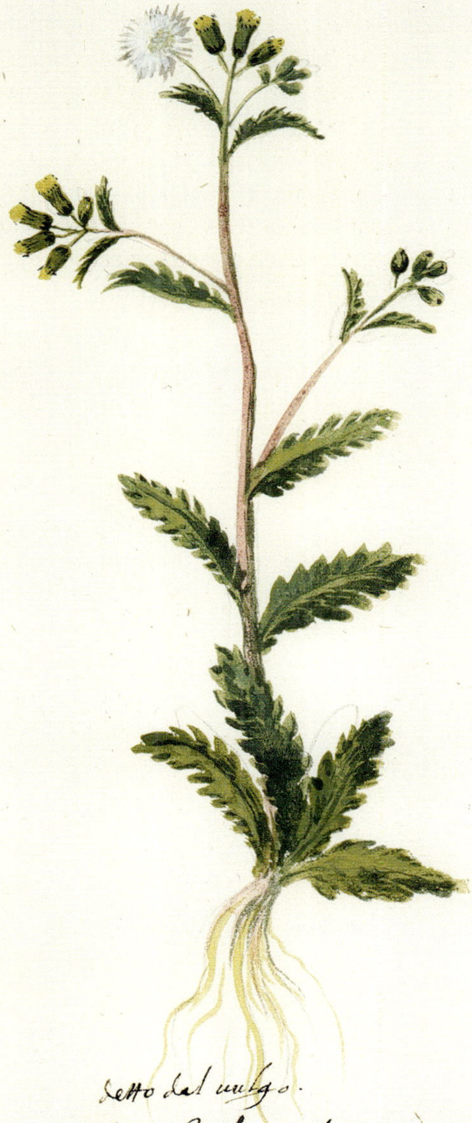

detto dal uulgo.

Il Crescione uolgare. ~~ha la medesima natura del uero Sio. mangiato tanto crudo quanto cotto. rompe le pietre è le fa orinare. prouoca e l'orina. i mestrui, è i parto.~~

Crescione

Sencio, ouero Crigero, le fronde è parimente i, fiori, hanno uirtu de infrigidire. sanano le infiamagione de li testicoli, è del sedere. mescolate con manna de incenso. medicano tutte le ferite. è particolarmente quelli de li nerui. sa medesimo la piuma de li suoi fiori. cotto tutti il fusto. è beuto con uino passo. sana i, dolori colerici, dello stomaco. 1191

70. Marsh ragwort, *Senecio aquaticus* Hill ssp. *erraticus* (Bertol.) V.A. Matthews

Erbario Miniato, fol. 70 (RL 27760)

NUMBERING: *568*

ANNOTATION: ~~*Senecio magiore. 1192*~~; *Virga aurea minore 1060* [erased] ('~~Greater *Senecio*. 1192~~; lesser golden rod 1060'). [From Mattioli 1568, pp. 1060, 1192]

The marsh ragwort is a herbaceous species of the family Asteraceae, native to Europe, northern Africa and the temperate zones of Asia, growing in damp, shady spots at altitudes from sea level to 1,500m. Like the common groundsel, *Senecio vulgaris* (**69**), it contains a toxic alkaloid, senecionine.

The artist has shown a flowering stem of a subspecies, the unusual marsh ragwort. The stem of the plant is erect and glabrous, with sessile leaves that are lobed when young and toothed when mature. Four flower heads, each made up of a cluster of tubular flowers surrounded by seven to nine ligulate flowers, are arranged in a terminal corymb.

Both annotations on the drawing are cancelled, suggesting some difficulty in identifying the plant. The lower note identifies it with Mattioli's 'Virga aurea' on p. 1060 of the *Discorsi* (*Solidago virgaurea*) while the reference on the right is to the 'Senecio maggiore' on p. 1192 (*Senecio jacobaea*). The latter identification seems to have prevailed, however, since the drawing was placed after the other 'Senecio' (**69**).

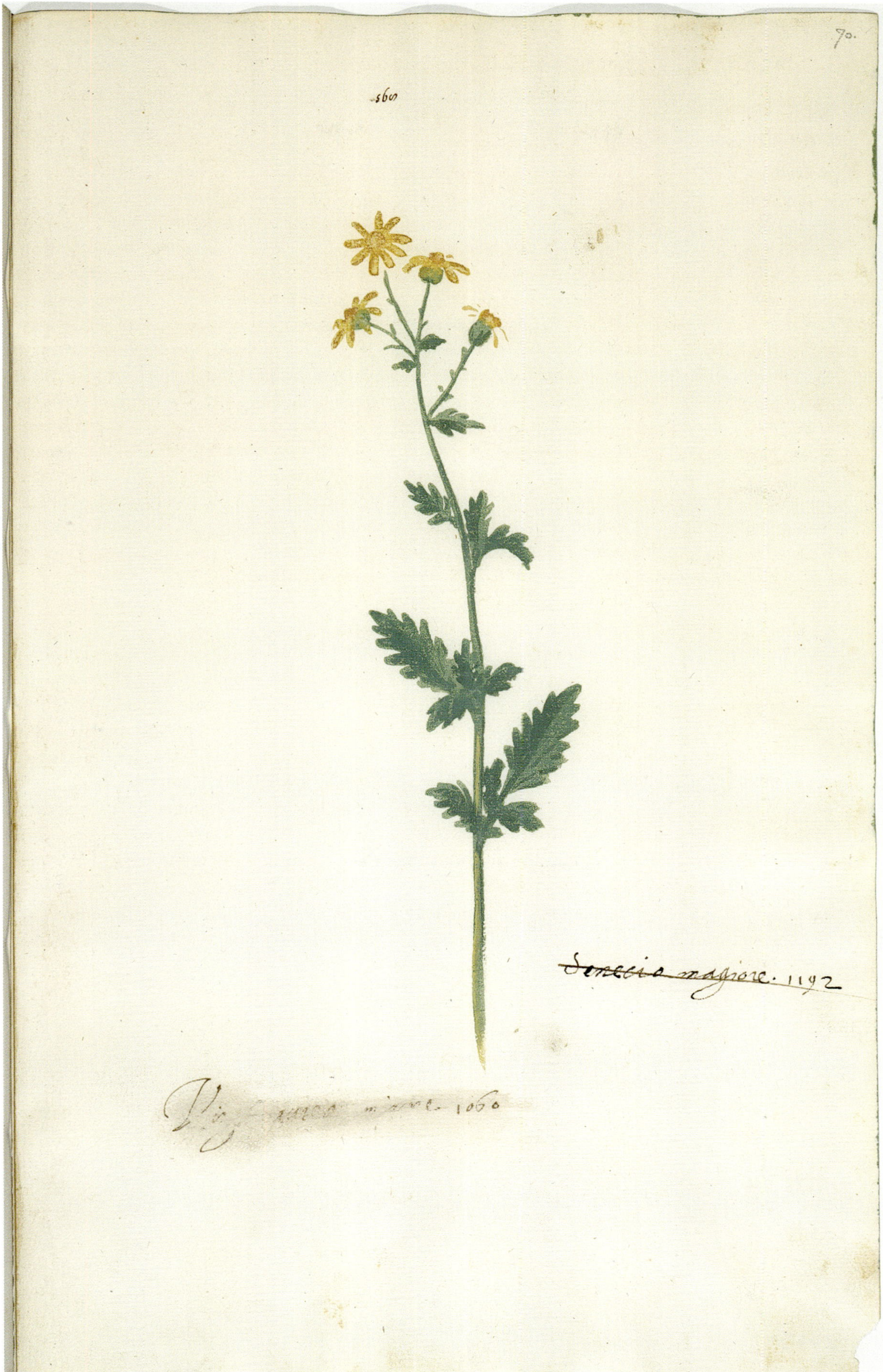
560
70.
magiore. 1192
1060

71. Aaron's rod, *Verbascum sinuatum* L.

Erbario Miniato, fol. 71 (RL 27761)

Watermark: Eagle 15

NUMBERING: *569*

ANNOTATION : *Un altro verbasco. / 1207.; Verbasco / salvatico.; Chiamasi volgarmente il verbasco Tasso barbasso. / el'erba fresca de la femina pesta con doi pietre / vive messa nelle inciodature dei, cavalli. subito li / guarisce: il succo de la sua radice. quando no*[*n*]*/ a'ancora prodotto ~~ancora~~ il fusto. cura la febre / quartano. il fiore. fregato in su quella spetie / di porri che sonno ruvidi, gli manda via. il me= / desimo fa la pervere* [M: *polvere*] *de la radice. fregatovi/ sopra le foglie aplicate con aceto. riso= / lvano le scrofole. giova alla lagrimatione / de gli occhi, alle erisipole, alle coture del / fuoco. I fiori impiastrati con rosso di uova. / midolla di pane. e fogli di porri, cotte vaglino / mirabilmente alle EMORRHOIDE. il medesimo / fa la polvere messa sopra un pezzo di pietra di / macina di molino. infocata. e' presene il funo* [M: *fumo*] *con / il sedere.* ('Another verbasco. 1207; wild *verbasco*; the *verbasco* is commonly called *Tasso barbasso*. The fresh female plant, ground between two stones and placed around the nails in horses' hoofs, immediately heals them. The juice of its roots, when the plant has not yet produced its stem, cures quartan fever. The flower, rubbed on those kinds of warts that are rough, makes them go away. Rubbing with the powdered root has the same effect. The leaves applied with vinegar cure scrofulas. Useful against watering eyes, erysipelas, burns. The flowers applied as a poultice with egg yolk, the soft part of bread and cooked leek leaves are a wonderful remedy for haemorrhoids. The same effect is obtained by taking in through the anus the fumes produced by the plant's powder when placed over a piece of burning hot millstone.'). [From Mattioli 1568, pp. 1204, 1207–9]

LITERATURE: Freedberg 2002, pp. 207 (fig. 8.4), 209

This drawing portrays a flowering stem of Aaron's rod, a herbaceous species of the family Scrophulariaceae distributed throughout the Mediterranean. It grows in the dry, sandy soil of uncultivated fields and along roadsides from sea level to an altitude of 800m. The name *Verbascum*, already in use at the time of Pliny, probably represents a corrupted form of the word *barbascum*, an allusion to the bearded appearance of the flower's stamens. Dioscorides instead called this plant 'Phlomos' ('burning') because the hairy leaves could be used as wicks for oil lamps.

The plant has been drawn in detail, though without its root system and basal rosette of leaves. The stem is thick, erect and branching. The two large sessile leaves are elliptical with blunt tips, slightly crenate margins and marked veins. Further along the stem are many smaller sessile leaves with pointed tips. The topmost branches carry a number of buds and flowers on short pedicels. The flowers' five yellow petals (which are joined at the base, a characteristic of the genus *Verbascum*) and five stamens covered with short, matted, bright orange hairs can be seen, though the calyx is not clearly shown.

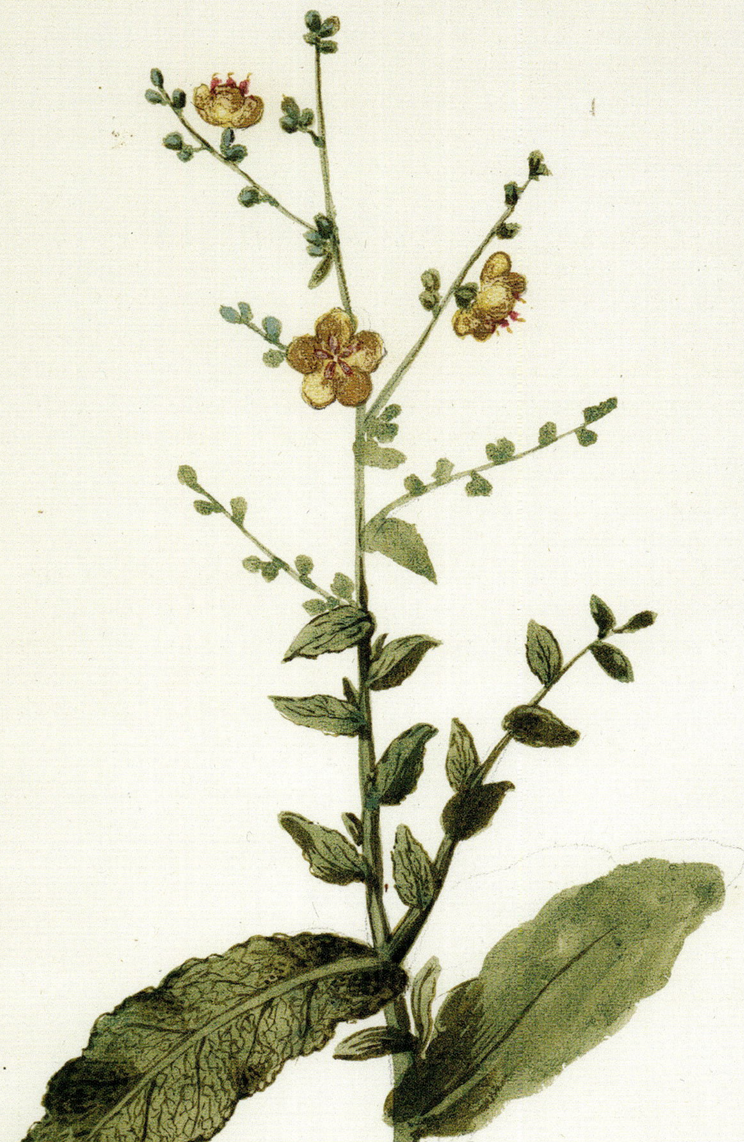

Vnaltro verbasco.
1207.

Verbasco
saluatico.

Chiamasi volgarmente il verbasco. Tasso barbasso. el'erba fresca de la femina. pesta con doi fiche crive. messa nelle incodature dei, cavalli subito li guarisce: il succo de la sua radice. quando no à ancora prodotto ancora il fusto. cura la febre quartana. il fiore fregato in su quella spetie di porri che sono umidi, gli manda via. il medesimo fa la peruere de la radice. fregatovi sopra. le foglie aplicato con aceto. riso=

lvano le scrofole. giova alla lagrimatione degli occhi, alle erisipole. alle cotture del fuoco. I fiori impiastrati con rosso di uova. midolla di pane. e foglio di porri, cotte vagliono mirabilmente alle EMORRHOIDE. il medesimo fa la polvere. messa sopra un pezzo di pietra di macina di molino. infocata. e presone il fumo con il sedere.

72. Primrose, *Primula vulgaris* Huds.

Erbario Miniato, fol. 72 (RL 27762)

NUMBERING: *570*

ANNOTATION: *e̶ fior' di primavera, .1209; Herba / Paralis̶x̶ p[er] li dolori delle gionuture, le radice. si cuocono. e' bevesi la / decotione. utilmente p[er] le opilatione delli reni, della vesica, dasse il succo / de lerba a' bere. e' parimente se impiastra, di fuore. nelle rotture / e' dislogagioni dell'ossa, usano le donne bagnarsi spesso la faccia / con il succo de i, fiori: inpero che vi fa distendere la pelle. / e' ne leva via ogni macchia.* ('Spring flower. 1209; *Herba Paralis* for pains in the joints. The root may be cooked and the decoction drunk against occlusions of the kidneys and of the urinary vesicle. The juice of the plant may be drunk or applied externally to broken and dislocated bones. Women often bathe their faces with the juice of the flowers; this relaxes the skin and eliminates all blemishes.'). [From Mattioli 1568, pp. 1205, 1206, 1209]

The primrose is a herbaceous perennial of the family Primulaceae, common all over Europe, Algeria and the temperate regions of Asia, and cultivated since at least the sixteenth century. It grows in meadows and deciduous broadleaved forests, particularly beech and oak, from sea level to 1,200m. The name *Primula* refers to the early blooming habit of this plant, which came to symbolize youth and was thus thought to have rejuvenating and healing properties.

The artist shows the plant with its short, curved rhizome and many secondary roots. Five fleshy lanceolate leaves grow directly from the base of the plant. The apex of each leaf is rounded and the margins are finely toothed. Two yellow flowers with broad, heart-shaped petals grow from long, slender pedicels. In the lower right the artist has added two details – a flower from a variety with white petals and a yellow throat, and a bud showing the deeply toothed calyx of the species.

The annotations are drawn from Mattioli's discussion of the 'Fior di primavera' or 'Herba Paralisis', a plant which he introduced in his commentary on Dioscorides' 'Phlomos' or 'Verbasco' (see **71**).

570

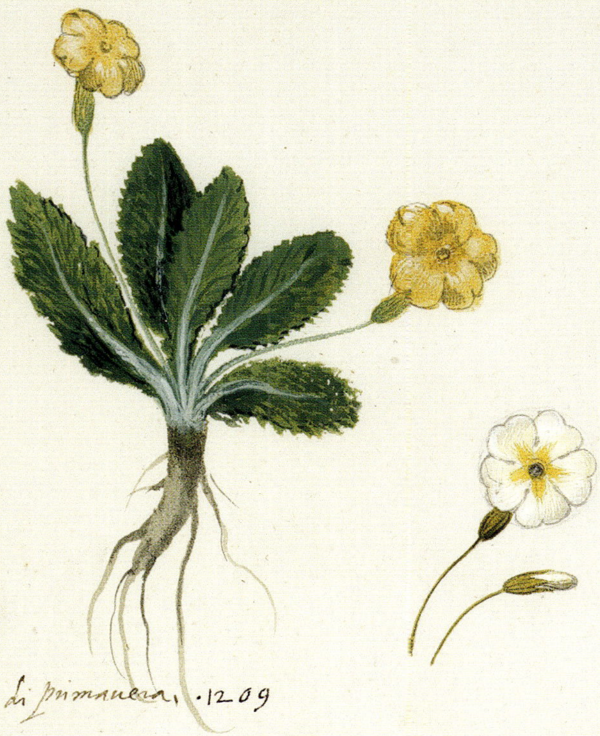

L'Herba + & fiori di primavera. .1209

Paralisi per li dolori delle giunture, le radice si cuocono è bevesi la decotione. utilmente per le opilatione delli reni, della vesica, dasse il succo de l'erba a' bere. è parimente se impiastra di fuore nelle rotture è dislogagioni dell'ossa, usano le donne bagnarsi spesso la faccia con il succo de i fiori: impero che vi fa distendere la pelle è ne leva via ogni macchia.

73. Cowslip, *Primula veris* L.

Erbario Miniato, fol. 73 (RL 27763)

NUMBERING: *571*

ANNOTATION: *PRIMAVERA MAGIORE* ('Greater *Primavera* [spring]')

The cowslip is a herbaceous perennial of the family Primulaceae, common throughout Europe and temperate regions of Asia, in dry meadows, thickets and forests of oak and conifers from sea level to an altitude of 2,300m. It was used to make sedatives, diuretics, spasmolytics, cough remedies and poultices for wounds, and to cure vertigo, palpitations and headaches. Cowslip wine, produced by flavouring white wine with the flowers, was once popular as a tonic.

This drawing shows a flowering stem of the plant without its root system or basal rosette of leaves. The long glabrous stem terminates in a cluster of six flowers carried on peduncles of varying lengths that grow out of the axils of six small, needle-like bracts. Each flower, protruding from its sharply toothed calyx, is made up of five broad, heart-shaped yellow lobes that darken in hue at the corolla's throat.

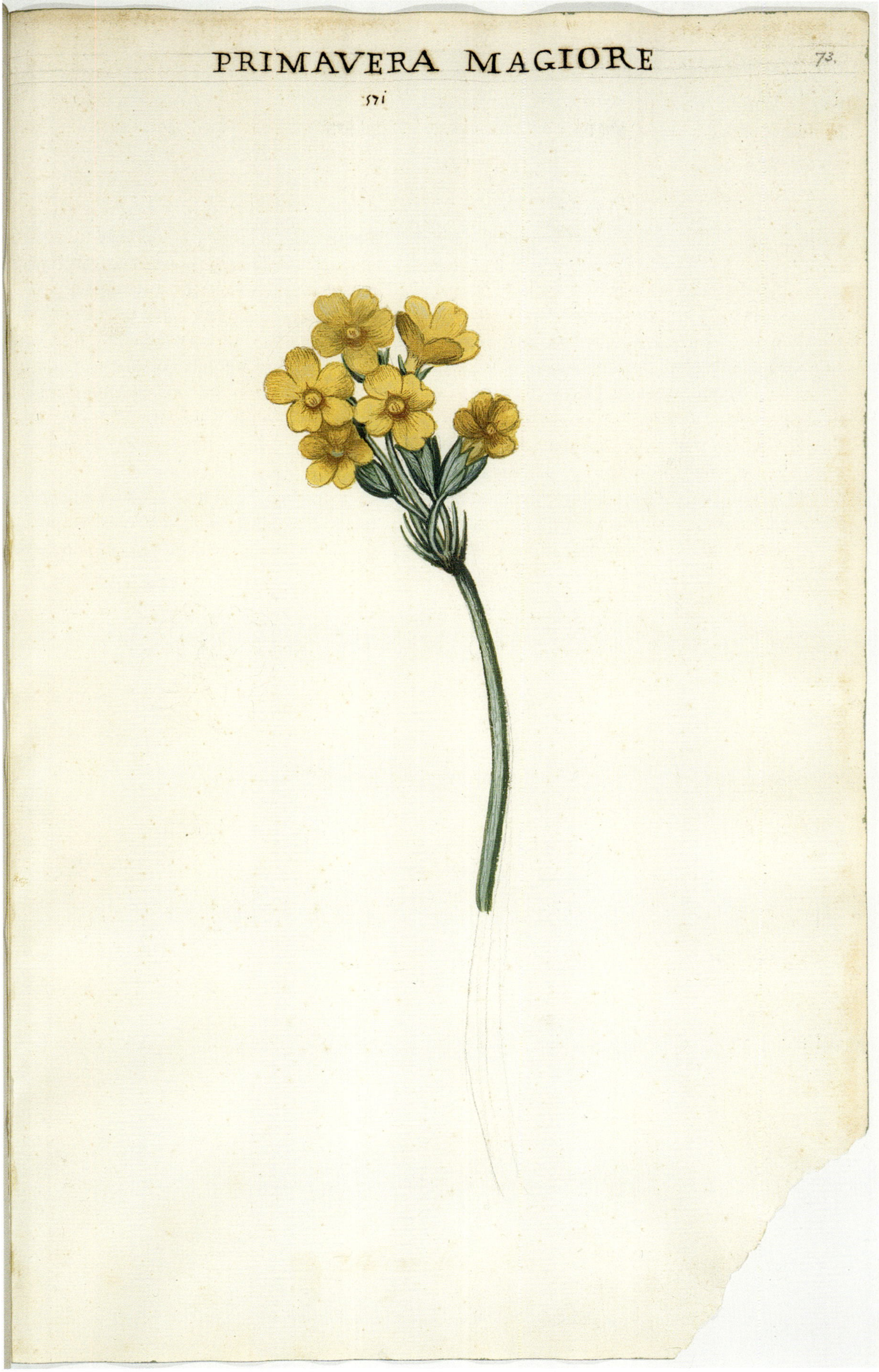
PRIMAVERA MAGIORE
73.
571

74. African sage, *Salvia aethiopis* L.

Erbario Miniato, fol. 74 (RL 27764)

Watermark: Eagle (unidentified)

NUMBERING: *572*

ANNOTATION: *Ethiopide. 1211.* [From Mattioli 1568, p. 1211]

African sage is a herbaceous perennial of the mint family, Lamiaceae. It grows in dry pastures in southern Europe as far east as the Caucasus (and naturalized in North America), as well as in North Africa and south-west Asia, at altitudes from 100m to 1,000m. The genus name *Salvia* is derived from the Latin word *salus*, 'health', as the therapeutic properties of many of the plants of this genus – in particular *Salvia officinalis* – have been known since antiquity. In 1832 the botanist George Bentham proposed a reorganization of the family Lamiaceae, including the division of the genus *Salvia* into various groups, placing *Salvia aethiopis* in a section of its own (*Aethiopis*). Bentham's classification system was eventually abandoned, but the morphological characteristics of the African sage do set it apart from the 700 other members of the genus.

In this unfinished drawing the root is not clearly portrayed, but appears to be quite broad. The stem, with its quadrilateral cross-section, is covered with conspicuous hairs. The broad, triangular leaves have either lobed or crenate margins and are arranged in a basal rosette; their petioles cannot be seen. White flowers with bilabial corollas and forked pistils grow in pairs out of large bracts along the one completed branch.

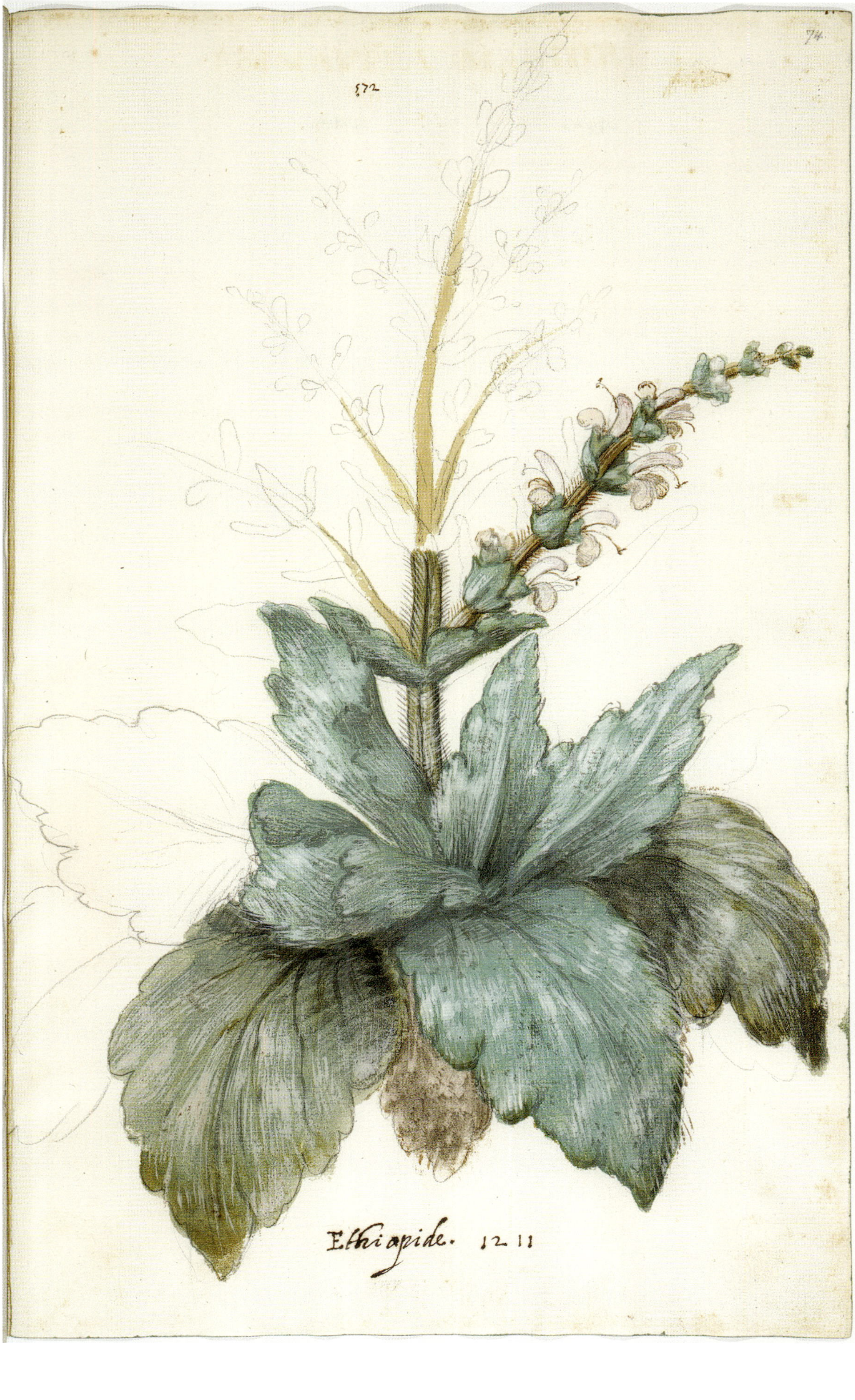
572
74
Ethiopide. 1211

75. Lesser burdock, *Arctium minus* (Hill) Bernh.

Erbario Miniato, fol. 75 (RL 27765)

NUMBERING: *573*

ANNOTATION: *La ~~Pratica~~ Personata overo lappa. La radice beuta al peso de una dramma. / con le pine giova a' coloro che sputano il sangue, e' la marcia / pesta e' impiastrata. mitiga il dolore de le gionture. impiastrinsi le frond[e] / utilmente in su lulcere antiche. . . 1213* ('*Personata* or *lappa*. The root in the weight of one drachm drunk with pine kernels helps those who spit blood and heals suppuration. Ground into a paste, it relieves pains in the joints. Applying the leaves is useful for chronic ulcers. 1213'). [From Mattioli 1568, pp. 1212–13]

The lesser burdock is a herbaceous, almost shrubby biennial species of the family Asteraceae. It is common in western Europe and temperate regions of Asia, along roadsides and riverbanks, under hedges and in uncultivated fields from sea level to an altitude of 1,500m. The hairiness of the plant, in particular of the flower's involucre, probably explains the name *Arctium*, derived from the Greek ἄρκτος (*arktos*), 'bear'.

This unfinished drawing shows only a portion of a plant. From the erect, pale green stem grow several broad, heart-shaped leaves, dark green in colour with almost white undersides, the margins with six or seven tiny teeth on each side. The dense clusters of flower heads are enveloped in whorls of tiny, scale-like bracts that come to sharp points.

The annotation is drawn from Dioscorides' chapter 'Della Personata, over Lappa' (p. 1212), and cites the page with Mattioli's illustration of the 'Personata maggiore' (p. 1213), which, however, corresponds to the great burdock, *Arctium lappa*. The lesser burdock was not illustrated by Mattioli; the 'altra Personata maggiore' depicted on p. 1214 is the woolly burdock, *Arctium tomentosum*.

75

573

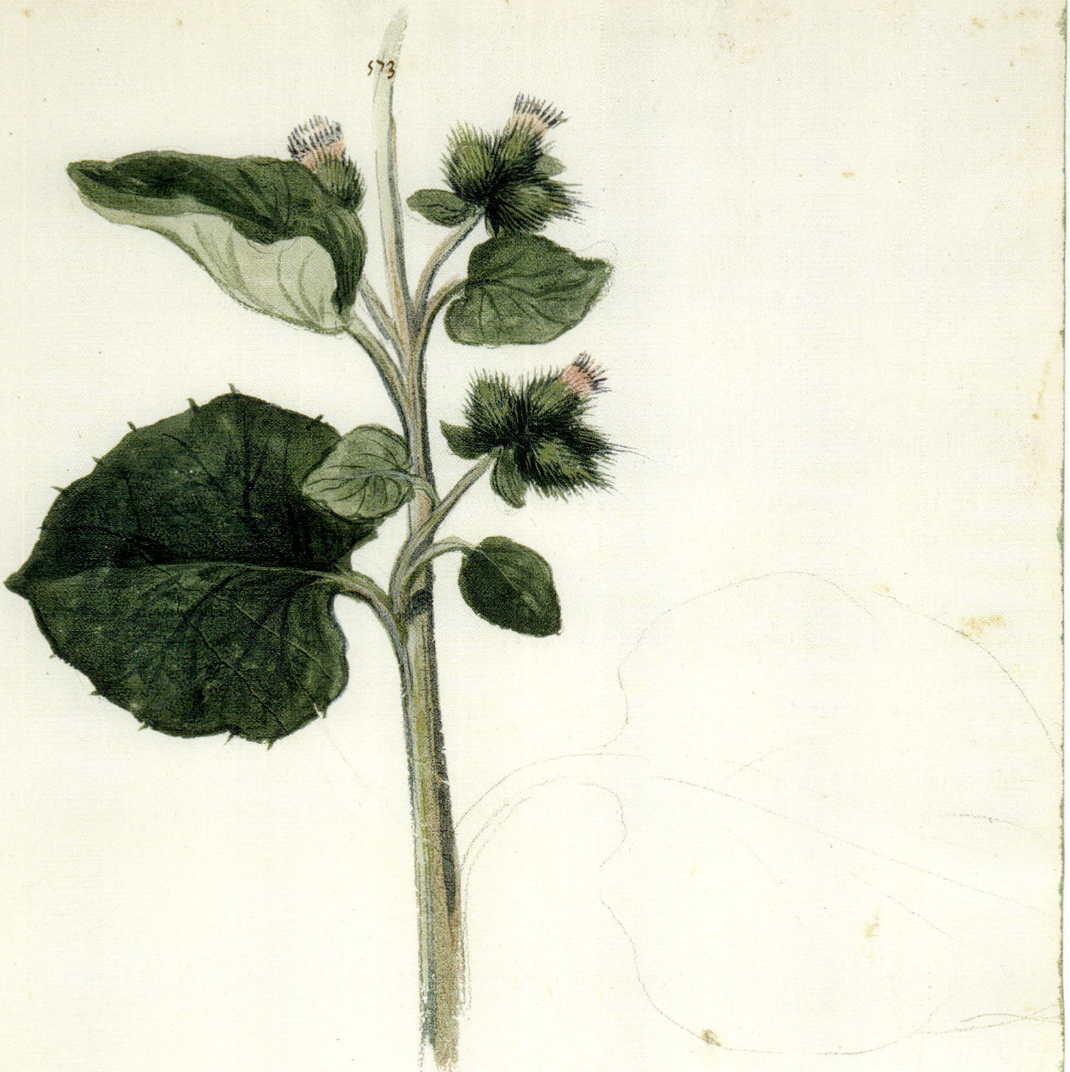

Personata.

La ~~[illegible]~~ ouero Lappa. La radice beuta al peso de una dramma. con le spine. giova a' coloro che sputano il sangue, e la marcia pesta e impiastrata. mitiga il dolore de le gionture. impiastrinsi le frond utilmente in su lucere antiche ...12.13

76. Thorow-wax, *Bupleurum rotundifolium* L.

Erbario Miniato, fol. 76 (RL 27766)

Watermark: Crown 46

NUMBERING: *574*

ANNOTATION: *Perfoliata. 1215.* [struck through: *Tithimalo characia / Perfoliata scritta dal Dodoneo.; sonno di sette spetie, vale il suo / latte, a' i pterigii delle dita e' a' i carbo= / ncelli, al ulcere corosive alle cancre = / ne e' alle fistole, i seme si racoglie/ el autunno e' secasi al sole, lav*[*a*]*se / la bocca con la decotione fatte de le fronde / con aceto p*[*er*] *il dolore de i, denti.*] ('Perfoliata. 1215. [*Tithimalo characia. Perfoliata* mentioned by Dodoens; there are seven types; its milk is useful for pterygia of the fingers and for carbuncles, corrosive ulcers, gangrene and fistulas. The seeds are gathered in the autumn and dried in the sun. Rinse the mouth with a decoction made from the leaves and vinegar for pain in the teeth.]') [From Mattioli 1568, pp. 1215, 1310–12]

The thorow-wax is a herbaceous annual of the family Umbelliferae. It is a weed of grain fields; indigenous to central Asia, it has followed the spread of agriculture and has become naturalized all over the world. It thrives in sloping terrain with calcareous, clayey soil from sea level to an altitude of 1,200m.

This slender branching green stem bears three perfoliate (with the stalk apparently passing through) leaves, broadly oval in shape with intact margins and pointed tips. The flowers are arranged at the ends of long peduncles in umbrella-like clusters, each of five large petaloid bracts surrounding a central disk of tiny yellowish-green flowers.

The plant was initially identified in the annotation as Dioscorides' 'Tithimalo Characia' (*Euphorbia characias*), illustrated by Mattioli on p. 1311, and the cancelled passages on medicinal usage are drawn from Dioscorides' chapter on that plant (pp. 1310, 1312). It appears, however, that after consulting Dodoens (1583, p. 104), Cesi correctly re-identified the plant as the thorow-wax illustrated on p. 1215 of the *Discorsi*.

574

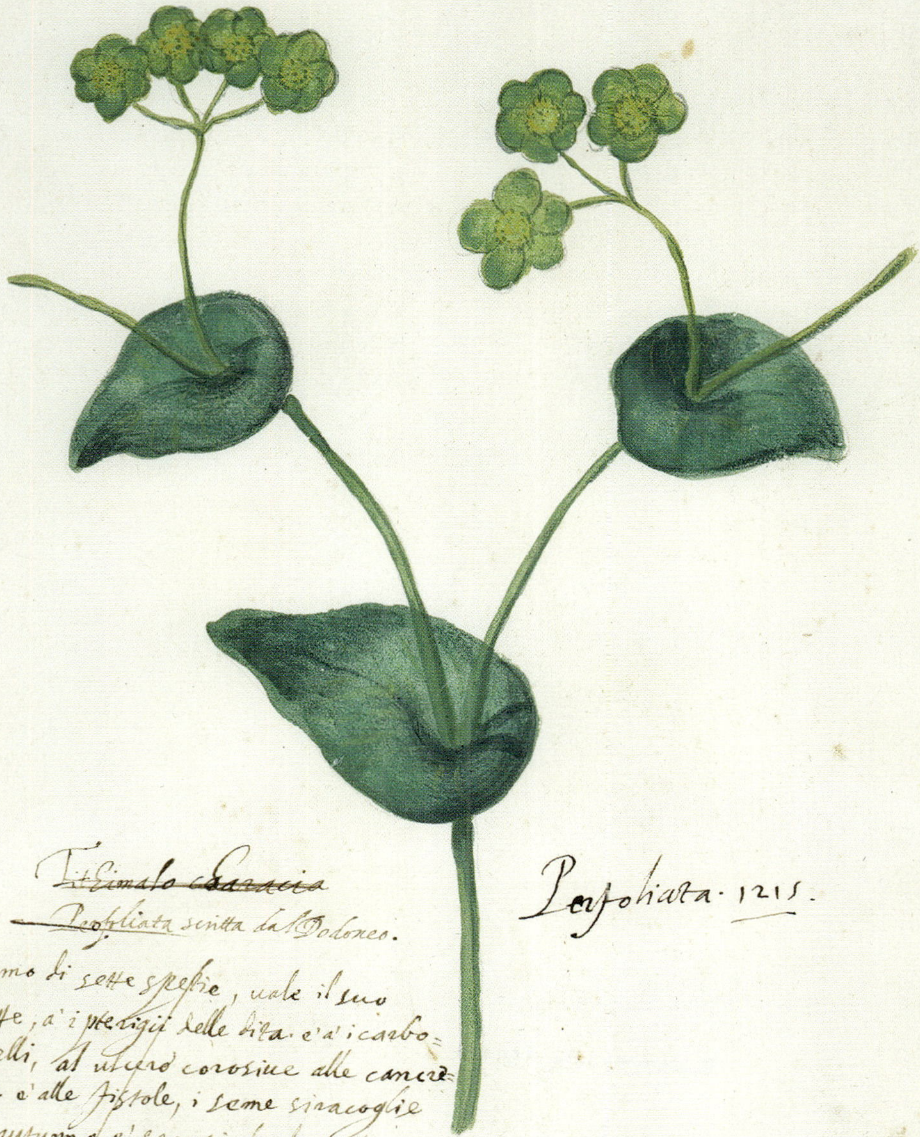

Perfoliata · 1215.

~~Titimalo caracia~~

~~Perfoliata~~ scritta dal Dodoneo.

Sono di sette spetie, vale il suo
latte, a' i pterigij delle dita, e a' i carbo=
ncelli, al ulcero corosive alle cancre=
ne e' alle fistole, i seme siracoglie
el autunno e' secasi al sole, lavse
la bocca con la decotione fatte de le fronde
con aceto per il dolore de i denti;

77. White helleborine, *Cephalanthera damasonium* (Mill.) Druce

Erbario Miniato, fol. 77 (RL 27767)

Watermark: Eagle 17

NUMBERING: *575*

ANNOTATION: *Eleborine falsa. non scritta da Matthiolo* ('False helleborine. Not mentioned by Mattioli')

The white helleborine is a herbaceous perennial of the family Orchidaceae (see also **183**). It may be found throughout the Mediterranean as far east as Turkey, in deciduous forests at altitudes to 1,600m. The common name of the plant comes from the similarity of its flower to those of the hellebores (hence the 'false' in the inscription).

Here the thick erect stem rises out of a greenish-white tunic and simplified root system consisting of a short horizontal rhizome with no evident bulb. The stem is enveloped in dark green, alternate, leaf-like bracts, with whitish undersides marked by a series of parallel veins. From the base of each bract springs a white flower made up of oval tepals and a labellum that is spotted with yellow near its base. There are two details of the flower, one showing the reproductive structures.

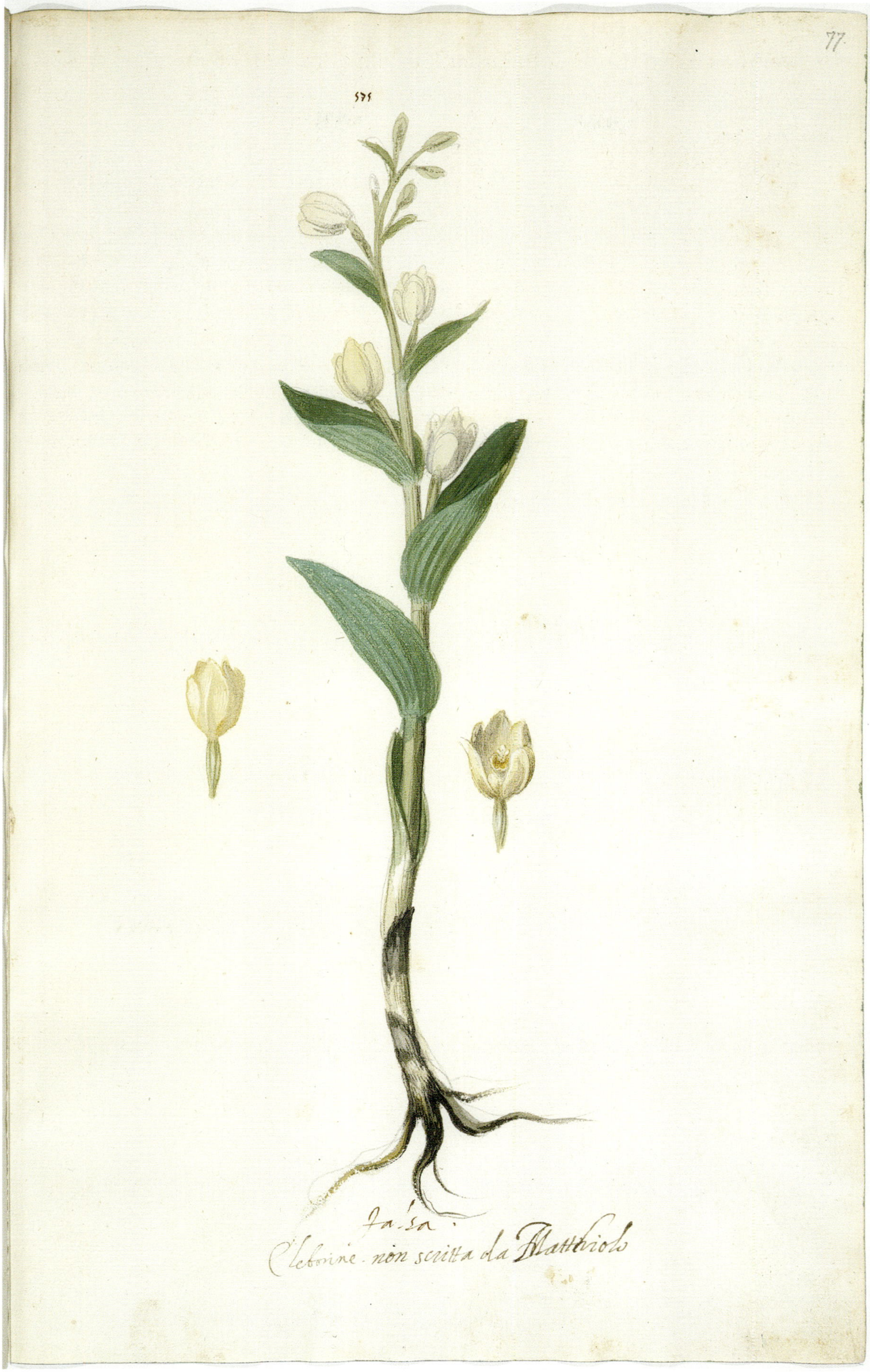
77
575
falsa.
Cleborine. non scritta da Matthiolo

78. Bulbous corydalis or hollowroot, *Corydalis cava* (L.) Schweigg. & Kört.

Erbario Miniato, fol. 78 (RL 27768)

ANNOTATION: *UN ALTRA FUMARIA* ('Another *Fumaria*')

The bulbous corydalis or hollowroot is a perennial bulbous species of the family Fumariaceae (see also **80**). It is common throughout Europe and temperate regions of Asia, in broadleaved forests from sea level to an altitude of 1,000m. The bulbous corydalis may be confused – as in the inscription here – with plants of the genus *Fumaria*, but can be distinguished by its fruit and the number of seeds. The tuberous roots of *Corydalis cava* are solid when young but soon become hollow. These and the lower part of the stem contain alkaloids and were used to treat skin conditions including the cutaneous symptoms of syphilis and malaria.

This drawing shows the upper part of the plant in flower, with its thick, smooth stem bearing several deeply lobed leaflets. The flowers grow from the axils of large green bracts and are arranged in terminal racemes. Each pink blossom is made up of petals fused for much of their length, forming a tube which ends in a paler curving spur. The pistils are barely visible, protruding from the throat of the flowers.

VNALTRA FVMARIA

78

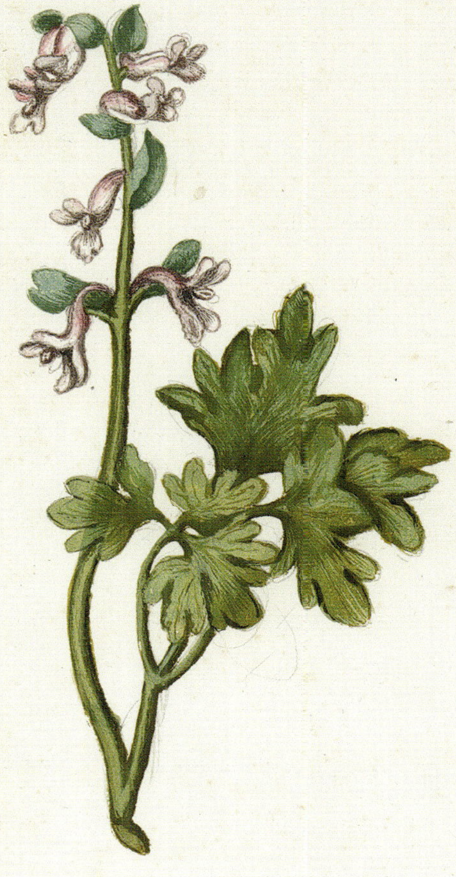

79. Common fumitory, *Fumaria officinalis* L.

Erbario Miniato, fol. 79 (RL 27769)

NUMBERING: *576*

ANNOTATION: *La fumaria chiamata da i' Medoci e' da li spetiali / fumus terre, el' erba beuta, purga copiosamente / la colera p*[*er*] *orina. si conumera tra le medecine benedette: / egli e' solutivo, corobera e' conforta anchora le viscere 1217. ~~Nº 55~~* ('The *fumaria*, called by physicians and by apothecaries smoke of the earth. When drunk the plant copiously expels choler by urination. It is counted among the blessed medicines: it is purgative and invigorates and soothes the bowels. 1217. ~~No. 55~~'). [From Mattioli 1568, pp. 1217–18, 1220]

This drawing shows the upper part of a common fumitory. This is a herbaceous annual of the family Fumariaceae common throughout Europe, the temperate regions of Asia and North Africa. It grows in cultivated fields, orchards and vineyards from sea level to an altitude of 1,600m. The slender, curving branch bears many finely fringed, compound leaves on short petioles, with tiny reddish-orange flowers growing in racemes from the axils of the leaves.

The fumitory derives its name (also in Latin and Italian, *fumaria*, and in Greek καπνός (*kapnos*), 'smoke') from its curious odour reminiscent of smoke or soot. Pliny thought that if the juice of the plant got into one's eyes they would begin to water as if they were filled with smoke.

576

79.

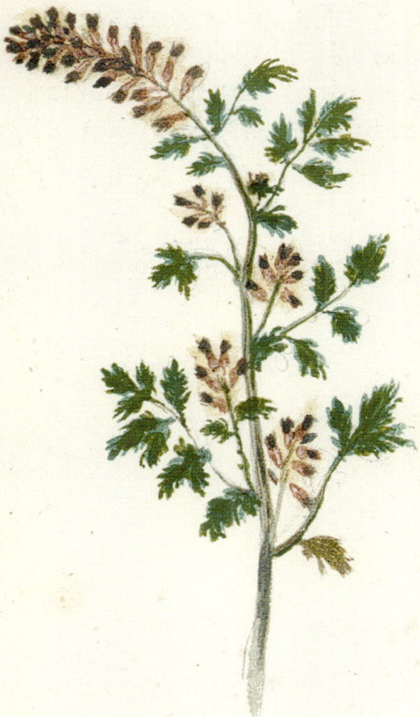

La fumaria chiamata dai Medoci e da li spetiali
fumus terre, e l'erba beuta, purga copiosamente
la colera p orina. si connumera tra le medecine benedette.
egli è solutivo, corobera e conforta ancora le viscere 1217.

N.o 55

80. Bulbous corydalis or hollowroot, *Corydalis cava* (L.) Schweigg. & Kört.

Erbario Miniato, fol. 80 (RL 27770)

NUMBERING: *577*

ANNOTATION: *Un altra Fumaria, nel Mattiolo. 1218 / Fumaria bulbosa flore albo. nel' Eicones. 38* ('Another *Fumaria*, in Mattioli [page] 1218. Bulbous *Fumaria* with white flower, in [Tabernaemontanus's] *Eicones* [page] 38'). [From Mattioli 1568, p. 1218; Tabernaemontanus 1590, p. 38]

This second drawing of a bulbous corydalis or hollowroot (see **78**) shows a fruiting branch and a detail of two flowers. The stem bears deeply lobed leaflets and four immature fruit borne on slender peduncles from the axils of well-developed bracts. The fruit takes the form of an elongated capsule, at the end of which are the vestige of its style and stigma. The detail of a raceme shows the unusual form of the pale pink flower.

The *Erbario* cites both the page in Mattioli's *Discorsi* which carries an illustration of *Corydalis cava*, and the equivalent in Tabernaemontanus's *Eicones plantarum* ('Fumaria bulbosa flore albo IV', p. 38). Tabernaemontanus included sixteen different 'Fumarie', many of which can be identified as members of the genus *Corydalis*.

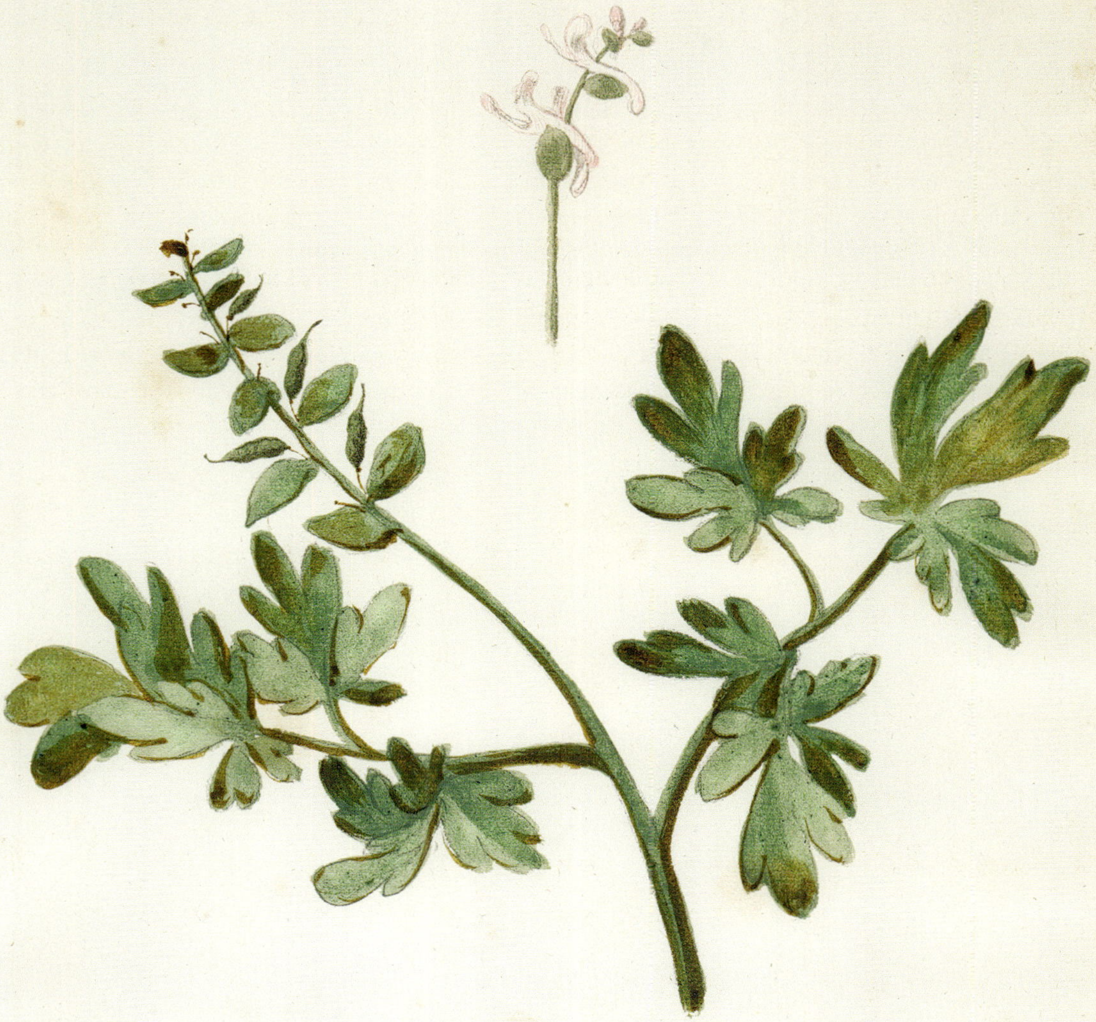

Vnaltra Fumaria . nel Mattiolo · 1218

Fumaria bulbosa flore albo · nel' Eicones · 38

81. Yellow corydalis, *Pseudofumaria lutea* (L. 1771) Borkh.

Erbario Miniato, fol. 81 (RL 27771)

Watermark: Fleur de lys 44

NUMBERING: *578*

ANNOTATION: *Coridali. da altri Split. nel Ma: 1219* ('Corydalis, called by others *Split*. In Mattioli [page] 1219'). [From Mattioli 1568, pp. 1219–20]

The yellow corydalis is a herbaceous perennial of the family Fumariaceae. Indigenous to the eastern and central Alpine regions of Switzerland and Italy, it became naturalized all over western Europe on walls and limestone cliffs at altitudes from 500m to 1,700m but is now rare in the wild. It has been cultivated since the middle of the eighteenth century, when it was called the yellow fumitory, hence its generic name *Pseudofumaria*.

This drawing shows a flowering stem, whose smooth, slender branches end in petioles bearing compound leaves made up of three to six trilobed leaflets. The nine flowers growing in a loose raceme at the apex of the plant have slender pedicels with no bracts.

The 'Coridali' illustrated on p. 1219 of Mattioli's *Discorsi* may be either this plant or the fumewort, *Corydalis ochroleuca*. As Cesi notes, an alternative name for the plant was 'Split'.

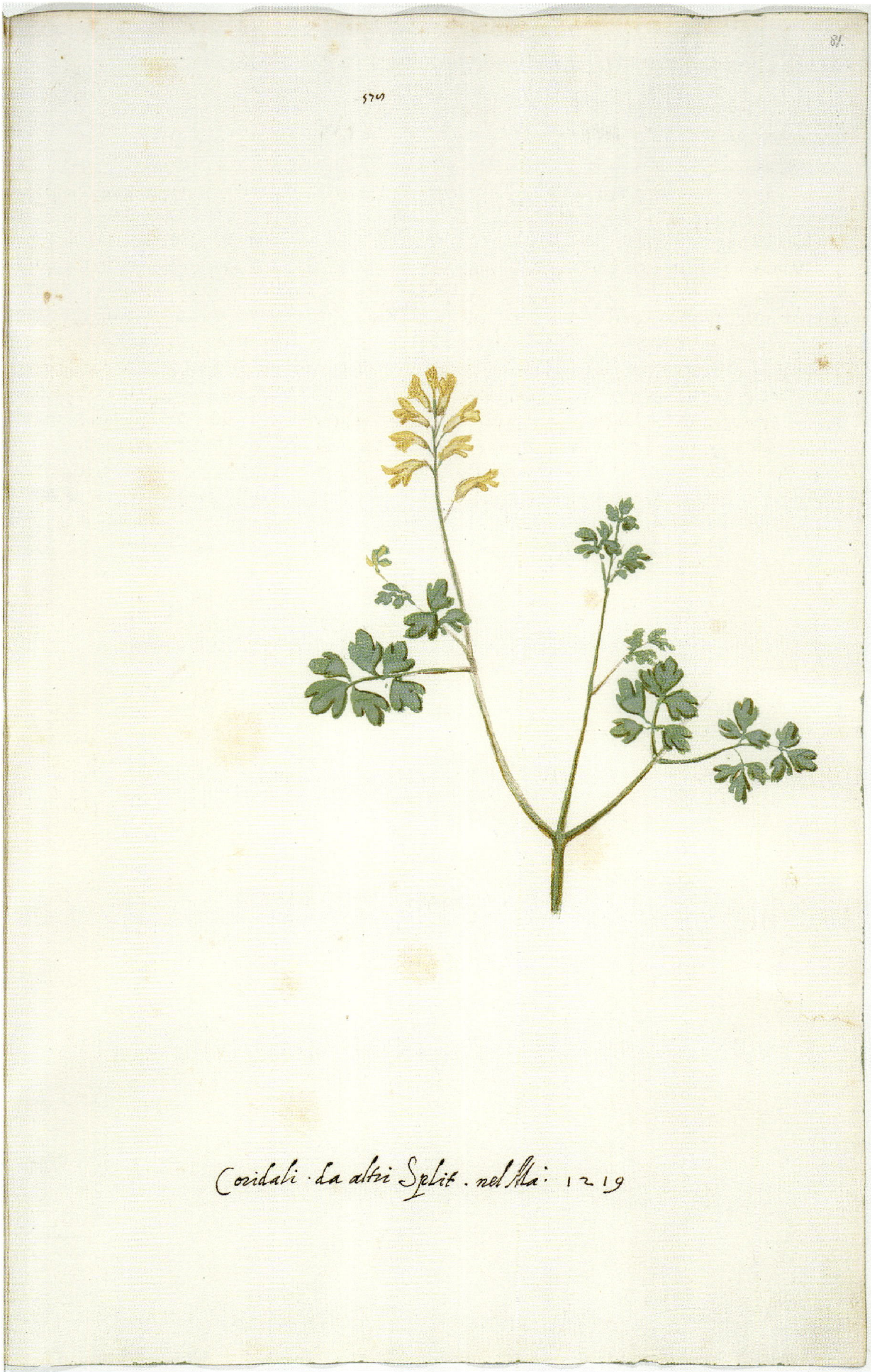
81.
Coridali · da altri Split · nel Mai · 1219

82. Ribbed melilot, *Melilotus officinalis* (L.) Pallas

Erbario Miniato, fol. 82 (RL 27772)

NUMBERING: *579*

ANNOTATION: *Loto ~~Domestico~~ Salvatico. 1221.; Tribulo, overo Loto Urbano; loto salvatico. a' virtu de scaldare. di costringere legiermente unto con / mele. purga le macole. e' altri difetti della faccia. fassi del fiore odorifera / e' sovavissima acqua. 1221* ('~~Domestic~~ Wild *loto*. 1221; *Tribulo* or urban *loto*; the wild *loto* has a warming and slightly astringent quality. Anointed with honey it clears spots and other imperfections on the face. From the flowers a fragrant and most delicate water is made. 1221'). [From Mattioli 1568, pp. 1220–2]

The ribbed melilot is a herbaceous biennial of the family Fabaceae, native to Europe and temperate regions of Asia, and naturalized throughout the world. It grows in uncultivated fields from sea level to an altitude of 1,500m. This slender stem carries seven compound leaves on short petioles; each leaf is composed of three leaflets that are narrowly elliptical in form with finely toothed margins. From their axils grow long, slender racemes of yellow flowers on long peduncles.

Melilotos was the Greek name for plants whose flower was attractive to honey bees. Mattioli discussed and illustrated two similar plants, the 'Loto domestico' or 'Tribolo' (the Roman name for the plant, according to Mattioli), which corresponds to *Melilotus officinalis*, and the 'Loto salvatico' (*Trigonella coerulea*). The notes here at first correctly identified this plant with the 'Loto domestico', but later this was erroneously amended to 'Loto salvatico'.

82.

579

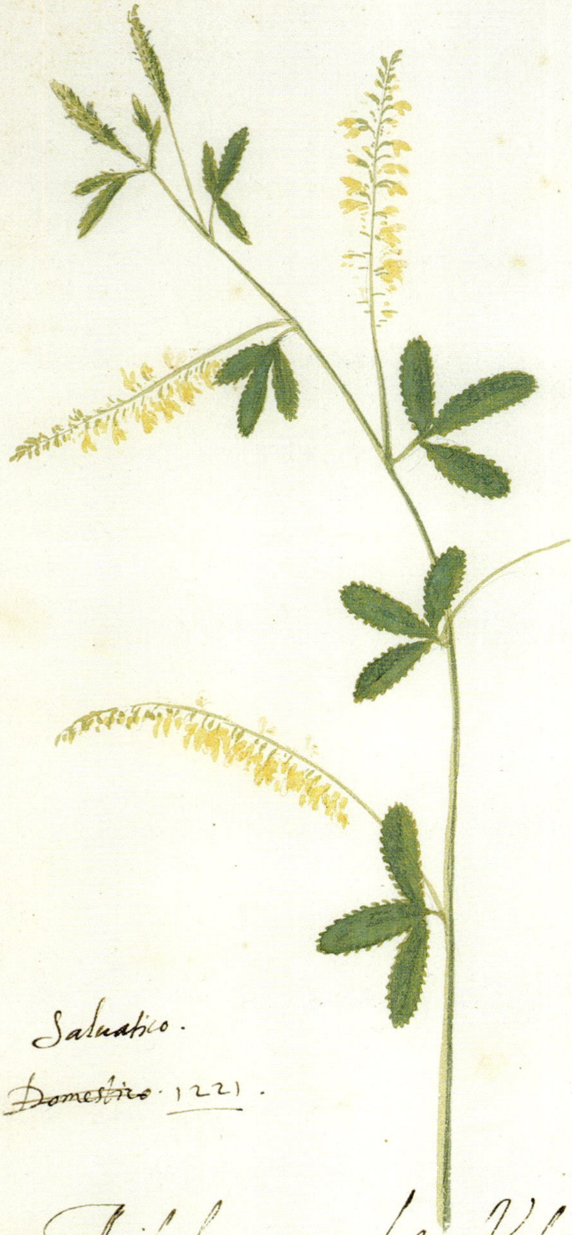

Saluatico.

Loto ~~Domestico~~ · 1221 ·

Tribulo, ouero Loto Vrbano

Loto Saluatico · a' uirtu de scaldare · di costringere · legiermente · unto con mele · purga le macole · e' altri difetti della faccia · fassi del fiore odorifera e' souauissima acqua · 1221

83. Yarrow, *Achillea millefolium* L.

Erbario Miniato, fol. 83 (RL 27773)

NUMBERING: *580*

ANNOTATION: *Sopraciglio di Venere; ~~Mille foglie~~; Miriophillo, prohibisce le / imfiamagione che vengano nelle / ferite, dassi a bere a' coloro che sonno cascati da alto, 1226*. ('Eyebrow of Venus; ~~*Mille foglie*~~; *Miriophillo*, prevents inflammations that develop in wounds; it is given to drink to those who have fallen from heights. 1226.'). [From Mattioli 1568, pp. 1225–6]

Yarrow is a herbaceous perennial of the family Asteraceae. It is native to Europe and temperate regions of Asia and naturalized in North America, being found in dry mountain meadows from the foothills to an altitude of 2,200m. This drawing shows a flowering stem with alternate, deeply dissected, lanceolate leaves on very short petioles. At its apex is a corymb of tiny flower heads made up of broad white petals surrounding a darker area representing the reproductive florets.

The yarrow has antiseptic and haemostatic properties, and has been used since antiquity to treat wounds, sores, ulcers and so on. Its generic name *Achillea* is derived from the Greek hero Achilles, who supposedly used it to staunch his soldiers' wounds. Some of its common names in various languages refer to this property; others such as *millefoglio* ('thousand leaves'), the English derivative milfoil, and the poetic 'eyebrow of Venus' refer to the fringed appearance of the leaves. Still other Italian common names including *camomilla selvatica* ('wild chamomile'), *finocchiella* ('little fennel'), or *trementina* ('turpentine') were inspired by the scent of its flowers.

The annotation first identified the plant as a 'Millefoglio'. Mattioli illustrated three plants of this name on pp. 1199–1201 of his *Discorsi*, the yarrow being the 'Millefoglio minore' on p. 1201. This identification was then changed to 'Miriophillo', but Mattioli's illustration of that plant on p. 1226 probably corresponds to the whorled water yarrow, *Miriophyllum verticillatum* (but while the leafy parts correspond to that plant, the flower does not). The name 'Sopraciglio di Venere' does not appear in Mattioli, but the rest of the note is taken from Dioscorides' passage on the 'Miriophillo' (p. 1225).

510

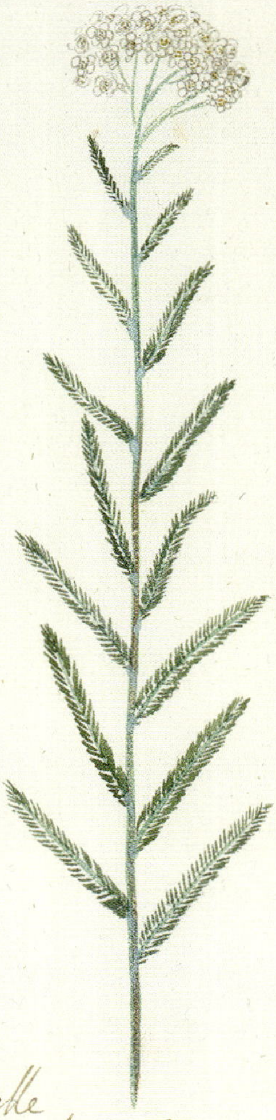

Sopraciglio di Venere

~~Mille foglie~~.

Miriophillo, proibisce le inflamagione che vengano nelle ferite, dassi a bere a' coloro che sonno cascati da alto, 1226.

84. Spreading hedge parsley, *Torilis arvensis* (Huds.) Link

Erbario Miniato, fol. 84 (RL 27774)

NUMBERING: *581*

ANNOTATION: *La Miride. provoca i, mestrui, il parto. e' le secondine: purga / le donne di parto: Dicano alcuni, che bevendosi ogni di doi o' / tre volte nel vino. la sua radice. e' salutifera alla pestilentia. / e' preserva da quella. chi la beve, 1228* ('The *Miride* induces menstruation, childbirth and the expulsion of the placenta; it purges women after childbirth. Some say that drinking its root two or three times a day in wine treats pestilence, and will preserve from it those who drink it. 1228'). [From Mattioli 1568, pp. 1227–8]

The spreading hedge parsley is a herbaceous annual of the family Umbelliferae, native to temperate regions of the northern hemisphere and growing weed-like in dry ground at altitudes from sea level to 800m. The drawing shows an entire plant, with a slender root and a lateral branch bearing several small, deeply lobed leaves and umbelliferous clusters of flowers. The stem of the hedge parsley is usually quite long and was probably shortened by the artist here.

Cesi identified this plant as the 'Mirrhide' illustrated on p. 1228 of Mattioli's *Discorsi*, which is actually cow parsley, *Anthriscus sylvestris*.

suri

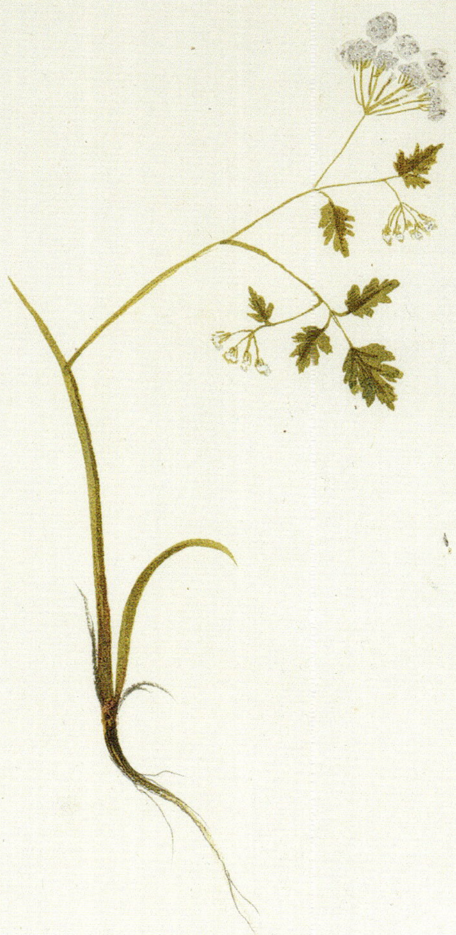

La Miride. prouoca i mestrui, il parto. e le secondine: purga
le donne di parto. Dicano alcuni, che beuendosi ogni dì doi o
tre uolte nel uino. la sua radice. è salutifera alla pestilentia.
è preserua da quella. e fa bene, 1228

85. Hogweed or cow parsnip, *Heracleum sphondylium* L.

Erbario Miniato, fol. 85 (RL 27775)

Watermark: Flower 4

NUMBERING: *582*

ANNOTATION: *Angelica odorata* ('Sweet-scented angelica')

The hogweed or cow parsnip is a herbaceous perennial of the family Apiaceae, common throughout Europe, the temperate regions of Asia, and North America. It grows in meadows, clearings and uncultivated fields to an altitude of 2,500m. In this large unfinished drawing the artist shows the plant's thick stem at the point of a large bract, from which grow two sets of compound leaves on long petioles. The leaflets on their short secondary petioles are oval in shape with sharp apices, toothed margins and prominent veins. Growing out of the same bract, slightly higher up on the axil, is a branch bearing two parasol-shaped clusters of white flowers, and another cluster in the fruiting stage. The flowers and fruits are merely sketched in.

Heracleum sphondylium was named by Linnaeus after Hercules (in Greek Herakles) who, according to a legend recounted by Pliny the Elder, used this plant to heal his wounds. *Angelica* was the Italian common name for *Angelica* spp. (see the annotation on **86**), introduced by Mattioli in his commentary on Dioscorides' 'Mirrhide' (see **84**), as it was held by some to correspond with that plant. Mattioli, however, thought that the root of the 'Angelica' was so fragrant that Dioscorides would not have neglected to mention it as a property of the 'Mirrhide' (p. 1228).

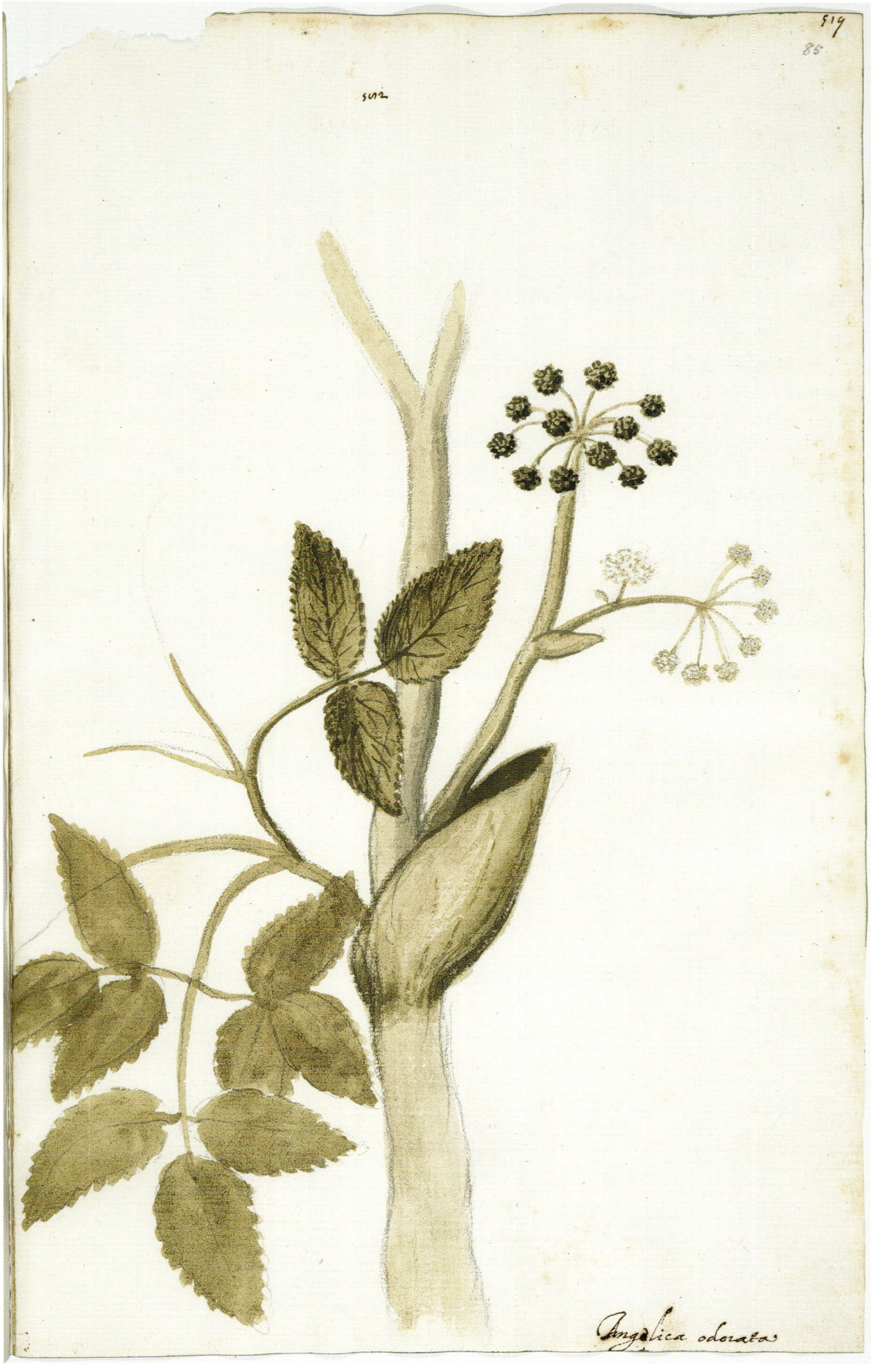
519
85
Angelica odorata

86. Ground elder, *Aegopodium podagraria* L.

Erbario Miniato, fol. 86 (RL 27776)

Watermark: Fleur de lys 51

NUMBERING: *583*

ANNOTATION: *Angelica, o' e' la terza, o' la quarta, spetie. e' calda e' secca, nel / prencipio del terzo ordine, apertiva, disecativa, e risolutiva, / vale unicamente contra a' i veleni, Giova mangiandola a' preserva= / rsi dalla peste, conferisce a' gli humori flematici, e' viscosi, guarisce / la tosse che si prende p[er] freddo. fortifica mangiata lo stomaco, vale ne / i difetti del cuore, fa ritornare lapetito perduto, libera da i morsi de/ i cani rabiosi, e' parimente dalle serpi, 1230* ('The third and the fourth species of *Angelica* are warm and dry, and beginning with the third order, aperient, drying and resolving. It is particularly effective against poisons. Eating it helps to protect one from the plague, is effective against phlegmatic and viscous humours, cures coughing induced by the cold. Eaten, it fortifies the stomach; it is valuable for heart defects, restores lost appetite, frees one from the effects of bites of rabid dogs and equally from those of serpents. 1230'). [From Mattioli 1568, p. 1230]

LITERATURE: Freedberg 2002, pp. 207 (fig. 8.5), 209

The ground elder is a herbaceous species of the family Apiaceae which is native to Europe and the temperate regions of Asia, and has become naturalized in the rest of the world. It grows in damp broadleaved forests and along riverbanks, and may easily infest gardens. It has a smooth green stem and compound leaves; the leaflets are oval in form with sharp apices, finely toothed margins and clearly visible veins. The inflorescence takes the form of a compound umbel; here the artist shows one cluster in flower and one in the fruiting stage. To the right is a detail of a short taproot and several small secondary roots.

Mattioli wrote of four different types of 'Angelica': 'Domestica', 'Salvatica', 'Acquatica' and a garden species to which he did not give a name. He described all four plants in the *Discorsi*, but provided illustrations of only two ('Domestica', *Angelica archangelica*, and 'Salvatica', *Angelica sylvestris*). The annotation is taken from Mattioli (p. 1230) but reveals uncertainty on which species is represented here: it mentions the third and fourth types of 'Angelica', but the page cited illustrates the second type (*Angelica sylvestris*).

503

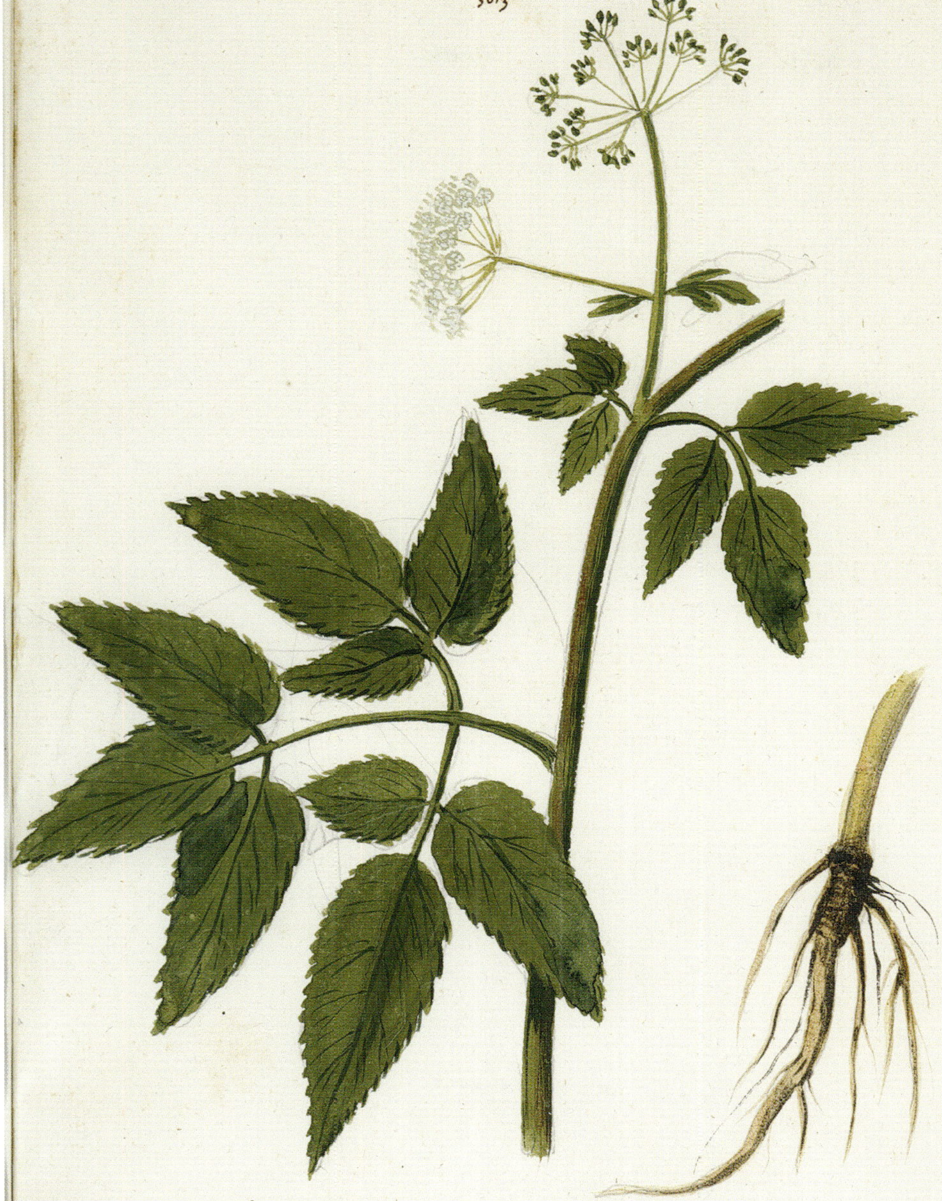

Angelica, ò è la terza, ò la quarta, spetie è calda e secca, nel
prencipio del terzo ordine, apertiva, diseccativa, e risolutiva,
vale unicamente contra à i veleni, Giova mangiandola à preserva=
rsi dalla peste, conferisce à gli humori flematici, e viscosi, guarisce
la tosse che si prende p freddo. fortifica mangiata lo stomaco, vale ne
i, difetti del cuore, fa ritornare l'appetito perduto, libera da i morsi de
i, cani rabiosi, è parimente dalle serpi, 1230

87. Spiny daisy, *Pallenis spinosa* (L.) Cassini

Erbario Miniato, fol. 87 (RL 27777)

NUMBERING: *584*

ANNOTATION: *Aster attico p.° del Matt:[1]; ~~Herba impia~~; Aster attico, rilieva in volgar nostro Stella de Athene: da altri Bubonio, e Ingui= / nale, p[er] essere egli molto eficacie rimedio p[er] le posteme dell'anguinaie, giova a' chi / essce il budello del sedere, nel mio 1233* ('*Aster attico* of the first type in Mattioli; ~~*Herba impia*~~; *Aster attico*, called in our vernacular Star of Athens, by others *Bubonio*, and also *Inguinale*, for being a very effective remedy against infections of the inguinal region. It is beneficial for those with piles. In my [Mattioli] 1233'). [From Mattioli 1568, p. 1233–4]

The spiny daisy is a herbaceous biennial of the family Asteraceae, common along roadsides in central and southern Italy and the Mediterranean generally, from sea level to an altitude of 1,400m. The drawing shows a straight, slender, branching stem covered with tiny hairs. The alternate leaves are long and narrow with blunt tips and entire margins. The inflorescence consists of a capitulum composed of numerous flowers, tubular at the centre and ligulate around the periphery, surrounded by a ring of external bracts that are twice as long as the flowers.

The plant corresponds to the illustration captioned 'Un'altro Aster attico' on p. 1235 of Mattioli's *Discorsi*, although the annotation cites the first of Mattioli's illustrations of 'Aster attico' on p. 1234 (*Aster amellus*: see **89**). The annotation is drawn from both Dioscorides' passage on p. 1233 and Mattioli's commentary on p. 1234.

87.

504

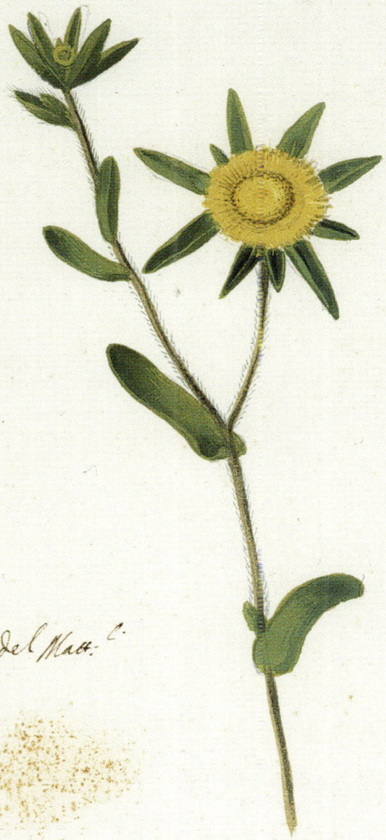

Aster attico p.° del Matt.c

~~Herba impia~~

Aster attico, ritiene in volgar nostro Stella de Atene: da altri Bubonio, e Inguinale. p essere egli molto eficacie rimedio p le posteme dell'anguinaie, giova a' chi esscie il budello del sedere, nel mo 1233

88. Common fleabane, *Pulicaria dysenterica* (L.) Bernh.

Erbario Miniato, fol. 88 (RL 27778)

Watermark: Eagle 15

NUMBERING: *585*

ANNOTATION: *Aster attico, overo amello, 1234* ('*Aster attico* or *amello*, 1234'). [From Mattioli 1568, p. 1234]

The common fleabane is a herbaceous perennial of the family Asteraceae, common throughout central and southern Europe in damp meadows and ditches from sea level to an altitude of 1,500m. The erect stem bears numerous pairs of sessile or subsessile leaves, ovate in shape with pointed tips. Dark veins are shown in the lower, more mature leaves. The upper part of the stem is branched and ends in a corymb of yellow flower heads, two in full bloom and one wilted, each composed of a central disk of tiny tubular flowers surrounded by many ligulate flowers.

Despite the annotation, this is not the plant illustrated by Mattioli on p. 1234 as 'Aster attico, overo Amello', which he describes as having a yellow and purple flower; that is the Italian aster (**89**).

505

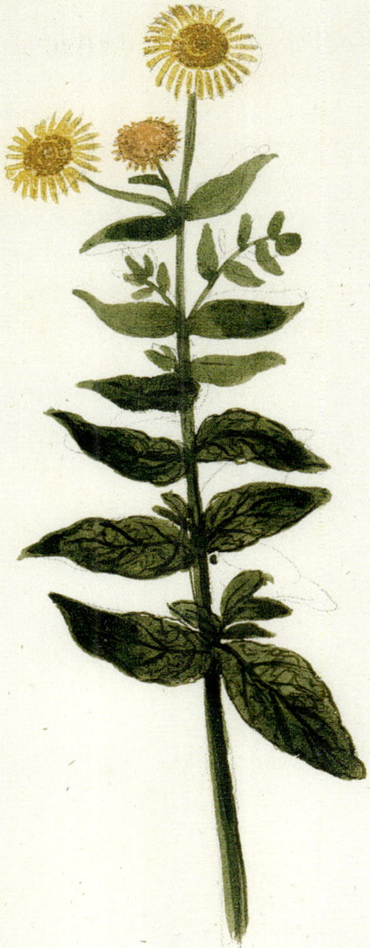

Aster attico, ouero amello. 1234

89. Italian aster, *Aster amellus* L.

Erbario Miniato, fol. 89 (RL 27779)

Lower specimen cut from another sheet and pasted on to the folio. *Watermark*: Eagle 20b

NUMBERING: *586*

ANNOTATION: *AMELLO DI VERGILIO* ('Virgil's *Amello*')

The Italian aster, a perennial of the family Asteraceae, is common in central and eastern Europe in forests, coppices and grassy glades below the tree line. The two specimens shown here have slender, slightly sinuous stems. The leaves are linear and sessile; in the first specimen they are as long as or longer than the flowering scapes, while in the second they are much shorter. Each flower head grows from a whorl of bracts and is made up of a central disk of bright yellow, tubular florets surrounded by ligulate ray florets, lilac in colour and extending like petals from the centre. In the first specimen the ligulate flowers are narrow and quite numerous; in the second they are broader and fewer in number.

The plant was well known in Roman times and is mentioned in Book IV of Virgil's *Georgics*, hence the common name recorded here, 'Amello di Vergilio'. Mattioli argued (on pp. 1236–7 of the *Discorsi*), probably correctly, that the 'Amello' described in some detail by Virgil corresponded with Dioscorides' 'Aster attico' (see **87**).

89

AMELLO DI VERGILIO

506

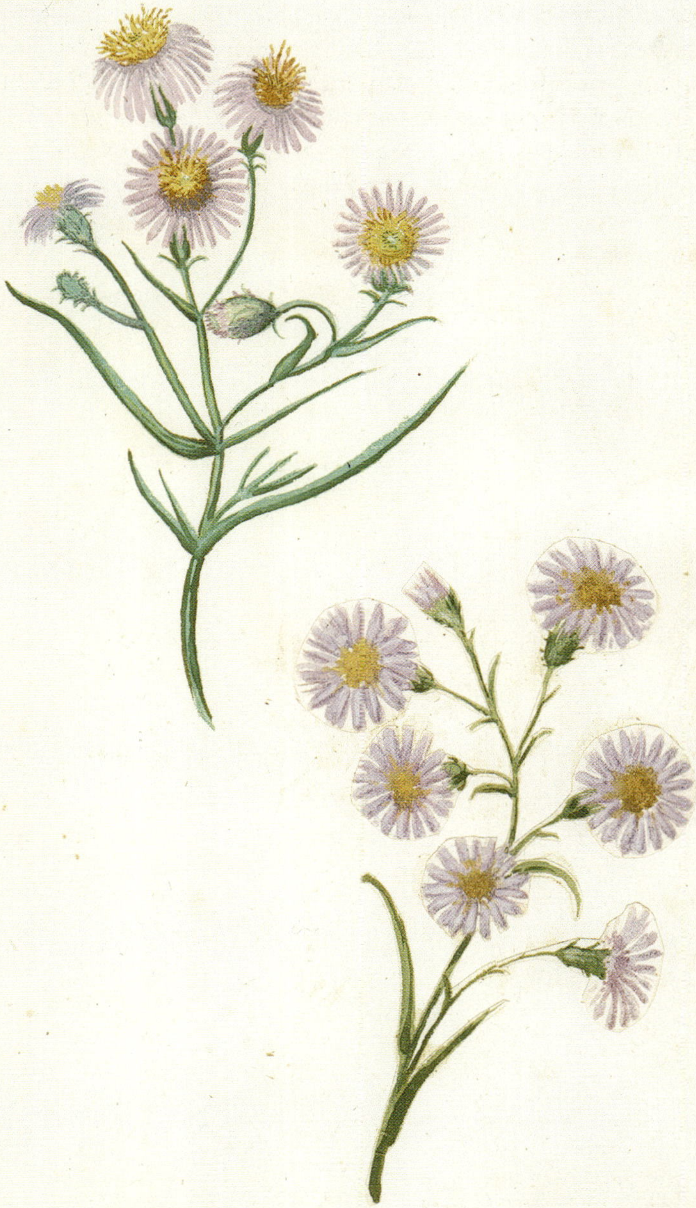

90. Sweet violet, *Viola odorata* L.

Erbario Miniato, fol. 90 (RL 27780)

Watermark: Eagle 16

NUMBERING: *587*

ANNOTATION: *le Viole Porporee respirano de sovavisimo odore., la virtu de la quale. / e' de infrigidire. 1239; N:º 30* ('Purple violets give out the sweetest scent and have a cooling quality. 1239. No. 30'). [From Mattioli 1568, pp. 1238–9]

The sweet violet is a herbaceous perennial of the family Violaceae, found across the Mediterranean in grassy spots and along the edges of forests, at altitudes from sea level to 1,200m. Plutarch recorded that sweet violets were widely planted in ancient Rome to counteract the smell of onions and garlic, and as ornamental plants they were prized by Renaissance gardeners. Many garden varieties exist today, but these may easily revert to the wild form.

The specimen here has a fairly short, slender main stalk with four leaves and four flowers growing on long petioles. The leaves are broadly oval, becoming heart-shaped as they mature, with finely toothed margins, acute apices, light green undersides and clearly marked veins. Each flower is made up of five purple petals with fine dark veins running down their centres; the pistil and stamens are not shown. The plant's slender grey root has many hair-like branches. To the left are details of a flower and a fruit consisting of a dark round capsule with a persistent calyx.

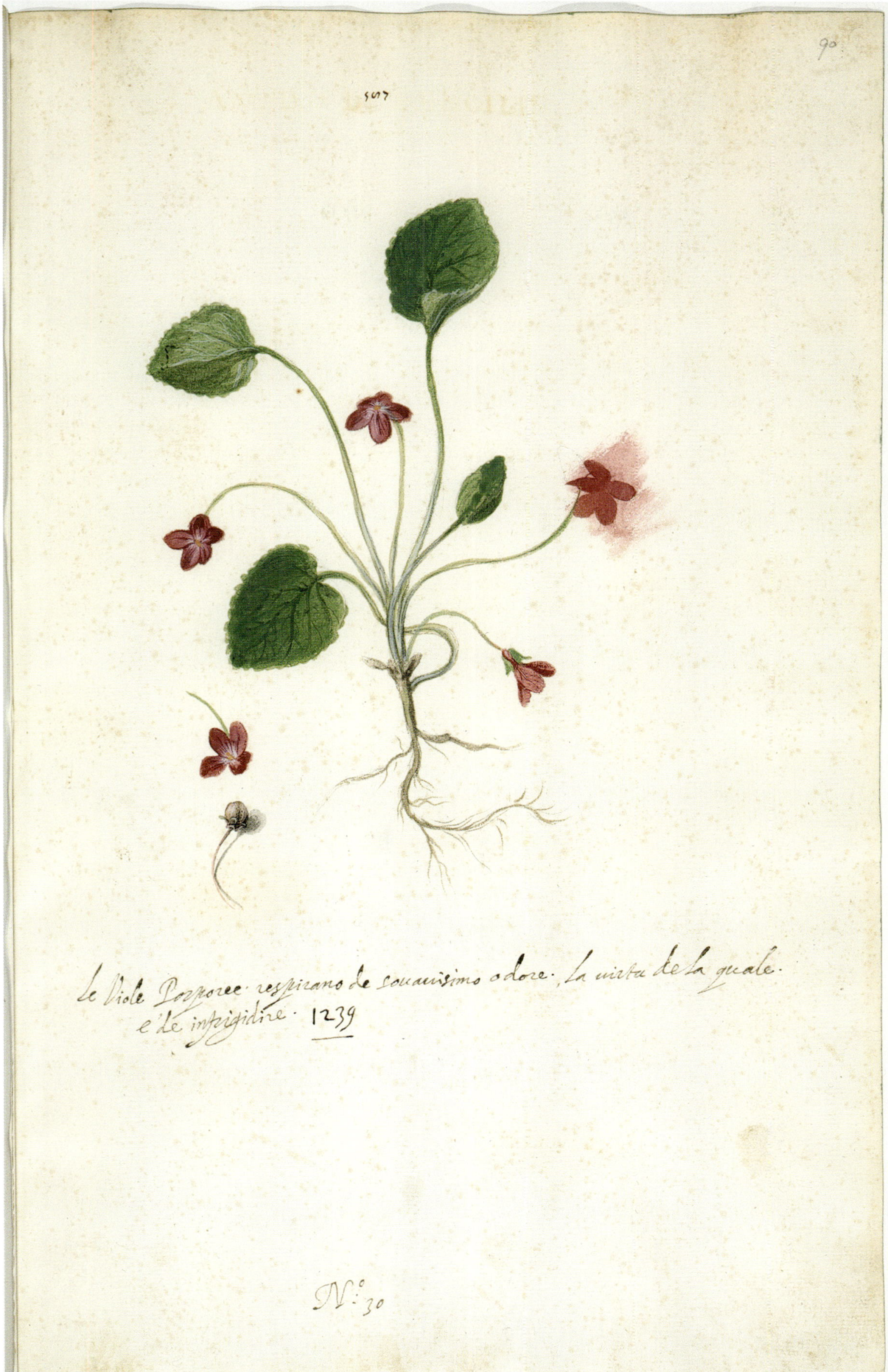
507
90
le Viole Porporee respirano de souauisimo odore, la virtu de la quale
e'de infrigidire. 1239
N.° 30

91. Wild pansy or heart's-ease, *Viola tricolor* L.

Erbario Miniato, fol. 91 (RL 27781)

Upper right figure and title inscription cut from other sheets and pasted on to the folio.
Watermark: Eagle 18

NUMBERING: *588*

ANNOTATION: *IACEA; viola bianca.; Iaccea. 1242.; Viola de tre colore. da altri Iacea magiore. / lacqua lambicata. e' otima p[er] il dolore del corpo de i fanciulli. / lerba impiastrata o' veramente data a' mangiare, guarisce i, / porci dalla schiranzia. e' no[n] li lascia strangolare.* ('Iacea; white violet; *Iaccea*. 1242. Violet of three colours, called by others greater *Iacea*. Its distilled juice is excellent for bodily pains in children. The plant applied externally or given as feed cures pigs of throat inflammations and prevents them from choking.'). [From Mattioli 1568, pp. 1240, 1242]

The wild pansy or heart's-ease is a herbaceous biennial of the family Violaceae. Originally from Eurasia, it has become naturalized all over the world and can be found growing in fields and woods from sea level to an altitude of more than 2,000m. The three colours of the wild pansy made it a popular garden flower and prompted a variety of names, such as 'Viola trinitatis' or 'flower of the Trinity'. The plot of Shakespeare's *A Midsummer Night's Dream* revolves around a love philtre concocted by Puck from the wild pansy (called 'love-in-idleness').

The plant on the left has a smooth, slender, sinuous stem, elliptical leaves with toothed margins and short petioles growing from widely separated nodes, and two flowers on long peduncles. Each flower is made up of five white petals; the three lower ones are faintly tinged with yellow at their base, while the two upper petals gradually shade to deep purple at their margins. The second specimen has a short, robust stem with closely spaced nodes, from which broad oval leaves with bluntly toothed margins extend on very long petioles. The flowers are similar to those of the first specimen, but grow on long, sinuous stems and are shown with their calyxes.

Details of two flowers, slightly enlarged, are depicted below. One is labelled 'viola bianca' (white violet) and shows a completely white blossom with a pale yellow throat. The other has the more typical colouring of the wild pansy – three white petals with a spot of pale yellow at the base, and two white petals marked by a broad band of purple at the margins.

The passages on medicinal usage are drawn from p. 1240 of the *Discorsi*, but the reference to p. 1242 identifies the plant with Mattioli's illustration of the second type of 'Iaccea' (captioned 'Un'altra Iaccea'), actually *Viola arvensis*. *Viola tricolor* is illustrated on p. 1241. The seventeenth-century index to the *Erbario Miniato* uses the name *suocer e nuora* ('mother- and daughter-in-law'), still a common name for this plant in Italy.

91.

IACEA

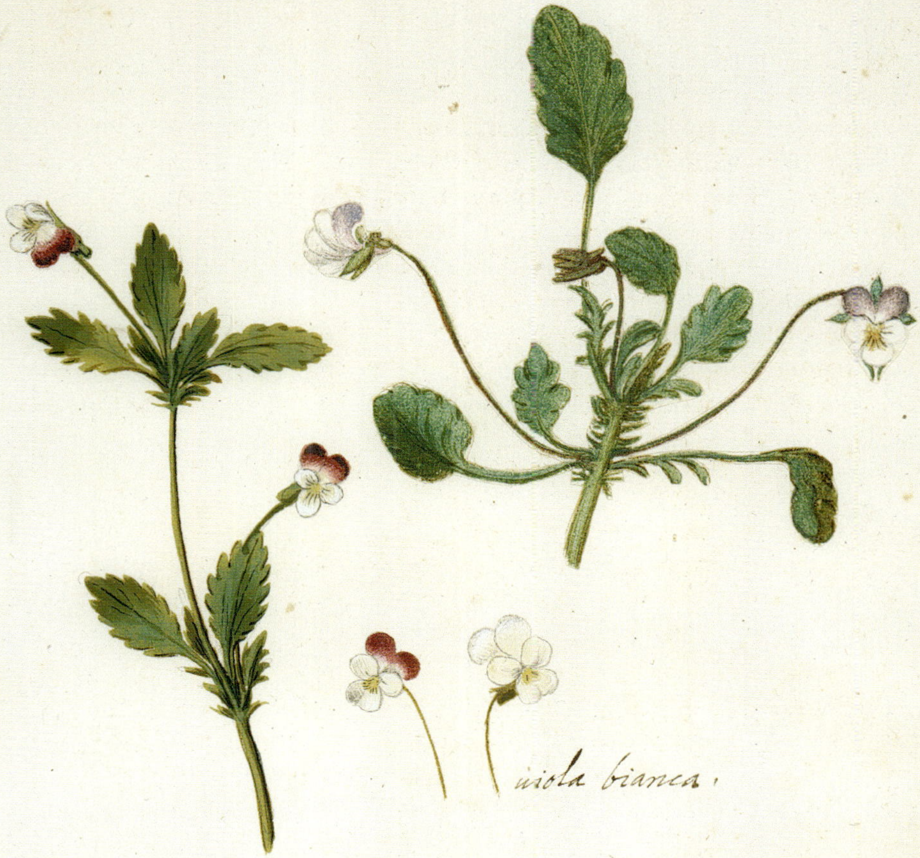

uiola bianca.

Jaccea·1242·

Viola de tre colore. da altri Jacea maggiore.

Lacqua lambicata. è ottima p il dolore del corpo de i fanciulli.
Lerba impiastrata o ueramente data a mangiare, guarisce i
porti dalla Scheranzia. e no li lascia strangolare.

92. Long-spurred pansy, *Viola calcarata* L.

Erbario Miniato, fol. 92 (RL 27782)

Watermark: Fleur de lys 47

NUMBERING: *589*

ANNOTATION: *Iacee*

In this unfinished drawing the artist shows three different flowers of the long-spurred pansy. A perennial of the family Violaceae, it is found in the Alps and the northernmost part of the Apennine mountain range, in meadows at altitudes between 1,500m and 2,800m.

The flower shown in two views at centre left is pale yellow with dark veins running along the length of its petals and a long, sinuous peduncle. A bud, a mature calyx made up of five linear sepals with blunt tips, and a few circular leaves with slightly scalloped edges are shown. The posterior view to the right displays the calyx.

The flower at centre right, which appears to be unfinished, is deep purple in colour with six rather than the usual five petals. Below is a flower made up of five white petals, the two upper ones violet at the margins, the three lower ones completely white with a spot of yellow at the base and dark veins running along their length. In none of the specimens is the characteristic spur of the flower visible.

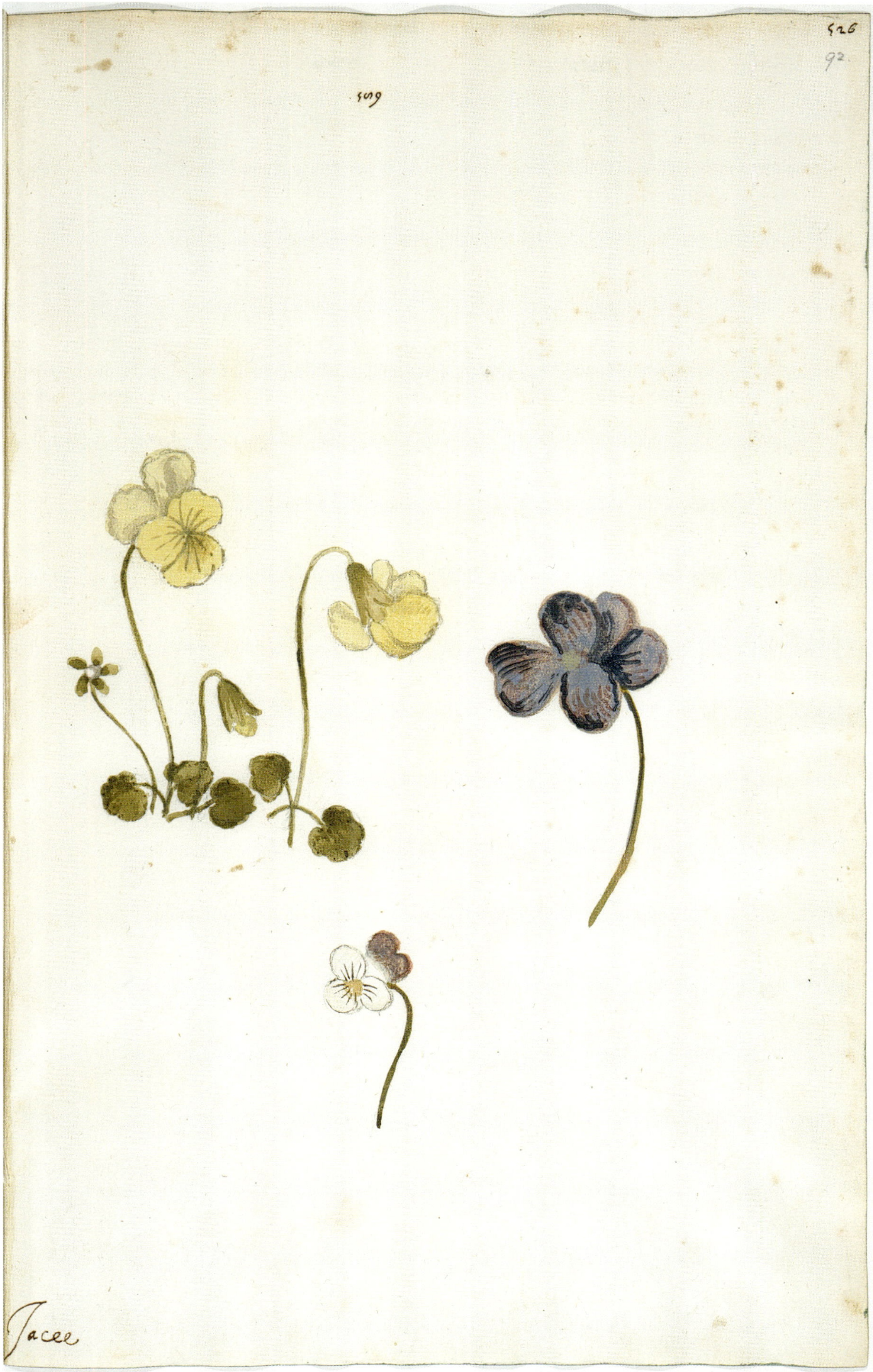
526
92.
509
Jacee

93. Borage, *Borago officinalis* L.

Erbario Miniato, fol. 93 (RL 27783)

NUMBERING: *590*

ANNOTATION: *Bugliosa / dal fior / bianco.; Bugliosa. o'vero Boragine: messe le sue fronde nel vino. usandolo il detto / vino continuamente. ralegra e' consola el animo.* *1245. N:º 28* ('White flowered bugloss. Bugloss or borage. Its leaves placed in wine, and this wine taken regularly, cheers and comforts the spirit. 1245. No. 28'). [From Mattioli 1568, pp. 1244–5]

LITERATURE: Solinas 1989, p. 60, n.19

Borage is a herbaceous annual of the family Boraginaceae, a family composed of at least 100 genera and 2,000 species. One of the best known and most widely consumed wild plants, it is common in southern Europe, North Africa and the temperate regions of western Asia, growing along ditches and roads, in vineyards and at the forest's edge from sea level to an altitude of 800m.

The thick stem tapers towards its apex, and bears oval leaves, sometimes on short petioles, sometimes directly from the stem. Both the stem and leaves are covered with short bristly hairs, a characteristic of the Boraginaceae (the name is derived from *borra*, a post-classical Latin word for a rough woollen cloth with long fibres). A blunt branch or a flower on a long peduncle grows from the axil of each leaf. The flower of the borage is made up of a star-like, five-lobed corolla, either sky-blue or light violet in colour, with black stamens that unite to form a cone at its centre. In this drawing most of the flowers are still closed, but the artist shows three in full bloom; the long, lanceolate sepals of their deeply indented calyxes are clearly visible. At lower right is a detail of a flower that is entirely white in colour. Contrary to the assertion of Solinas, the page does not appear to have been modified in any way.

The annotation is mostly drawn from Dioscorides' short chapter on the 'Buglossa' (p. 1244), to which Mattioli added a long commentary and the observation that 'the flowers have the form of a star of a vivid sky-blue colour, although there are also those that produce white flowers', hence the detail of the white flower in this drawing. The cited p. 1245 illustrates a 'true bugloss' ('Buglossa vera'), which corresponds correctly to *Borago officinalis*.

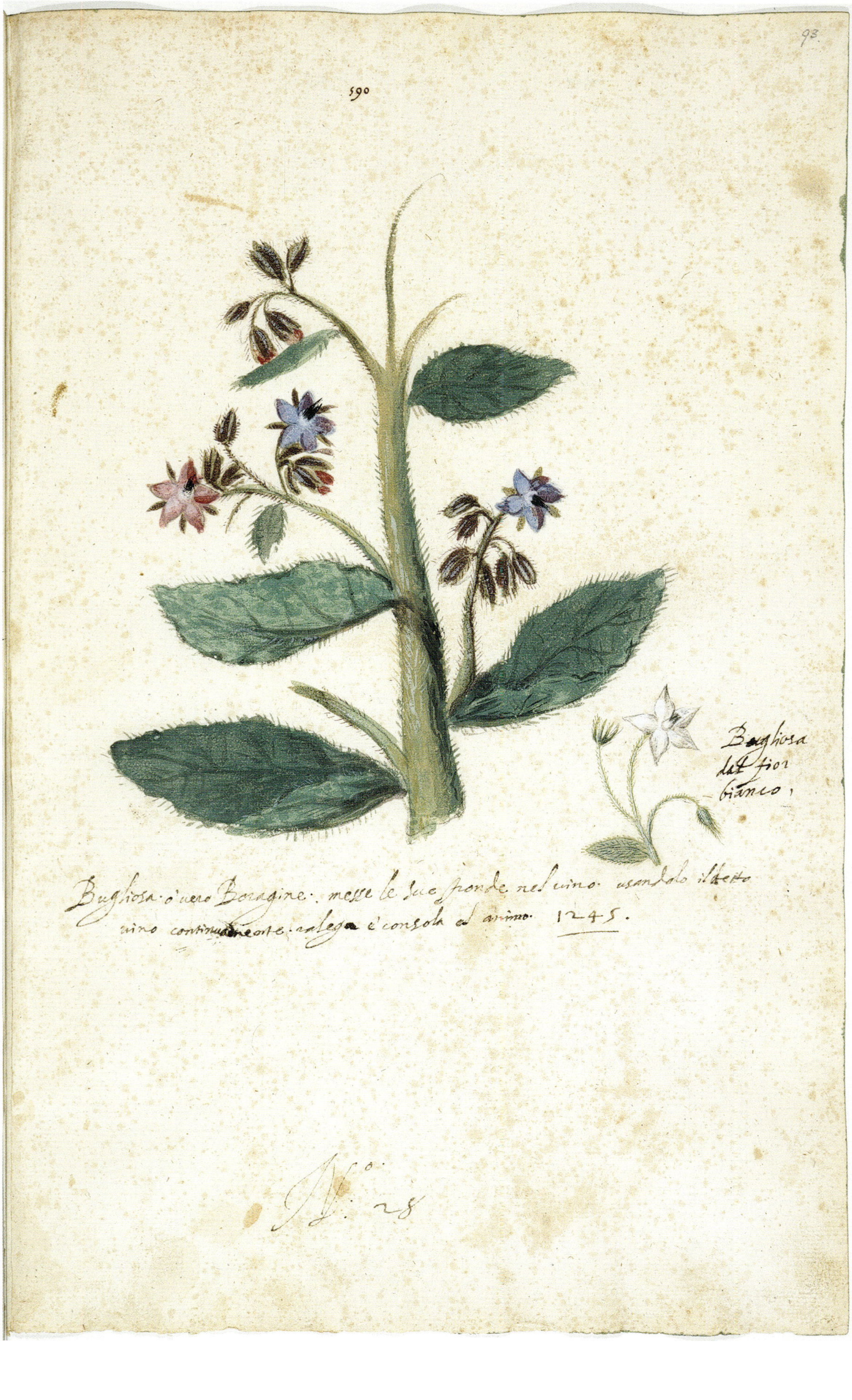
93
590
Buglosa dal fior bianco.
Buglosa o'uero Boragine. messe le sue fronde nel uino usandolo il detto uino continuamente, ralegra e consola el animo. 1245.
N.o 28

94. Green alkanet, *Pentaglottis sempervirens* (L.) Tausch ex L.H. Bailey

Erbario Miniato, fol. 94 (RL 27784)

NUMBERING: *591*

ANNOTATION: *La vera Buglossa. tritandosi con il suo seme e' radice. / giova beuta contra al rigore della febre terzana. / e' anco alla quarttana, Messe le fronde nel vino, p[er] / ralegrare e' consolare el animo, 1245.* ('True bugloss. Its seed minced and drunk with the root is efficacious against the rigour of tertian fever, and also of quartan. The leaves placed in wine cheer and comfort the spirit. 1245.'). [From Mattioli 1568, pp. 1244–5]

The green alkanet is a perennial of the family Boraginaceae, common in western and south-western Europe on uncultivated land, from sea level to an altitude of 600m (see also **95**). The specimen shown here has a thick, erect stem with two alternate sessile leaves, oval in shape with entire margins and acute apices. Both the stem and leaves are covered with short, downy hairs. From the axil of each leaf springs a flower with a slender, hairy peduncle, almost as long as the leaf itself. The flowers have large bracts and tubular corollas that divide into five broad lobes with rounded margins; the corollas are bright blue in colour with white throats. Neither the apex nor the lower part of the plant is shown.

The *Erbario* again cites p. 1245 of Mattioli's *Discorsi*, mistakenly identifying this plant as another 'vera Buglossa' (*Borago officinalis*: **93**). The passage on medicinal usage repeats some of the comments copied in **93**.

591

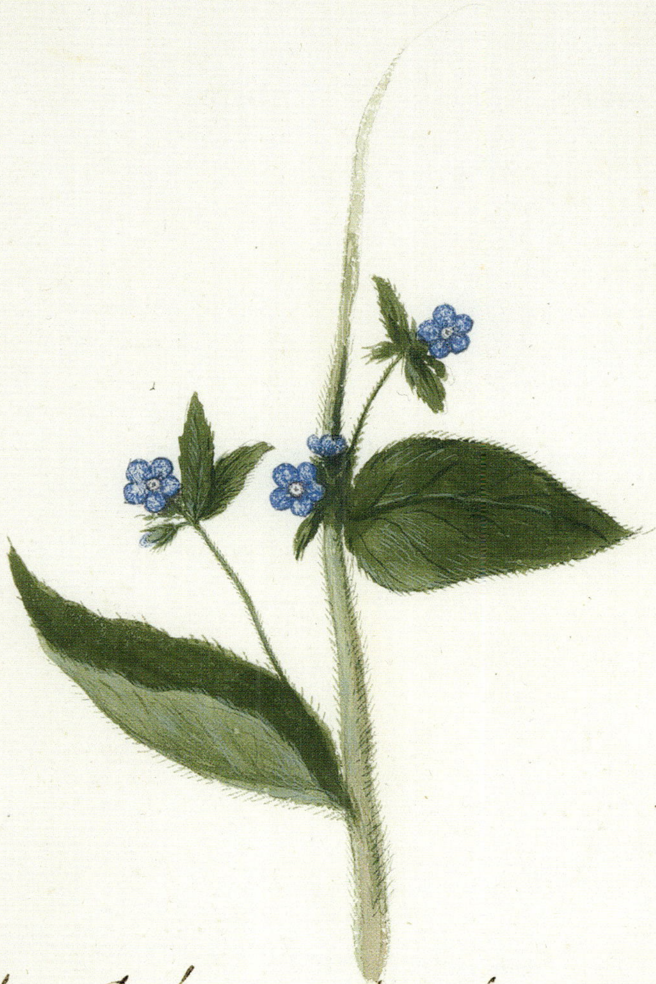

La uera Buglossa. tritandosi con il suo seme e' radice.
giova beuta contra al rigore della febre terzana.
e' anco alla quartana. Messe le fronde nel uino, ꝑ
ralegrare e' consolare el animo, 1245.

95. Green alkanet, *Pentaglottis sempervirens* (L.) Tausch ex L.H. Bailey

Erbario Miniato, fol. 95 (RL 27785)

NUMBERING: *592*

ANNOTATION: *1246 carte nel mio Matiolo grande; Buglossa volgare* ('[Page] 1246 in my large Mattioli; common bugloss'). [From Mattioli 1568, p. 1246]

This is another specimen of the green alkanet (see **94**). Like the previous drawing, it shows a section of the plant, with an erect stem thickly covered with short, soft hairs. The leaves are alternate, ovate and sessile with prominent veins, and the tiny hairs that cover both surfaces are clearly drawn. Long flowering stems grow from the axils of two leaves at different heights; these are also covered with tiny hairs. Each flower has a slender, reflexed peduncle, a leafy bract and a long, hairy tubular calyx divided into toothed segments. The tubular corolla is bright blue in colour, becoming white at the throat, and is divided into five rounded lobes. The apex of the plant and its lower part, including the root system, are not shown.

The inscription identifies the plant as a 'Buglossa volgare' illustrated on p. 1246 of Mattioli's *Discorsi*, which is in fact the Italian bugloss or large blue alkanet, *Anchusa italica*.

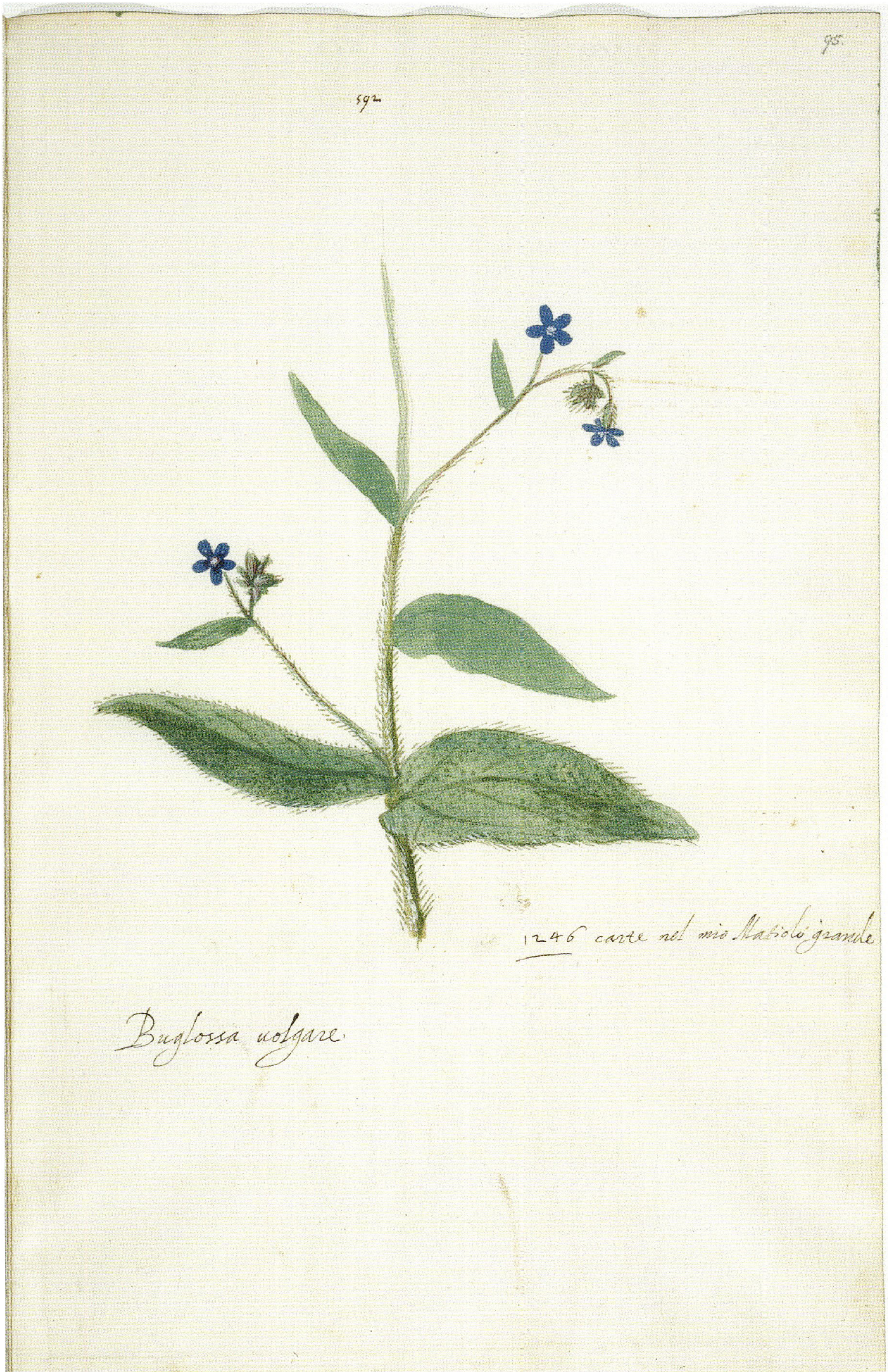
95.
592
1246 carte nel mio Matiolo grande
Buglossa uolgare

96. Hound's tongue, *Cynoglossum officinale* L.

Erbario Miniato, fol. 96 (RL 27786)

NUMBERING: *593*

ANNOTATION: *CINOGLOSSA VOLGARE* ('Common hound's tongue')

The hound's tongue is a herbaceous biennial of the family Boraginaceae. It is common all over Europe and in the temperate regions of Asia, growing along the edges of fields and paths from sea level to an altitude of 1,300m. This drawing shows an entire specimen, with a thick, erect stem tapering towards its apex. The leaves are lanceolate with entire margins and pointed tips; the lower leaves narrow at their base to form stem-like attachments while the upper leaves are sessile. Tiny flowers grow on long peduncles from the axils of the leaves; their corollas are divided into five lobes and vary in colour from light blue to purple (like many species in the family Boraginaceae, the flowers may vary in colour on a single plant). The thick, dark root ends in a wide collar that carries dried leaves from the preceding year. Also growing from the root is a lateral branch with a new stem.

The plant owes its scientific and common name to the shape of its leaves, which supposedly resemble a dog's tongue (from the Greek κύων (*kyon*), 'dog', and γλώσσα (*glossa*), 'tongue'). The leaves contain a poisonous alkaloid, and were used in traditional medicine to brew sedatives and other remedies. Mattioli illustrated *Cynoglossum officinale* on both pages 1249 (as 'Cinoglossa volgare') and 1250 ('Cinoglossa volgare fiorita') of the *Discorsi* (see Fig. 8, p. 25, for Fuchs's earlier illustration of this plant).

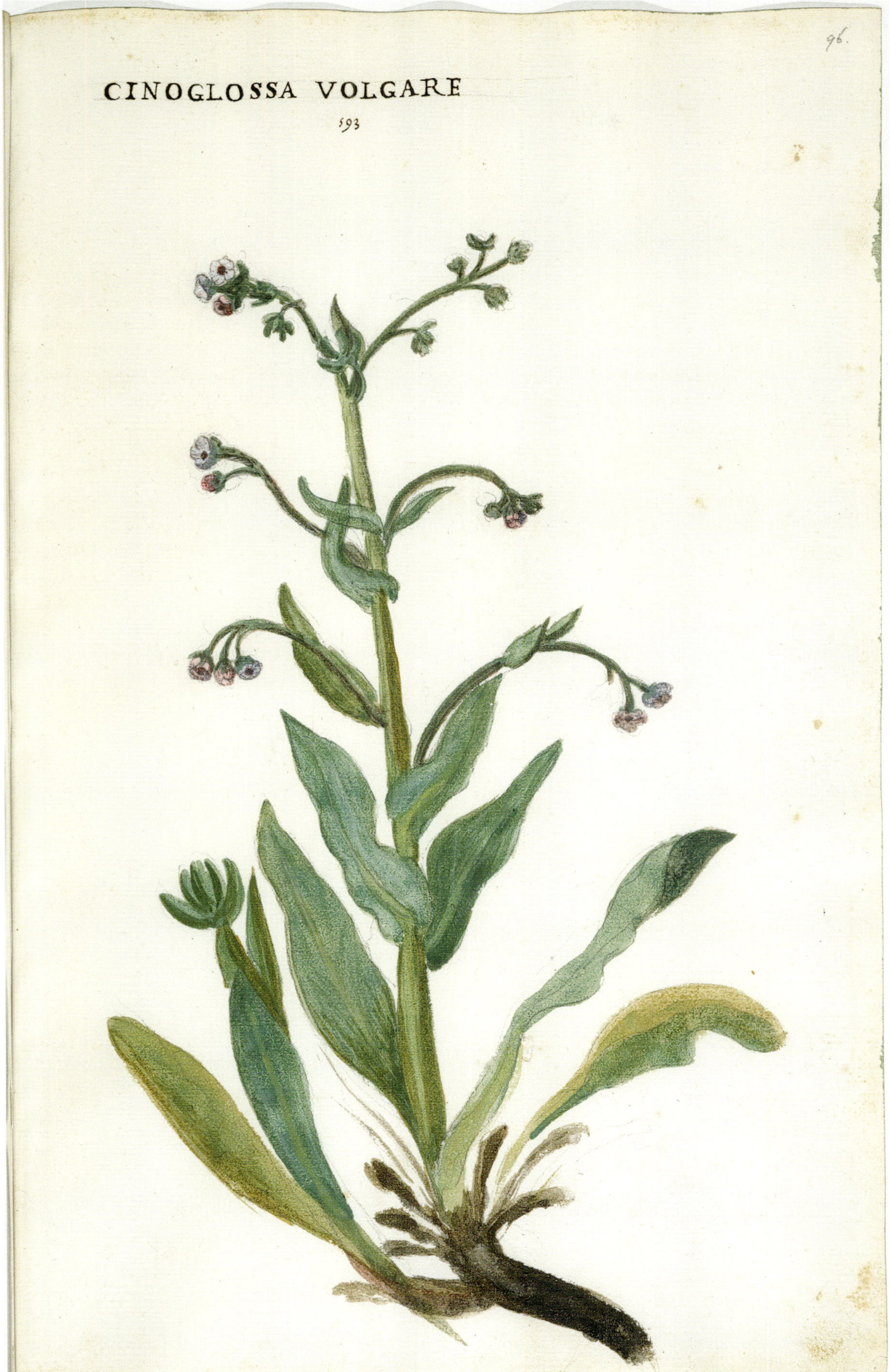
96.
CINOGLOSSA VOLGARE
593

97. Horse-tongue, *Ruscus hypoglossum* L.

Erbario Miniato, fol. 97 (RL 27787)

Watermark: Eagle 17

NUMBERING: *594*

ANNOTATION: *Chiamasi l Hippoglosso in toscana Bislingua e' in alcun altri luoghi de Italia. / Bonifacia: Dandosi un cucchiaro de pollvere dele sue frondi, overo delle / radice nelle prefocationi della Madrice, libera subito da quelle. e' oltre a / questo. Rimedio valerosissimo e' quasi divino p*[*er*] *le ~~rotture~~ ROTTURE, che scendano / nelle borscie* [M: *borse*]. *bevendosi continuamente una dramma e mezza ogni matina / con decotione di Simphito magiore; vale ancora particolarmente a' trogli* [M: *quegli*], / *che maragevolmente parlano, 1254* ('The horse-tongue is called in Tuscany *Bislingua* and in some other parts of Italy *Bonifacia*. Taking a spoonful of the powder of its leaves or of its root for inflammations of the uterus provides instant relief. It is in addition the most effective remedy, almost divine, for inguinal hernias. Drinking a drachm and a half regularly every morning with a decoction of common comfrey is particularly efficacious for those with speaking difficulties. 1254'). [From Mattioli 1568, pp. 1253–4]

The horse-tongue is an evergreen shrub with an unusual leaf structure, belonging to the family Ruscaceae. It is distributed throughout the eastern Mediterranean, where it thrives in the underbrush of broadleaved forests from sea level to an altitude of 1,400m. It is cultivated as a garden ornamental and has a tendency to naturalize.

The artist shows a slender, tapering stem bearing nine cladophylls, modified stems which take the form of leaves; the true anatomical origin of these appendages can be deduced from the fact that the plant's flowers grow from the centres of these 'leaves'. The conspicuous bract enveloping the flower distinguishes this species from the more common *Ruscus aculeatus*. Unlike Mattioli's woodcut of the 'Hippoglosso' cited here, which presents the cladophylls with marked veins, this drawing accurately depicts them as being fairly smooth.

594

97.

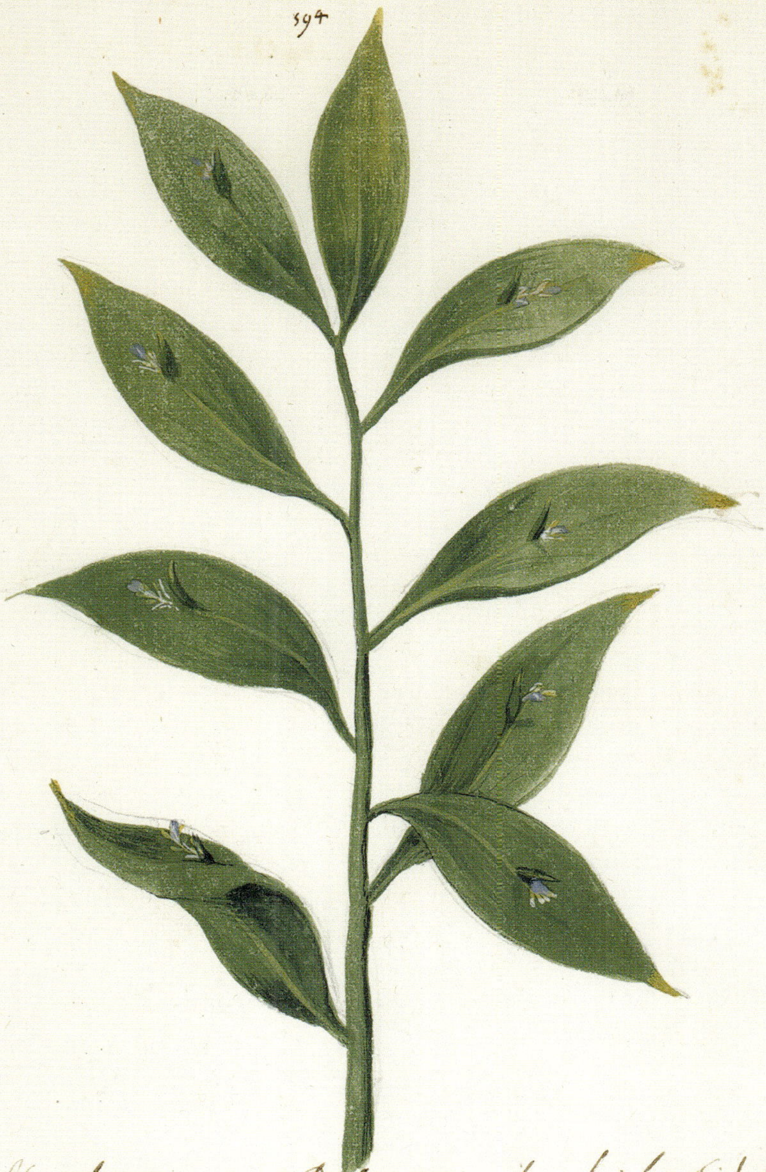

Chiamasi l'Hippoglosso in toscana Bislingua e in alcun altri luoghi de Italia.
Bonifacia. Dandosi un cucchiaro de polvero delle sue frondi, overo delle
radice nelle prefocationi della Madrice, libera subito da quelle. e oltre a
questo. Rimedio valerosissimo e quasi divino p le ~~[illegible]~~ (ROTTVRE) che scendano
nelle borscie. bevendosi continuamente una dramma e mezza ogni matina
con decotione di Simphito magiore; vale ancora particolarmente à trogli,
che malagevolmente parlano, 1254

98. Snapdragon, *Antirrhinum majus* L. cv.

Erbario Miniato, fol. 98 (RL 27788)

The flower at lower left cut from another sheet and pasted on to the folio; likewise the whole of the stem to the right excepting its lowest flower, which is drawn directly on to the folio. *Watermark*: Eagle 15

NUMBERING: *595*

ANNOTATION: *ANTIRRHINO; Antirrhino Primo. 1255. chiamano / alcuni anarrhino, e' altri lichnide sal= / vatica. Si fa lolio de il ⸗ Seme. pe*[*r*] *// ungersi la faccia. misto con olio / di giglio. e di ligustro. diventano bellissimi / quegli che la doperano. e' portandosi / il detto olio adosso. e' contrario a' i veneficii, / et a' i medicamenti nocivi.* ('Antirrhinum; first type of antirrhinum. 1225. Some call it *anarrhino* and others wild *lichnide*. The seed is used to make an oil for the face which is mixed with lily and privet oil. Those who use it become most beautiful, and applying it on one's person protects against poisoning and noxious medications.'). [From Mattioli 1568, p. 1255]

The snapdragon is a partially woody species belonging to the family Scrophulariaceae, native to the north-west Mediterranean, naturalized in temperate regions of the rest of the world, and widely cultivated (see also **99–100**). It flourishes on stony ground, cliffs and walls from sea level to an altitude of 800m. The sack-shaped protuberance at the throat of the flower gives it the appearance of a gaping mouth (a characteristic of the Scrophulariaceae), and thus many of its names – the English snapdragon, the Italian *bocca di leone*, *gola di lupo* and *testa di bue* (lion's mouth, wolf's throat, ox's head) and the scientific name *Antirrhinum* from the Greek αντί (*anti*), denoting equivalence, and ρίς or ρινός (*ris/rinos*), meaning nose. In ancient Rome, priests believed that they could read the future in the movements of its flowering stem.

The flowering stems of two different cultivars of the snapdragon are shown here; in one the stem is robust, erect and smooth, while in the other it is slender and flexible. Long, narrow leaves grow in pairs on opposite sides of the stem. The terminal racemes bear large pink flowers on short, well-developed peduncles. The calyx has five lanceolate teeth that are much shorter than the corolla, which is bilabial and bright pink in colour. The pistils and stamens are not visible, but each stem bears several immature capsules at the base of the inflorescence.

The annotation is drawn from Dioscorides' description of the properties of the 'Antirrhino' on p. 1255, where Mattioli's first type of 'Antirrhino' is also illustrated (corresponding to *Antirrhinum majus*). Mattioli added that the plant was 'such an enemy to scorpions that at the mere sight of it they remained petrified, as if struck senseless' (p. 1257).

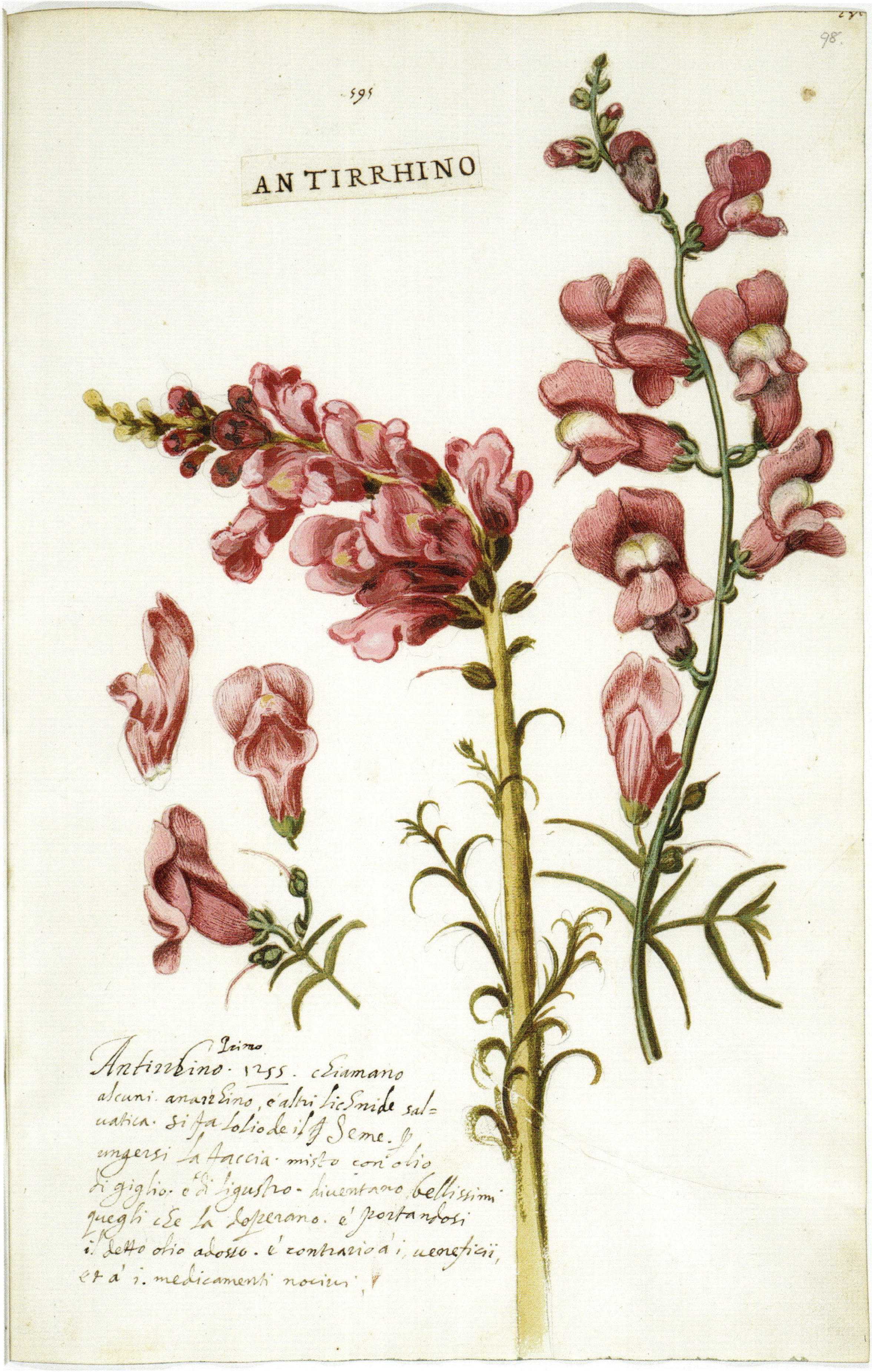
595
98.
ANTIRRHINO
Primo
Antirrhino. 1255. chiamano
alcuni anarrhino, e altri licnide sal=
uatica. si fa l'olio de il seme.
ungersi la faccia misto con olio
di giglio. e di ligustro. diventano bellissimi
quegli che lo dosperano. e portandosi
il detto olio adosso. è contrario a i uenefici,
et a i medicamenti nocivi.

99. Snapdragon, *Antirrhinum majus* L. cv.

Erbario Miniato, fol. 99 (RL 27789)

NUMBERING: *596*

ANNOTATION: *Anterrini*

This work shows two stems of the snapdragon (see **98**), one with pink and one with yellow blossoms, and the detail of a flower. The specimen on the left has a smooth, flexible stem and alternate leaves that become increasingly linear and acute near the apex, with slender petioles. The short raceme bears three flowers on erect, slender peduncles; the calyx is broadly toothed and fairly short. The corolla is bilabial with light pink petals that are fused at the base, while the pouch-like protuberance at the throat of the corolla is yellow. An immature capsule can also be seen. The specimen on the right is similar, although the raceme is less erect and the flowers are yellow in colour, shading to almost white at the base. The five broad lobes of the calyx are not clearly depicted.

The single flower, enlarged but somewhat summarily drawn, is yellow in colour with a slender peduncle and a calyx whose five teeth are narrower and more marked than those in the blossoms depicted above. The pistils and stamens of the flowers are not shown.

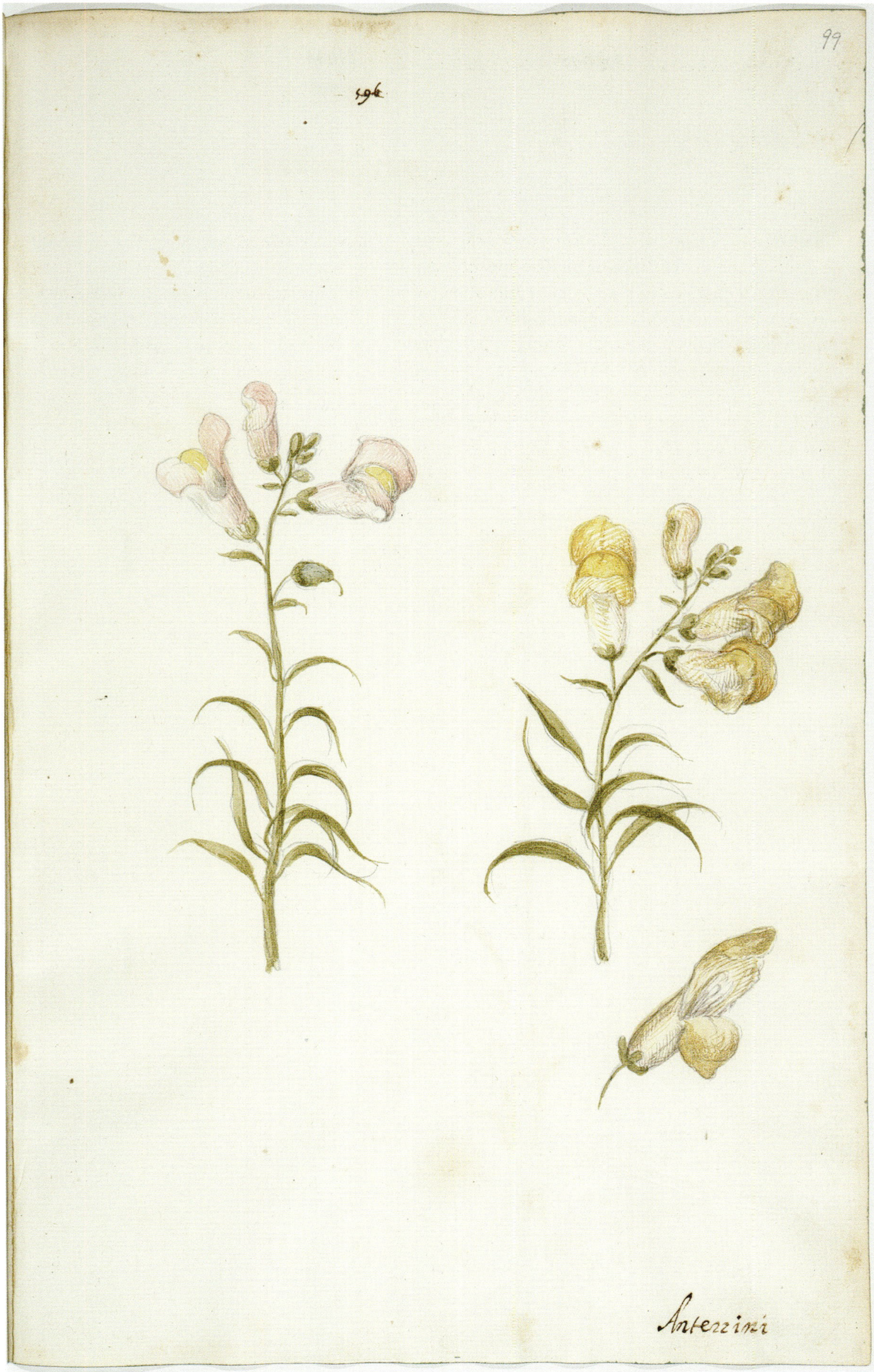
99
596
Anterrini

100. Snapdragon, *Antirrhinum majus* L. cv.

Erbario Miniato, fol. 100 (RL 27790)

Watermark: Eagle 19

NUMBERING: *597*

ANNOTATION: *ANTIRRHINO*

This drawing shows the curving stem of a white snapdragon (see **98**), together with two details of a flower seen from above and laterally. The stem is thick, smooth and erect, with two small branches bearing long, narrow, sessile leaves. The flowers at the apex have short peduncles and small, toothed calyxes. The bilabial corolla is white with splashes of yellow at the opening of the throat. The stamens and pistils are not shown, except in the two immature capsules at the base of the inflorescence whose corollas have fallen, leaving the calyx and persisting stylus.

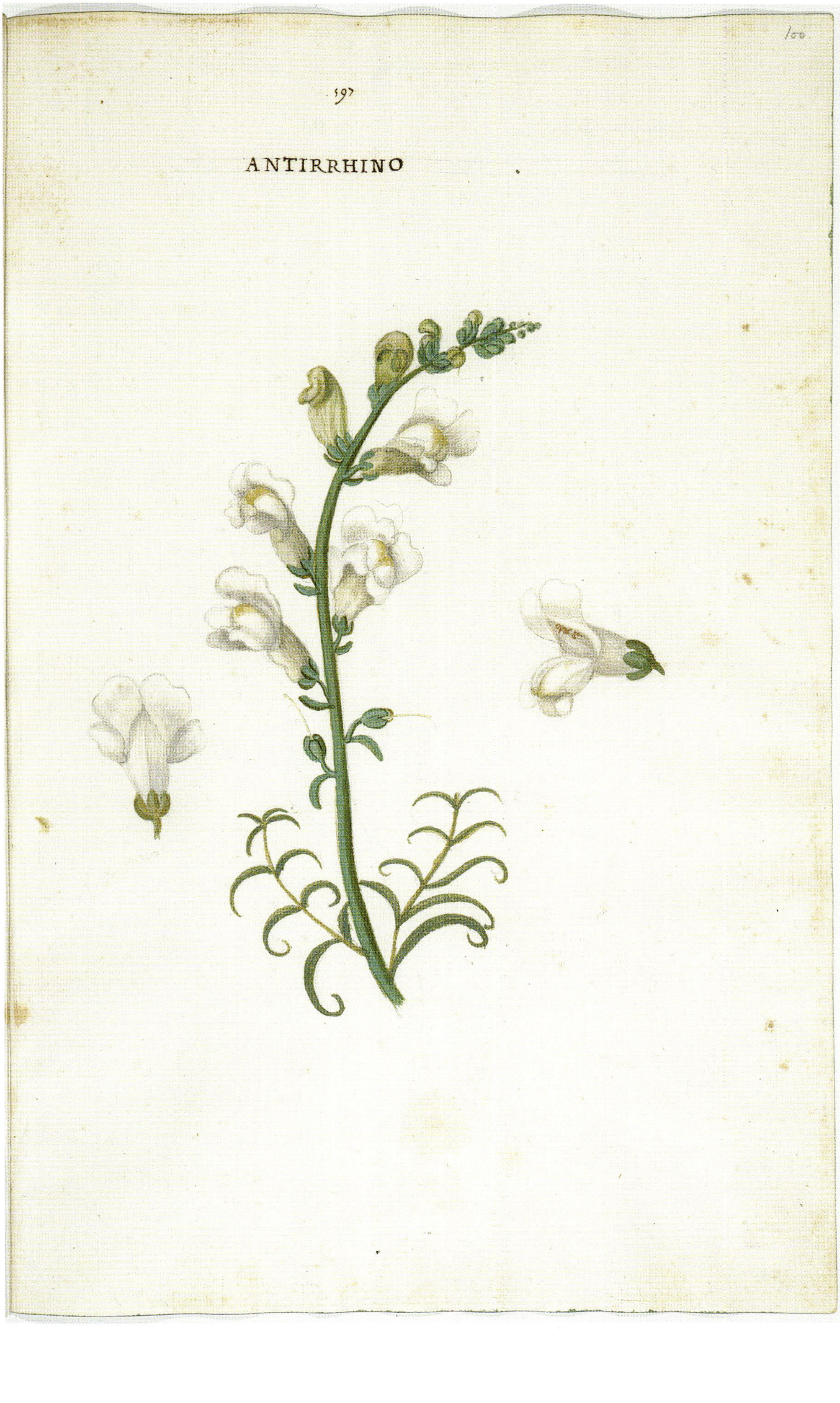
100
597
ANTIRRHINO

101. Red hemp-nettle, *Galeopsis angustifolia* Ehrh. ex Hoffm.

Erbario Miniato, fol. 101 (RL 27791)

Watermark: Eagle 18

NUMBERING: *598*

ANNOTATION: *Antirrhino terzo* ('Third antirrhinum'). [From Mattioli 1568, p. 1257]

The hemp-nettle, a member of the family Lamiaceae, is common in Europe and has become naturalized in the rest of the world. An invasive weed, it flourishes in arid, stony, uncultivated terrain at altitudes from sea level to 1,600m.

This drawing shows the entire plant with its root system. The smooth, slender, erect stem bears opposite, lanceolate, linear leaves with broadly toothed margins and new leaves growing from the base of each pair. The three flowers are arranged in a loose whorl; two are in full bloom while the third is still closed. The calyxes, which are one-fifth the length of the corollas, are not clearly depicted; the artist shows them growing from short peduncles, though they are actually sessile. The bilabial corolla is bright pink; its upper lip is hood-like in form, while the lower one is divided into three lobes. Beneath the upper lip, the tips of the flower's yellow anthers are just visible. The root system consists of a taproot with hair-like branches.

In the *Discorsi* four types of 'Antirrhino' are illustrated. Cesi identifies this plant with the third of these, illustrated on p. 1257, which actually shows the dwarf snapdragon, *Chaenorrhinum minus*.

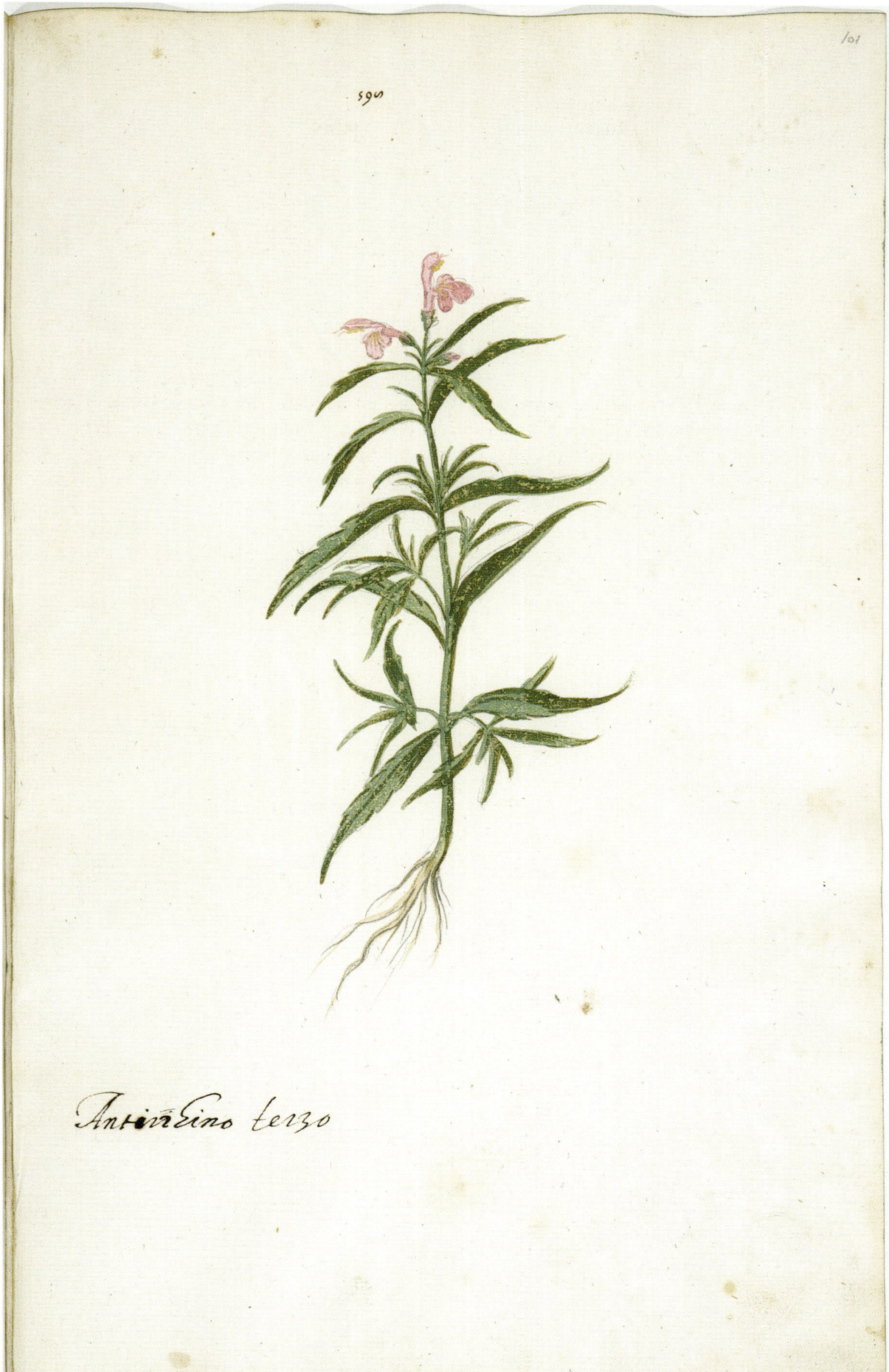
101
590
Antirrino terzo

102. Maidenhair fern, *Adiantum capillus-veneris* L.

Erbario Miniato, fol. 102 (RL 27792)

Watermark: Eagle 14

NUMBERING: *599*

ANNOTATION: *Lo Adianto, overo Politricho, detto vulgarmente Capelvenere, / giova la decotione del'herba. beuta. agli. stretti de petto, a' coloro / che malagevolmente rispirano, a' idifetti de milza, al trabo= / cco di fiele. al' orina retenuta, rompe le pietre ristagna il / corpo. conferisce ai morsi de i, serpi: bevesi nel vino p*[*er*] *il / catarro, che discende dallo stomaco, provoca i mestui, rista= / gna li sputi del sangue. impiastrasi lerba cruda su i, morsi de / le serpe. fa rinascere i capelli cascati, risolve le scrofole: / fatta bulire nella liscia molifica* [M: *mondifica*] *la farfalla* [M: *farfarella*], *e' el ulcere del capo / fattene untione con ladano. isopo. olio mirtino. di gigli, e' vino, / prohibisce il cascare de i, capelli, fa il medesimo la decotione / fatta nella liscia, e' nel vino, e' infusa, piantasi ~~vi~~ ne i pascoli / p*[*er*] *le pecore.* 1260. ('*Adianto* or *Politricho*, popularly called Hair of Venus. The decoction of the plant when drunk is useful for constrictions of the chest in those with breathing trouble, for spleen problems, for excess bile and for urine retention. It breaks up kidney stones, sets bodily fluids and heals snake bites; drunk in wine it is good for catarrh descending from the stomach. It induces menstruation and stays the coughing up of blood. The raw plant is applied to snake bites. It makes hair grow back again, and resolves scrofulas. Boiled in lye it clears dandruff and ulcers on the head. An ointment made with laudanum, hyssop, myrtle- and lily-oil and wine prevents hair from falling out. An infusion of the decoction made in lye and wine has the same effect. It is grown in meadows for sheep. 1260.'). [From Mattioli 1568, pp. 1259–61]

The maidenhair fern is a perennial of the family Adiantaceae, common in temperate and tropical zones of Africa, Europe and America, on damp limestone formations from sea level to an altitude of 1,500m. This delicate drawing shows the dark brown midrib with its fronds of tiny leaflets on either side. The leaflets vary in form from round to rhomboid to fan-shaped, with irregular incisions on their distal margins.

The Greeks dedicated this plant to Venus (hence its specific epithet and the popular name given in the annotation), and in the Middle Ages it was associated with the Virgin Mary, giving names such as Madonna's hair, Virgin's hair or the current maidenhair. The generic name *Adiantum* comes from the Greek αδίαντος (*adiantos*), 'unwetted', because the leaves repel water and drops of rain or dew roll off the surface. In the seventeenth century a syrup made from the plant was added to hot tea and milk to create a drink known as the *bavarese*, a popular remedy for respiratory illnesses (Cattabiani 1996, p. 354), and the leaves were used to prepare cough medicines, emollients and expectorants. Following the doctrine of signatures, the maidenhair fern also offered a remedy against hair loss.

599

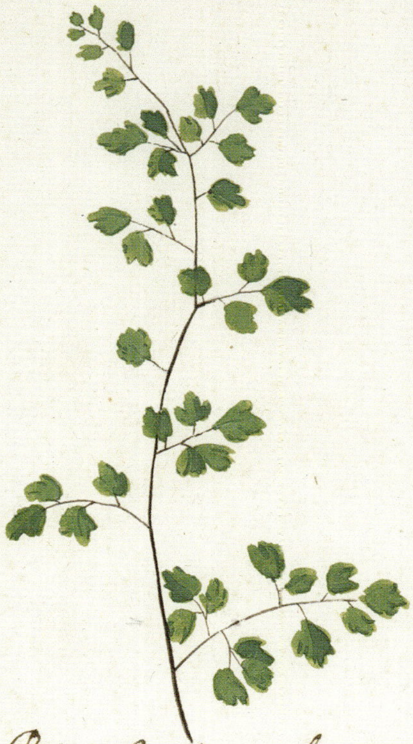

Lo Adianto. ouero Politricco, detto uulgarmente Capeluenere,
gioua la decotione del' herba. beuta. agli stretti de petto, a' coloro
che malageuolmente rispirano, et a' i difetti de milza, al trabo=
cco di fiele. al' orina retenuta, rompe le pietre ristagna il
corpo. conferisce ai morsi de i, serpi: beuesi nel uino p il
catarro, che discende dallo stomaco, prouoca i mestrui, rista=
gna li sputi del sangue. impiastrasi lerba cruda su i, morsi de
le serpe. fa rinascere i capelli cascati, risolue le scrofole.
fatta bulire nella liscia mortifica la forfalla, e' l' ulcere del capo,
fattene untione con ladano. isopo. olio mirtino. di gigli, e' uino,
prohibisce il cascare de i, capelli fa il medesimo la decotione
fatta nella liscia, e' nel uino, e' infusa, piantosi ~~uine~~ ne i passoli
p le pecore. . 1260.

103. Wall rue, *Asplenium ruta-muraria* L.

Erbario Miniato, fol. 103 (RL 27793)

Watermark: Crown 5

NUMBERING: *600*

ANNOTATION: *Paronichia overo cape[l] / venere bianco.* ('*Paronichia* or white hair of Venus.')

This tiny drawing depicts the wall rue, a perennial fern of the family Aspleniaceae found in the temperate zones of Europe, North America and Asia. It thrives in cool, damp areas, particularly in the cracks of walls (especially of calcareous stone), from sea level to an altitude of 2,400m. Each frond is made up of a slender green central rib bearing two to three symmetrical pairs of rounded, trilobed leaflets. The rhizome consists of a mass of black, hair-like roots.

Since antiquity various species belonging to the genus *Asplenium* were considered to be remedies against spleen. Like the maidenhair fern (**102**), the wall rue was also thought to prevent baldness.

Mattioli illustrates a wall rue on p. 1095, in Dioscorides' chapter on the 'Paronicchia'. The placing of this drawing in the *Erbario* between representations of *Adiantum capillus-veneris* (p. 1260 in the *Discorsi*) and *Asplenium trichomanes* (p. 1261), however, and the short annotation, suggest that Cesi thought that the plant was equivalent to Mattioli's second type of 'adianto' or 'capelvenere' (see **102**), the 'white' one (p. 1262).

600
103
Paronichia ouero cape
uenere bianco.

104. Maidenhair spleenwort, *Asplenium trichomanes* L.

Erbario Miniato, fol. 104 (RL 27794)

Watermark: Eagle 14

NUMBERING: *601*

ANNOTATION: *Trichomanne e' de la medesima natura che e' ell' Adianto. / overo politricho, o' Capel venere. 1261.* ('*Trichomanne* has the same nature as *Adianto*, that is *politricho* or hair of Venus. 1261.'). [From Mattioli 1568, p. 1261]

The maidenhair spleenwort is a perennial fern of the family Aspleniaceae, common in temperate regions on rocks and walls, at altitudes from sea level to 500m. It was considered, like maidenhair fern (**102**) and wall rue (**103**), to be a remedy against hair loss. The name 'Trichomanes' is the Latinized form of the Greek term τριχομανές (*trichomanes*) introduced by Theophrastus, from the Greek τρίχ (*trich*), 'hair', and μανός (*manos*), 'sparse'.

The dark central rib is lined with oval leaflets growing on very short petioles. The frond on the right is seen from below, showing the plant's sporangia – Mattioli's illustration of the 'Trichomane' also shows the underside of a frond.

601

104

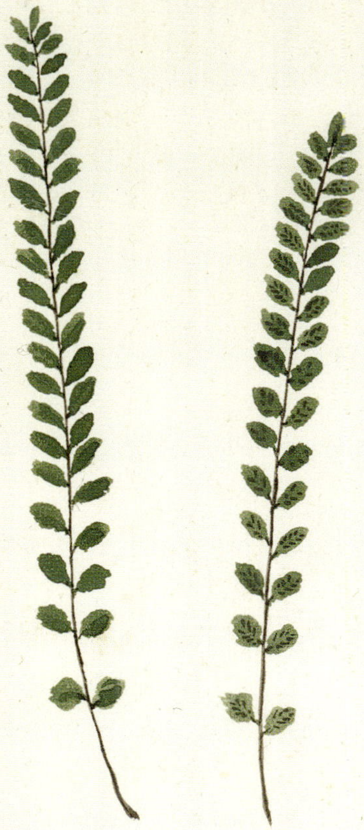

Tricomanne é de la medesima natura che é ell' Adianto. ouero politricco, ó Capel uenere. 1261.

105. Rough cocklebur, *Xanthium strumarium* L.

Erbario Miniato, fol. 105 (RL 27795)

NUMBERING: *602*

ANNOTATION: *Xanthio il succo de il suo frutto. fa negri i, capelli, / il seme se impiastra in su le posteme. 1263* ('*Xanthio*. The juice of its fruit makes hair black. The seed is applied to abscesses. 1263'). [From Mattioli 1568, pp. 1262–3]

The rough cocklebur is an annual of the family Asteraceae, growing all over the world on uncultivated soil, often close to the sea. The stem here is erect and branching; the ovate-triangular leaves have three distinct lobes, toothed margins and a prominent central vein, and grow from petioles as long as the leaves themselves. Each branch ends in three to five capitulums; the spiny pods with their characteristic apical beaks have been carefully drawn.

The generic name derives from the Greek ξανθόν (*xanthon*), 'yellow', because a dye of this colour could be extracted from the leaves. The rough cocklebur was also used to dye hair, and to treat scrofula and bronchial infections.

105.

602

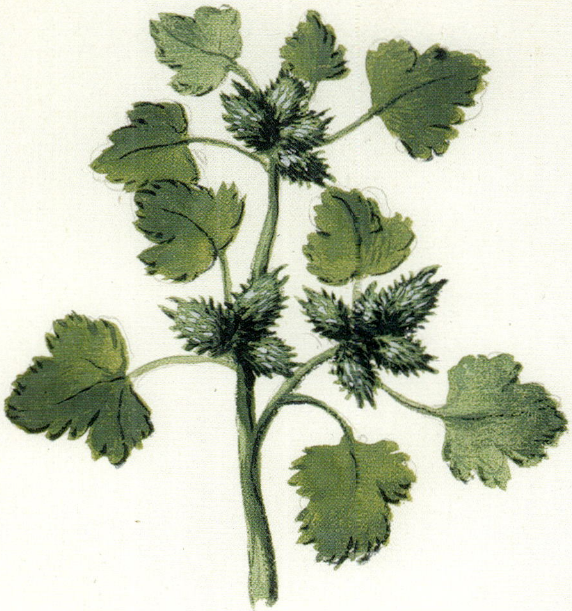

Xanthio il succo de il suo frutto. fa negri i capelli, il seme se impiastra in su le posteme. 1263

106. Drooping brome or downy chess, *Bromus tectorum* L.

Erbario Miniato, fol. 106 (RL 27796)

Watermark: Fleur de lys 49

NUMBERING: *603*

ANNOTATION: *fenice.; Egilopa, impiastrata lerba con farina, giova alle fistole / lagrimali, risolve le durezze, .1265.* ('*Fenice; Egilopa*. The plant applied with flour is beneficial against tear-gland fistulas. It resolves hardnesses. 1265.'). [From Mattioli 1568, pp. 1264–5]

The drooping brome is a herbaceous annual of the family Poaceae. It is common in temperate areas of Europe, Asia and Africa, growing in arid and uncultivated areas from sea level to an altitude of a few hundred metres. This specimen has a slender erect stalk and short linear leaves. The panicle is reflexed and ends in brown spikes growing from short peduncles. The spikelets have awns that are twice the length of the spikes. The roots are slender and bundled.

The annotation cites p. 1265 of the *Discorsi*, where the second of the two types of 'Egilopa' is illustrated (see also **107** for the name Egilopa/ Aegilops). That woodcut depicts ovate goatgrass, *Aegilops geniculata*, however, and not drooping brome.

Fenice.

Egilopa, impiastrata lerba con farina, gioua alle fistole lagrimali, risolue le durezze, .1265.

107. A form of goatgrass, *Aegilops neglecta* Req. ex Bertol.

Erbario Miniato, fol. 107 (RL 27797)

NUMBERING: *604*

ANNOTATION: *Unaltro Egilope. 1265* ('Another *Egilope*. 1265'). [From Mattioli 1568, p. 1265]

This drawing shows a stem of *Aegilops neglecta*, a herbaceous annual of the family Poaceae. It is common around the Mediterranean in dry pastures and uncultivated land to an altitude of 600m. The stem of the plant is slightly curved, and the leaf blade is slender, linear and fairly short. At the apex of the culm is a spike composed of three spikelets with slightly swollen, empty lemmas terminating in numerous reflexed awns.

The generic name *Aegilops* derives from the Greek αιγιλώπιον (*aigilopion*), an unidentified bearded grass. Such grasses are considered a nuisance by farmers, as is reflected in such popular names as *frumeint dal diavel* ('devil's grain') in Emilia and *frumentu saracinescu* ('Saracen grain') or *frumintieddi di turchi* ('Turks' grain') in Sicily. As in **106**, the annotation cites p. 1265 of the *Discorsi*, where 'Egilopa II' is illustrated, though that plate corresponds to the ovate goatgrass, *Aegilops geniculata*.

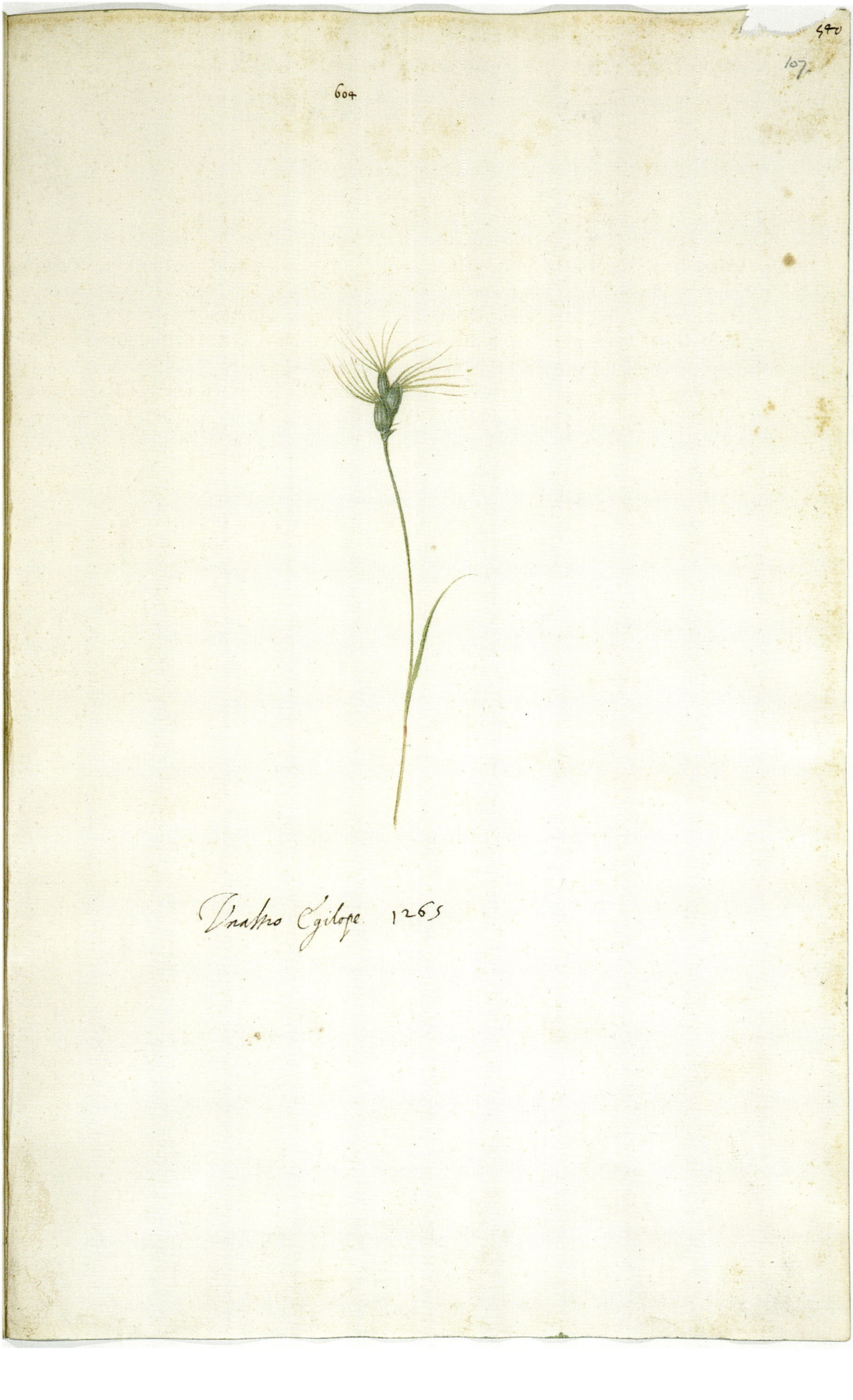
590
107
604
Vnaltro Egilope 1265

108. Montpellier milk vetch, *Astragalus monspessulanus* L.

Erbario Miniato, fol. 108 (RL 27798)

Watermark: Eagle 15

NUMBERING: *605*

ANNOTATION: *Poligala, 1267.; Questa beuta fa abondare / il latte.* ('*Poligala*, 1267. When drunk this increases the flow of milk.'). [From Mattioli 1568, p. 1267]

The milk vetch is a herbaceous perennial of the family Fabaceae, common around the Mediterranean on arid hillsides and in pastures at altitudes between 500m and 1,400m. From the plant's short stem spring three slender branches, each bearing ten or eleven pairs of leaves. The spike-like inflorescence is made up of numerous pink flowers with butterfly-like corollas (typical of the Fabaceae). Another long peduncle carries three erect, curved pods with reddish calyxes and short peduncles. The plant has a thick, tapering, sparsely branched taproot.

The Greeks used the word αστράγαλο (*astragalo*) to refer to a number of shrubs whose roots supposedly resembled the astragalus, a bone in the tarsus of the foot. The genus *Astragalus* includes about 1,500 species, most of them found in the steppes of Asia and Europe. Many plants belonging to the genus (although not *A. monspessulanus*) produce gum tragacanth, used by artists and by pharmacists in making lotions and ointments.

The note identifies the plant as the 'Poligala' illustrated on p. 1267 of the *Discorsi*, but that is actually the crown vetch, *Coronilla coronata*. Botanists of the period did not have a clear idea what Dioscorides' 'Poligala' was. Mattioli wrote that the plant depicted in his work had been gathered by the herbalist Francesco Calzolari of Verona; in an appendix to his *Compendium de plantis* (1571), Mattioli included an account of the plants collected by Calzolari on Mount Baldo (see Arber 1986, p. 279). However, he admitted his uncertainty as to whether it was the same species as the 'Poligala' described by Dioscorides, who stated that the plant was as high as a man's palm, with fronds similar to the lentil, and a bitter taste.

605

108

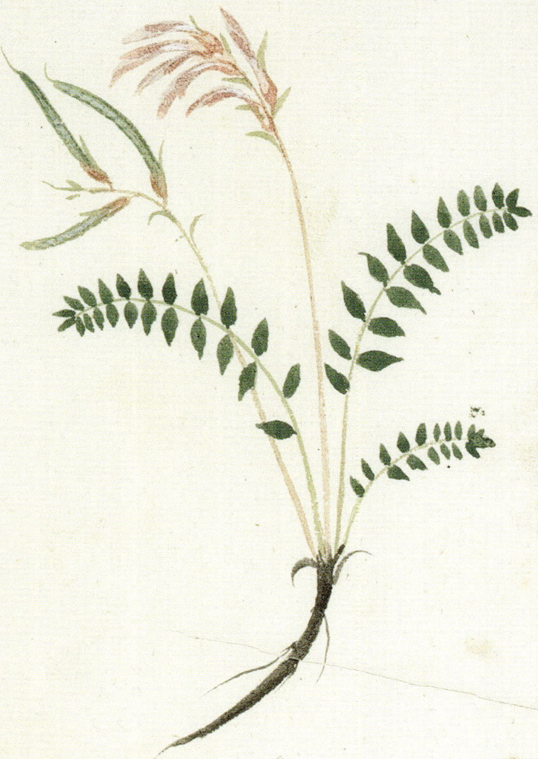

Poligala, 1267.

Questa herba. fa abondare il latte,

109. Common toadflax, *Linaria vulgaris* Mill.

Erbario Miniato, fol. 109 (RL 27799)

NUMBERING: *606*

ANNOTATION: *Osiride, la decotione beuta sana il trabocco / del fiele, 1268.* ('*Osiride*. The decoction when drunk cures excess bile. 1268.'). [From Mattioli 1568, p. 1268]

This common toadflax is a herbaceous perennial of the family Scrophulariaceae, native to Europe and temperate regions of Asia, and naturalized in other parts of the world. It grows in uncultivated soil at altitudes from sea level to 1,500m. An infusion made from the plant was used to treat inflammation of the gall ducts or intestinal dysfunction.

This specimen has a slender, erect stem bearing numerous long, narrow leaves, verticillate near the base and alternate near the apex. The stem terminates in a short raceme of flowers, yellow with light orange blotches at the swelling of the throat. The corolla of the toadflax (like that of the snapdragon, **98–100**) resembles a mask and terminates in a long spur. The genus *Linaria* owes its name to fact that its leaves are similar to those of the genus *Linum*.

606

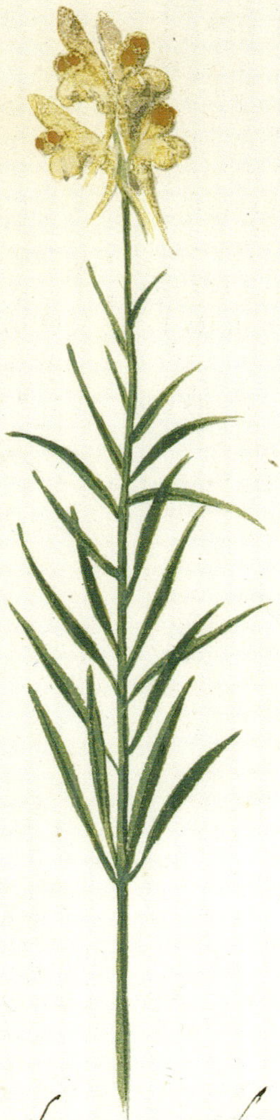

Osiride. la decotione beuta sana il trabocco del fiele. 1268.

110. Rough greenbrier, *Smilax aspera* L.

Erbario Miniato, fol. 110 (RL 27800)

Watermark: Fleur de lys 49

NUMBERING: *607*

ANNOTATION: *Smilace Aspra, overo, spetie de salsapariglia, da alcuni in Tosca= / na, Hedra spinosa, e' da altri Rovo cervino,: le fronde e' gli acini / beuti avante e' doppo. sonno antidotto contra i, veleni, .1270.* ('Bitter smilax or type of sarsaparilla, called by some in Tuscany spiny ivy, and by others deer bramble. The leaves and the berries, drunk before and after, are an antidote for poisons. 1270.'). [From Mattioli 1568, pp. 1269–70]

The rough greenbrier is a perennial liana of the family Smilacaceae. It is common in North Africa, Asia and Europe, typically growing near oak groves, in thickets and in the underbrush beside fallen trees at altitudes from sea level up to 1,200m.

The stem is slender, contorted and covered with spines. From its nodes grow alternate leaves, broadly cordate with smooth margins, long petioles and stipules that take the form of long tendrils. Both the male and female inflorescences are shown, the former composed of clusters of two to three tiny white flowers growing from the nodes of a short twig, the latter of mature red berries arranged singly or in groups or two or three.

110.

607

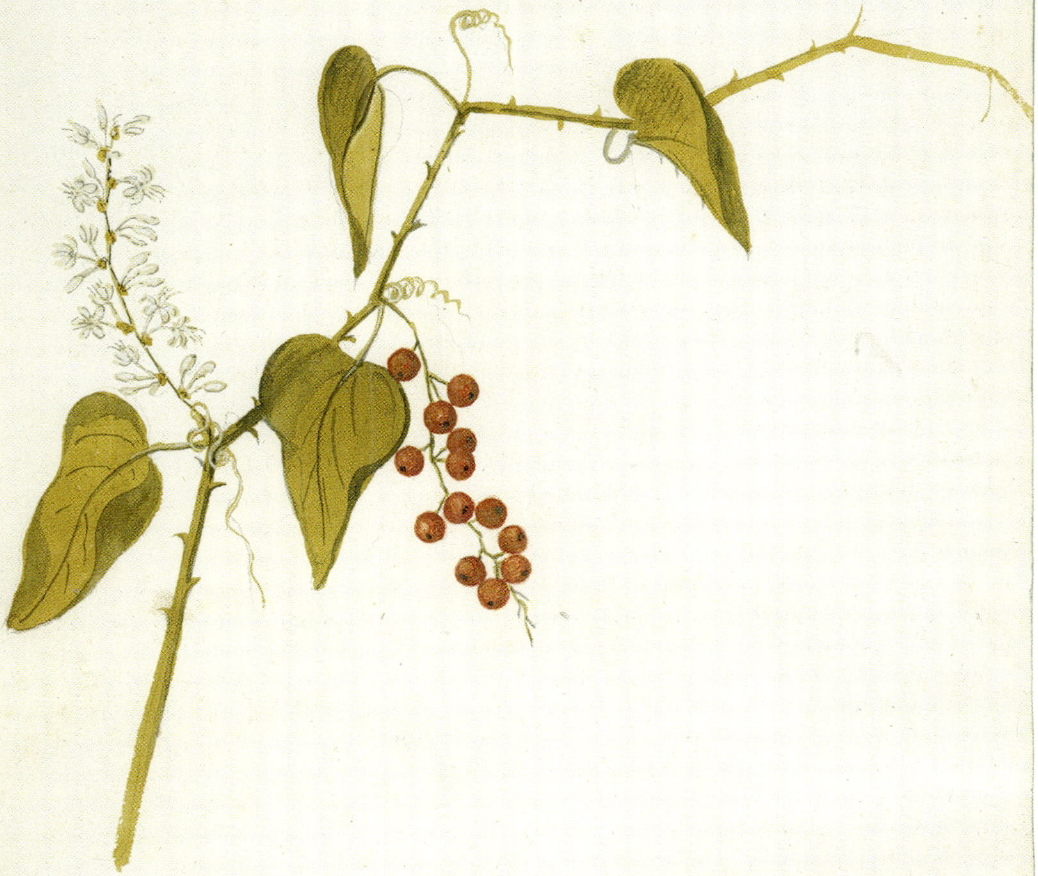

Smilace Aspra, ouero, spetie de salsapariglia, da alcuni in Tosca-
na, Hedra spinosa, é da altri Rouo ceruino;: le fronde é gli acini
beuti auante é doppo. sono antidotto contra i, ueleni, .1270.

111. Great bindweed, *Calystegia sylvatica* (Waldst. & Kit. 1806–12) Griseb. ssp. *fraterniflora* (Mack. & Bush) Brummitt

Erbario Miniato, fol. 111 (RL 27801)

NUMBERING: *608*

ANNOTATION: *velucchio magiore* ('great bindweed')

The great bindweed is a perennial climbing vine of the family Convolvulaceae, widespread in Europe and temperate areas of Asia, and naturalized in North America, Australia and elsewhere in the southern hemisphere. It grows along hedgerows and in uncultivated areas at altitudes from sea level to 800m. The stem is slender, smooth and sinuous. The leaves are alternate and heart-shaped with smooth margins and dark veins. The petioles are short in the young leaves near the apex of the stem and longer in the mature leaves. Three flowers are shown, one wilted, one in full bloom and one still in the bud. The white corolla is funnel-shaped with five broad, barely indented lobes, borne on a long, sinuous floral peduncle. The pistil and stamens with their yellow anthers have been loosely sketched in the throat of the flower.

The name *Calystegia* is derived from the Greek κάλυξ (*kalyx*), 'calyx', and στέγος (*stegos*), 'cover', a reference to the unusual form of the bracts that completely envelop the calyx. The characteristics that distinguish the genus *Calystegia* from the more familiar *Convolvulus* are well defined, but plants of the two genera have often been confused and the properties of the former attributed to the latter. Like the hedge bindweed (*Calystegia sepium*), the leaves and root of this plant contain substances with medicinal properties that can act on the digestive system.

This plant is illustrated on p. 1272 of the *Discorsi* (where it is captioned 'Smilace liscia', smooth smilax). On p. 1270 Mattioli observed that Dioscorides' 'Smilace liscia' was identical with the plant known in Tuscany as 'Vilucchio maggiore', although Dioscorides' plant may in fact have been *Convolvulus sepium*. *Vilucchio maggiore* remains the Italian common name for the great bindweed.

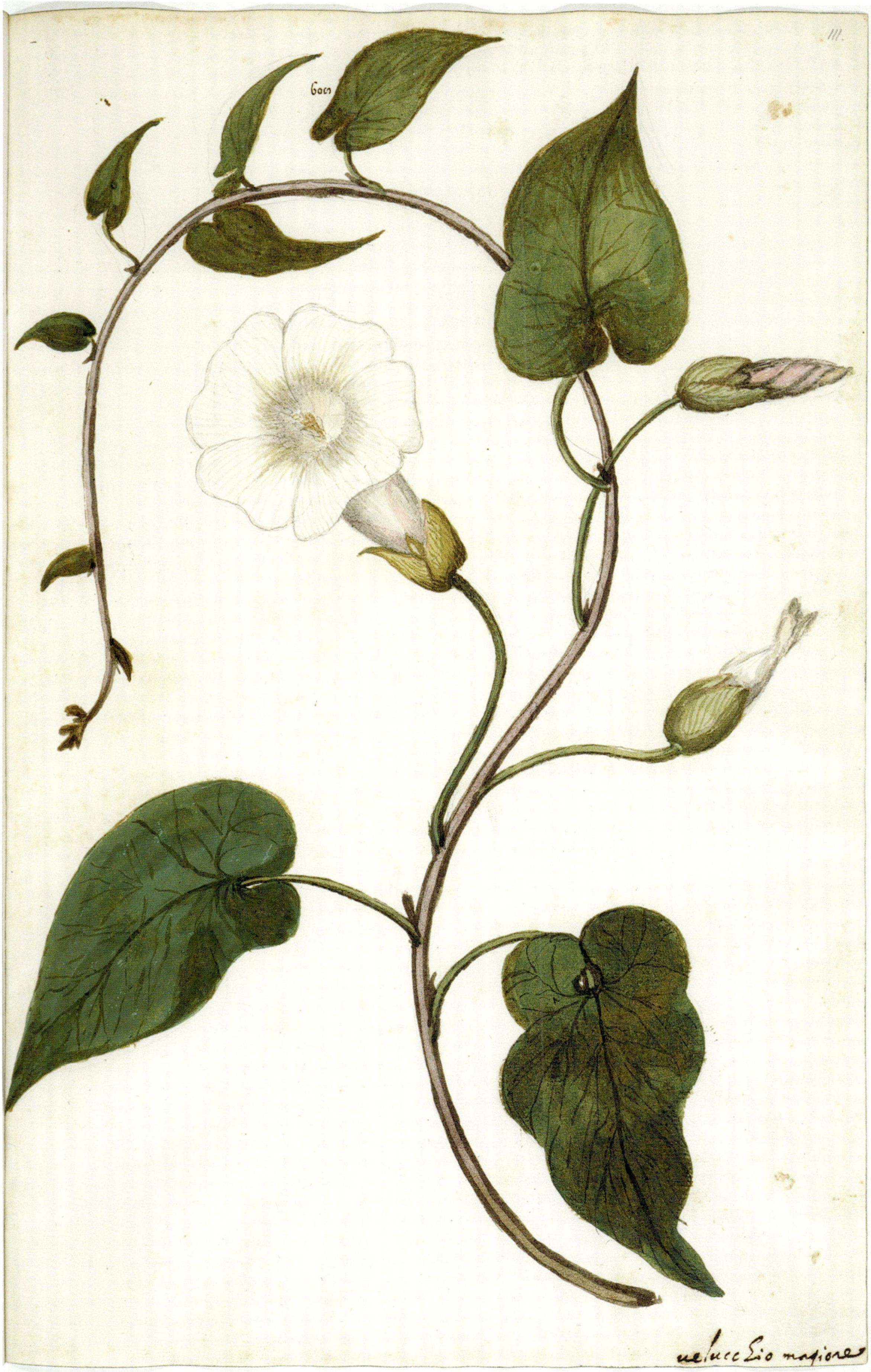
111.
velucchio magiore

112. Hop, *Humulus lupulus* L.

Erbario Miniato, fol. 112 (RL 27802)

NUMBERING: *609*

ANNOTATION: *lupolo solve un certo che di colora gialla, e' mondifica il sangue da quella, e' lo chi= / arifica, il suo siroppo beuto. rimuove il trabocchho del fiole. ma e' veramente gran cosa, / che cosi poco l'usano i medici de i tempi nostri, essendo egli medecina cosi buona / l'herba, e parimente il succho incorporato con polenta d'orzo, sana il dolore del / capo, causato p[er] umore calido. conferisce alla riscaldagione del fegato. e de lo sto= / maco, giova il suo siroppo alle febre CO~~R~~LERICHE. e' sanguigne ~~458~~ 1273; N°: 34* ('The hop resolves jaundice, purifying and clearing the blood. Drinking its syrup gets rid of excess bile. It is truly incredible that such an effective medicine should be so little used by the physicians of our time. The plant, as also its juice, incorporated with pearl barley, cures headaches caused by warm humours. It is beneficial to the functioning of the liver and stomach. Its syrup is effective against choleric fevers, and those of the blood. ~~458~~ 1273; No. 34'). [From Mattioli 1568, pp. 458, 1272–3]

The hop is a perennial liana of the family Cannabaceae, native to the northern hemisphere where it grows in damp forest glades and hedgerows at altitudes from sea level to 1,200m. The genus *Humulus* is composed of only two species, *H. lupulus* and *H. japonicus*. The name *Humulus* is believed to derive from *humlo* or *humlon*, an old Germanic word for the hop (Marzell 1972, cols 902–7). The epithet *lupulus* means 'small wolf', and is derived from a Latin vernacular name for the plant, *lupus salictarius*, or 'willow wolf', from its tendency to climb over willow trees.

The plant is an essential ingredient in the production of beer, imparting a bitter taste to the sweet malt obtained from barley, preventing acidic fermentation and serving to clarify the liquid by precipitating its albuminous substances. The female flower contains an oily alkaloid resin in its bracts that has long been used as a sedative. Stomach remedies and bitter tonics were also concocted from the plant.

Unlike most drawings in the *Erbario*, here the artist shows the plant harvested and bound together. The stems are slender, sinuous and covered with erect spines. The opposite leaves are palmate with three deep lobes, toothed margins and long petioles. The ovate-lanceolate stipules are not always visible.

The annotation is drawn entirely from Mattioli's discussion of the hop in his commentary on Dioscorides' chapter on the 'Smilace liscia' (see **111**). The mistaken citation of p. 458 is a reference to the similarly named 'lupino'.

609

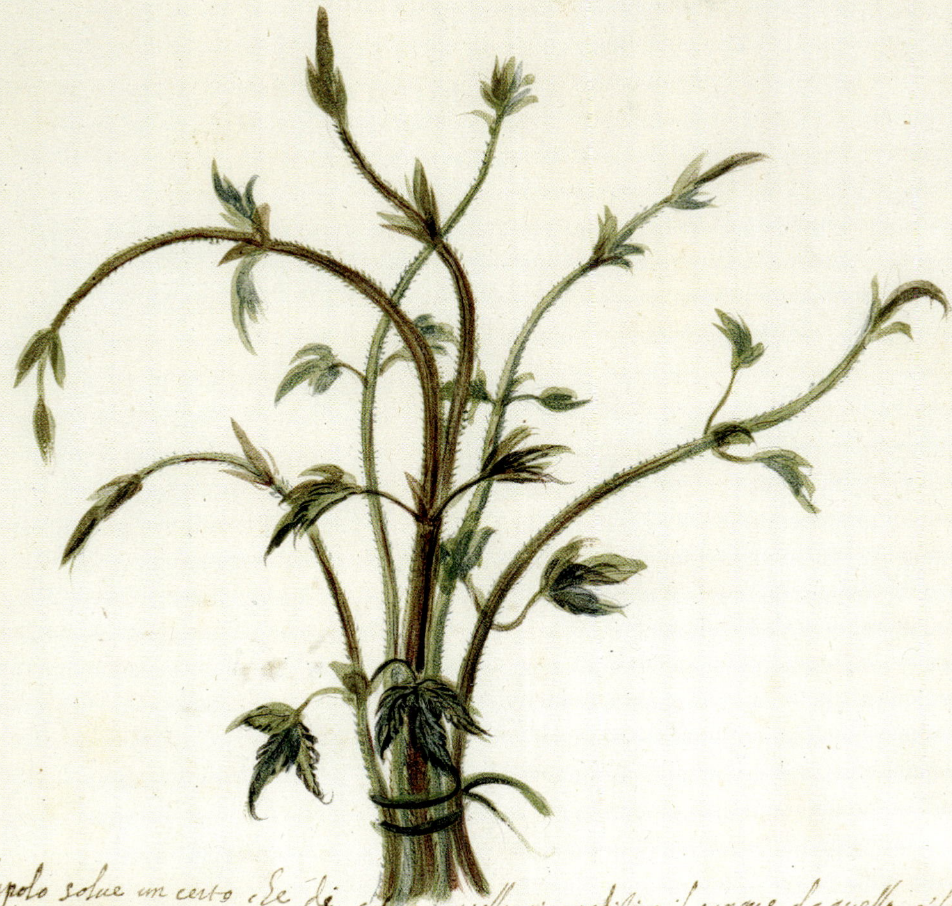

Lupolo solue un certo che di colora gialla, e' mondifica il sangue da quella, e lo chiarifica: il suo siroppo beuto. rimuoue il trabocco del fiele. ma e veramente gran cosa, che cosi poco l'usano i medici de i tempi nostri, essendo egli medecina cosi buona. L'herba, e parimente il succo incorporato con polenta d'orzo, sana il dolore del capo, causato per humore calido. conferisce alla riscaldagione del fegato. e de lo stomaco, giova il suo siroppo alle febre COLERICHE. e sanguigne. ~~458~~ 1273

N.o 34

113. Butcher's broom, *Ruscus aculeatus* L.

Erbario Miniato, fol. 113 (RL 27803)

Watermark: Crown 46

NUMBERING: *610*

ANNOTATION: *Fiore del Rusco.; il Rusco. chiamato da i Greci Mirto salvatico, e volgarmente a' Perugia / picchasorci: le frondi e parimente i frutti. beuti nel vino, fanno orinare, / provocano i mestrui, rompano le pietre de la ƀ vescica, giovano alla / distilatione de la orina, sanano il dolore del capo. il traboccho del' fiele, / mangansi i suoi gamboncelli, quando sonno freschi, in luogho de asparrac*[–]; *.1274*. ('Flower of butcher's broom; butcher's broom, called by the Greeks wild myrtle, and popularly in Perugia mouse-pricker. Drunk in wine, the leaves, as also the fruit, induce urination and menstruation, break down bladder stones, are beneficial in purifying urine, cure headaches and excess bile. Its stems may be eaten, when young, in place of asparagus. 1274.'). [From Mattioli 1568, p. 1274]

The butcher's broom is a perennial rhizomatous plant of the family Ruscaceae. It grows in groves of oak and other deciduous trees in the Mediterranean, at altitudes from sea level to 600m. The slender, tapering stem shown here, branching near its base, is lined with cladophylls, branches resembling leaves (see the horse-tongue, **97**) that are oval in form and terminate in short spines. Many carry a mature red berry. At lower left are details of two smaller cladophylls, each bearing a flower composed of six small blue-green tepals. The rhizome of the plant is not shown.

Because of its spines, and the red berries that appear during the winter, the butcher's broom had the same symbolic associations as the holly plant. Its leaves provided a defence against evil spirits while the colourful berries represented the rebirth of the sun at the winter solstice and a positive omen for the new year. The rhizome was ground and used to prepare infusions with diuretic, laxative, vasoconstrictive or anti-inflammatory properties.

The annotation is mostly drawn from Dioscorides' chapter on the 'Rusco' in the *Discorsi* (p. 1274). Mattioli added that the plant was known in Tuscany as 'pungitopo' or 'mouse-pricker' (still an Italian common name for the butcher's broom) because it was placed over salted meat to protect it from mice (as was holly: see **161**). The *Erbario* notes, however, that in Perugia the plant was called 'picchasorci' (also 'mouse-pricker'). Heckius had spent several years in Perugia (cf. **242a**), and Cesi's residence at Acquasparta was 40km south of the city, perhaps explaining why the annotation should differ from Mattioli's text on this point.

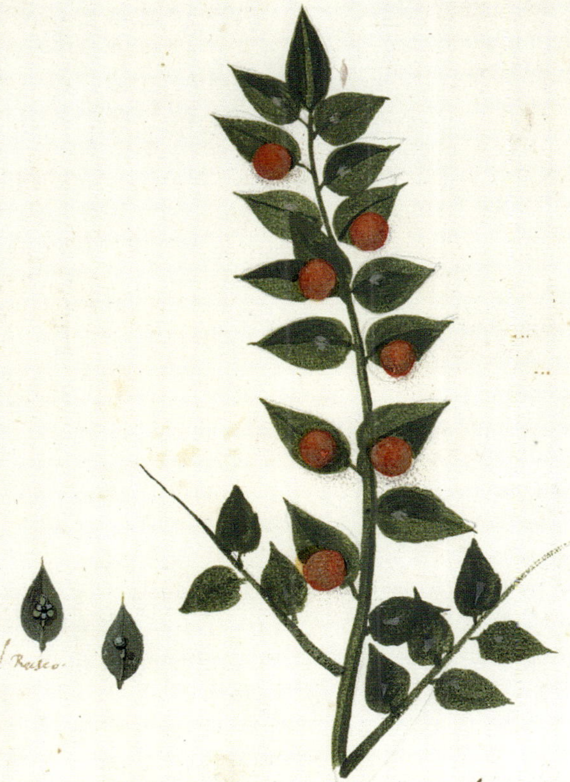

il Rusco. chiamato da i Greci Mirto saluatico; & uolgarmente a' Perugia piccasorci: le frondi e parimente i frutti. beuti nel uino, fanno orinare, prouocano i mestrui, rompano le pietre de la uescica, giouano alla distillatione de la orina. sanano il dolore del capo. il trabocco del' fiele, manganzi i suoi gambarcelli, quando sono freschi, in luogo de asparagi.

. 1274 .

114. Black false helleborine, *Veratrum nigrum* L.

Erbario Miniato, fol. 114 (RL 27804)

NUMBERING: *611*

ANNOTATION: *Elleboro Bianco 1279* ('White hellebore 1279'). [From Mattioli 1568, p. 1279]

The black false helleborine is a perennial rhizomatous plant of the family Melanthiaceae, which grows in coppices and glades in Europe and Asia at altitudes from sea level to 1,400m. The leaf (shown greatly enlarged) is oval in form with smooth margins and prominent, parallel veins running along its length. The flowers are borne on a panicle that is branched near the base and covered with erect, patent hairs. The brownish-red corolla of the flower is composed of six tepals that bend downwards, completely exposing the flower's dark stamens.

The generic name *Veratrum* is derived from the Latin *verum* because it was believed that this plant could clear the mind and sharpen the intelligence. In reality the black false helleborine has the same toxic properties as the more common white hellebore (*Veratrum album*). Accidental poisoning may occur when the plant is confused with the gentian, which has similar but opposite leaves and is used in the preparation of tonic wines. The annotation mistakenly identifies the specimen as the 'white hellebore' illustrated by Mattioli, while labelling the specimen on the next folio 'black false hellebore' (though it is a *Helleborus foetidus*).

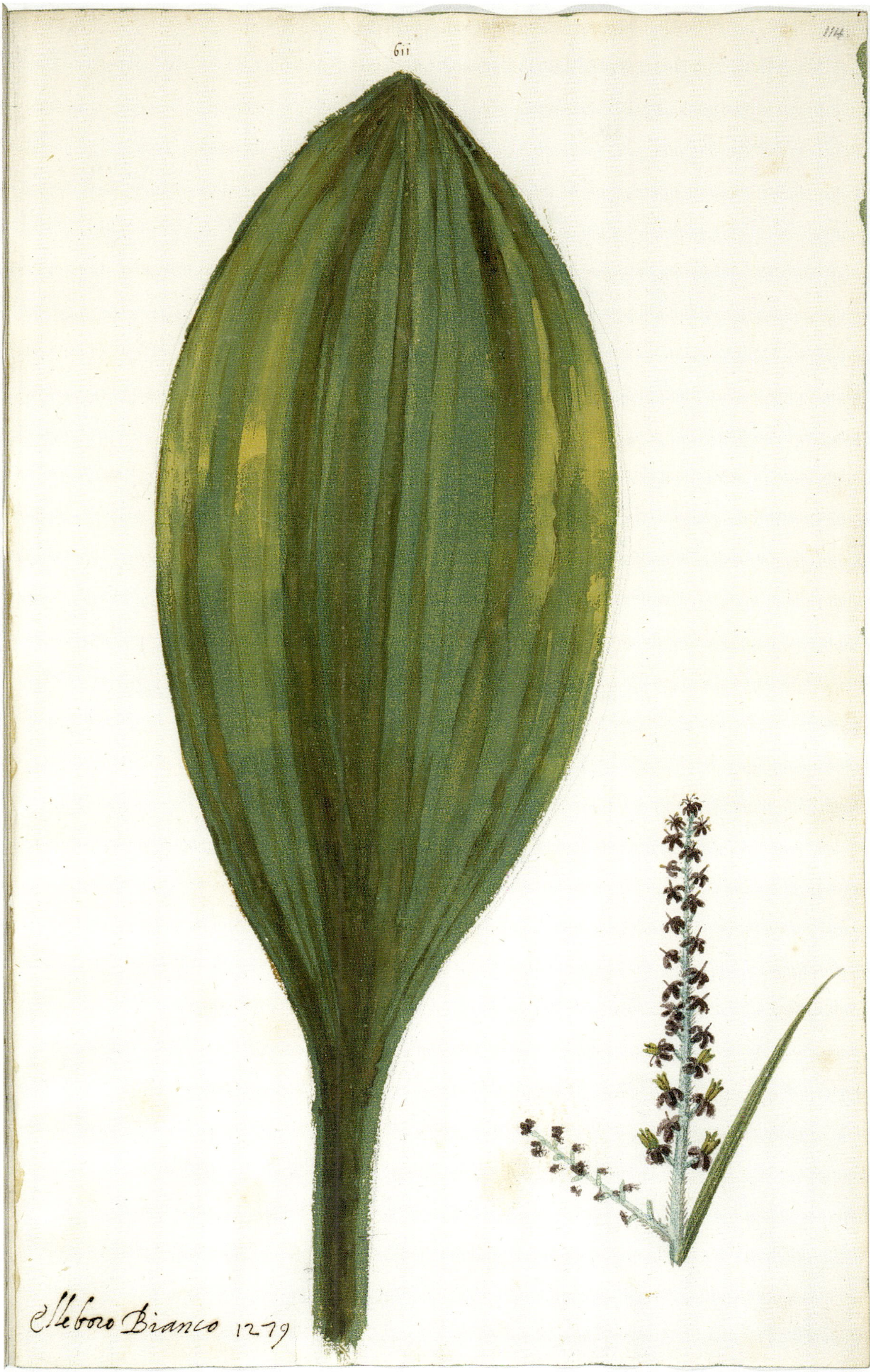
611
114
Elleboro Bianco 1279

115. Stinking hellebore, *Helleborus foetidus* L.

Erbario Miniato, fol. 115 (RL 27805)

NUMBERING: *612*

ANNOTATION: *Ellebro nero falso . 1280.; lo Ellebro nero si chiama Melampodio: Purga lo stomaco: solve la colera, e la flemma. / dato cosi solo. overo con scamonea. Giova al mal Caduco, a' i, malinconici, a' coloro che impa= / ziscano. a'i dolori delle giunture e a' i paralitici, Provoca aplicato disotto. i, mestrui, purga / le fistole. mettise p[er] la sordita nelle orechie. Unto con incenso, overo cera. et pece, e' olio / cidrino, sana la rogna; Mitiga i, dolori de i, denti, lavandosene la bocca con la sua / decotione, Mettisi utilmente' informa de impiastro. con farina de orzo, e' vino in su'l / ventre degli hidropici, piantato apresso alle radice de le vite, fa il vino purgativo.* ('False black hellebore. 1280. The black hellebore is called *Melampodio*. It purges the stomach, eliminates choler and phlegm when administered alone or with scammony. It is beneficial for epileptics, the melancholic, those going mad, for arthritic pains and paralysis. It induces menstruation when applied below, it clears fistulas. It is administered in the ears for deafness. Rubbed on with incense or wax, pitch and cedar oil, it heals scabies. Washing the mouth with its decoction relieves toothache. It is beneficial when placed as a poultice with barley flour and wine on the stomach of dropsy patients. Planted close to the roots of vines, it makes the wine purgative.'). [From Mattioli 1568, pp. 1280–2]

The stinking hellebore is a herbaceous perennial of the family Ranunculaceae. It is native to Europe, as far east as the Caucasus, growing along the forest edge at altitudes from sea level to 1,000m.

This unfinished drawing shows a specimen with an erect, tapering stem bearing four alternate leaves, deeply divided into eight or nine lobes with toothed margins. Near the apex are flowers carried on branching scapes that grow from lanceolate bracts. Each perianth is composed of five light green sepals with a faint reddish band near the base. Some of the flowers already bear maturing fruit that can be seen emerging from the sepals together with three follicles. At upper right are details of two flowers, one open and one closed.

There are some doubts regarding the identification of the 'black hellebore' described by Dioscorides and discussed by Mattioli. Dioscorides discussed just one 'black hellebore' which may be the Lenten rose, *Helleborus orientalis*. Mattioli, however, described three types of 'black hellebore' that could be distinguished by the colour of their flowers, purple, white, or green and yellow. He admitted, though, that he had never seen the purple variety and provided only two illustrations, of a Christmas rose (*Helleborus niger*) on p. 1280 and of a green hellebore (*Helleborus viridis*) on p. 1281.

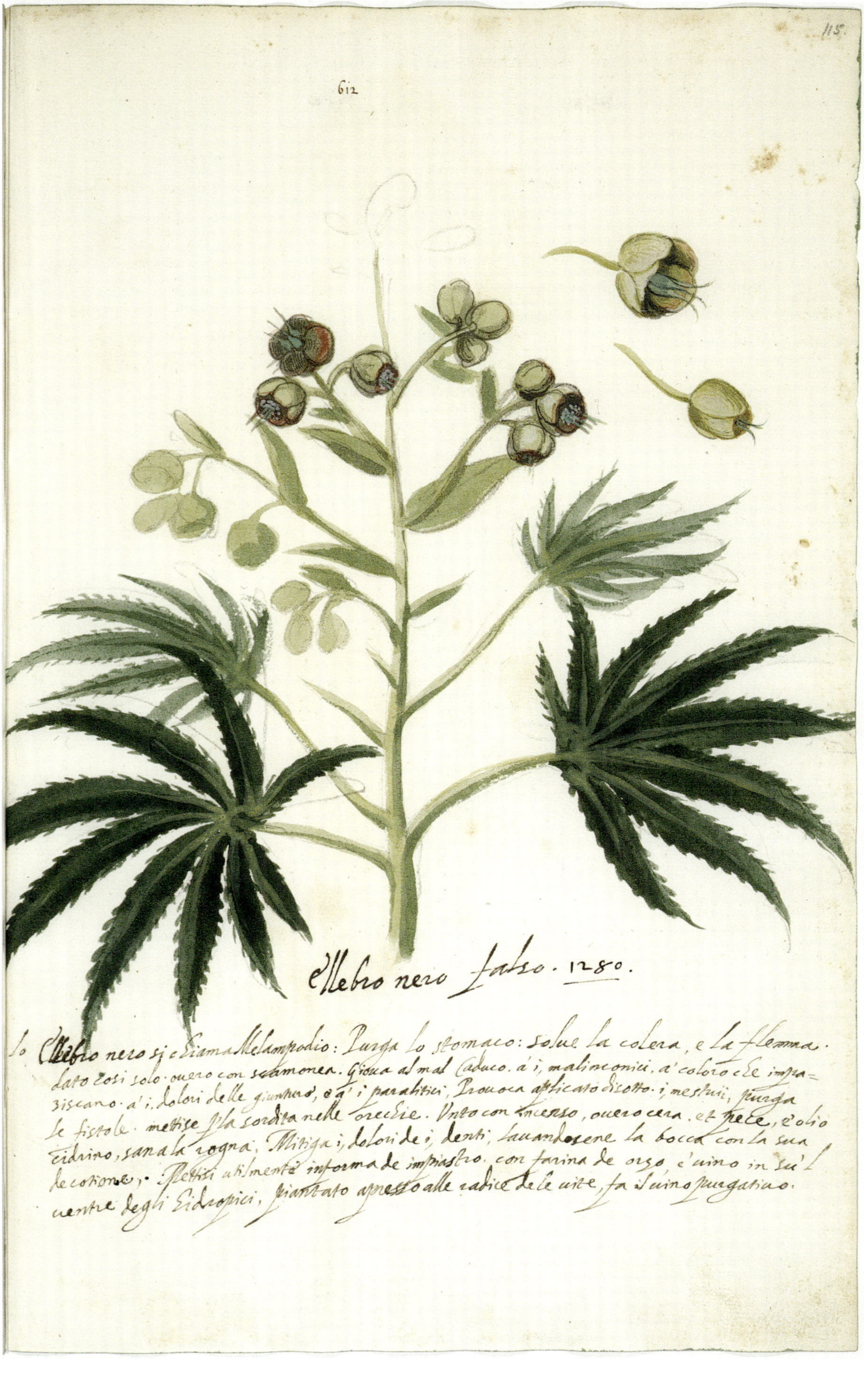

115.

612

Ellebro nero falso. 1280.

Lo Ellebro nero si chiama Melampodio: Purga lo stomaco: solue la colera, e la flemma.
dato cosi solo. ouero con scamonea. Gioua al mal Caduco. a' i, malinconici. a' coloro che impa=
ziscano. a' i. dolori delle giunture, e a' i paralitici, Prouoca applicato disotto. i mestrui, purga
le fistole. mettise per la sordita nelle orecchie. Vnto con incenso, ouero cera. et pece, e olio
cidrino, sana la rogna, Mitiga i, dolori de i, denti, lauandosene la bocca con la sua
decotione, . Mettisi utilmente in forma de impiastro. con farina de orzo, e uino in su'l
uentre degli Hidropici, piantato apresso alle radice dele uite, fa il uino purgatiuo.

116. Scented hellebore, *Helleborus odorus* Waldst. & Kit. 1809

Erbario Miniato, fol. 116 (RL 27806)

Watermark: Eagle 18

NUMBERING: *613*

ANNOTATION: *Fiore de Elebro nero vero, la cui virtù e' dove / si legge, Elebro nero falso, 1280.* ('Flower of the true black hellebore, whose properties are found where one reads false black hellebore, 1280.'). [From Mattioli 1568, p. 1280]

The scented hellebore is a perennial plant of the family Ranunculaceae, which grows in woodland throughout southern Europe from sea level to an altitude of 1,700m.

The specimen is shown from the front and from the side. The flower is composed of five broad, yellowish-green sepals with at their centre a number of stamens surrounding the pistils; it springs from the axil of a leafy bract that is divided into lobes with toothed margins. The annotation identifies the specimen as another 'black hellebore' – this time a 'true' one – and directs the reader to the drawing labelled 'false black hellebore' (**115**) for the plant's medicinal properties.

. 613

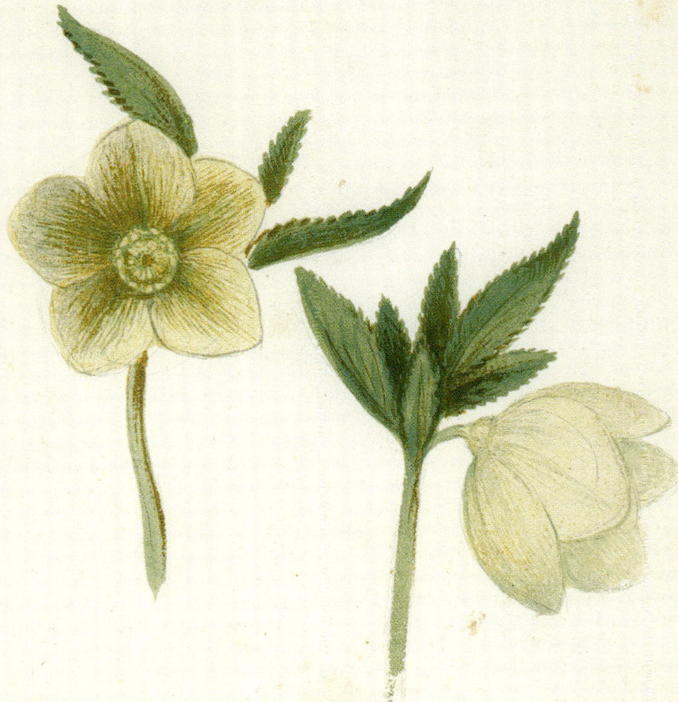

Fiore de Elebro nero. uero, la cui uirtù è doue
Si legge, Elebro nero falso. 1280.

117. Squirting cucumber, *Ecballium elaterium* (L.) A. Rich. 1824

Erbario Miniato, fol. 117 (RL 27807)

Watermark: Star 4

NUMBERING: *614*

ANNOTATION: *il succo de le fronde. del Cocomero salvatico. distilato nelle orecchie / ne cava il dolore. mettise ne i, chistieri che si fanno p*[*er*] *le sciatiche: lavandosi / con la sua decotione. li denti che doglino, purga senza molestare punto lo stomaco: / lavandosi le mano con il succo de i, zucarelli. o' questi pomi. guarisce i, / porri che nascono sule mano. cosa provata 1288.* ('The juice from the leaves of the squirting cucumber relieves earache when dropped in the ears. It is employed in enemas for treating sciatica. The decoction is used for rinsing aching teeth. It purges without irritating the stomach. Washing one's hands with the juice from the fruit heals the warts that develop on hands, a proven thing. 1288.'). [From Mattioli 1568, pp. 1288–9]

The squirting cucumber is a perennial plant of the family Cucurbitaceae. It is native to the Mediterranean region, and is usually found growing on wasteland, particularly along the coast but also at altitudes of up to 800m. The stem is short, thick and covered with erect hairs. The leaves are triangular with irregular, toothed, undulating margins and long petioles that are also covered with erect hairs. A single female flower and an oval fruit are shown growing from the axil of the lowermost leaf. The flower has a long, thick peduncle which carries the ovary and a pale yellow corolla divided into five deep lobes.

The generic name *Ecballium* is derived from the Greek εκβάλλω (*ekballo*), 'to expel or throw out'. When mature the fruit falls to the ground, and from the hole in the mericarp where it was attached to the peduncle a liquid containing the seeds is sprayed out. The bitter pulp of the fruit (and in particular the juice of the unripe fruit) was used to prepare a laxative called *elaterio* (hence the specific epithet), and it is used today by Bedouins to treat jaundice. In the countryside around Siena the plant is still used to treat earache, an application mentioned in the annotation.

614

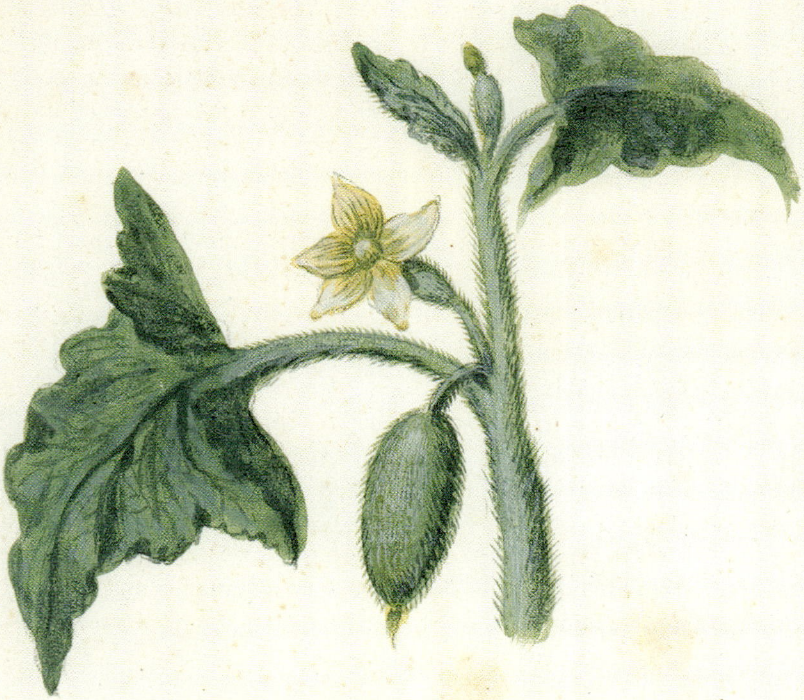

il Succo de le fronde. del Cocomero saluatico. distilato nelle orecchie
ne caua il dolore. mettise ne i, cristieri che si fanno per le sciatiche: lauandosi
con la sua decotione. li denti che doglino. purga senza molestare punto lo stomaco:
lauandosi le mano con il succo de i, zuccarelli. o' questi pomi. guarisce i,
pori: che nascono sule mano. cosa prouata 1288.

118. Stavesacre, *Delphinium staphisagria* L.

Erbario Miniato, fol. 118 (RL 27808)

Watermark: Eagle 15

NUMBERING: *615*

ANNOTATION: *Staphis Agria, Purga p*[*er*] *vomito gli umori / grossi. dieci o' vero quindeci de li suoi seme beuti / inacqua melata. trita lerba. con olio amazza i, / pidochi, e' vale al provito* [M: *prurito*]. *e' alla rogna. masti= / cata fa sputare asaissima flemma, lavandosi / la bocca con la sua decotione guarisce i dolor*[*i*] */ de i denti, e' ristagna il flusso de le gengiv*[*e*] */ mettisi nelli impiastri che brusiano. 1291* ('*Staphis Agria*. Drinking ten or fifteen of its seeds in honey water purges strong humours by vomiting. The plant minced with oil kills lice and is effective against itching and scabies. When chewed it makes one spit out large amounts of phlegm. Rinsing the mouth with its decoction cures toothache, and staunches bleeding of the gums. It is applied in burning poultices. 1291'). [From Mattioli 1568, pp. 1290–1]

LITERATURE: Morton 1990, pp. 16–17

The stavesacre is a herbaceous plant of the family Ranunculaceae, which grows close to inhabited areas at altitudes from sea level to 800m. The stalk of the plant is erect and slender; the alternate leaves grow from long petioles and are deeply incised into five lobes, some of which are further divided into three parts. The flower stems are long and slender and extend from deeply lobed bracts. The flowers, whose deep blue colour has been realistically captured by the artist, have five petals and a short spur.

The generic name *Delphinium* was in use during the first century AD for this plant. The plant was cultivated in southern Europe as an insecticide: the seeds in the form of a pomade protected against lice and other parasites, and were also used to treat neuralgia and heart ailments. The alkaloids in the seeds are, however, highly toxic and can be fatal.

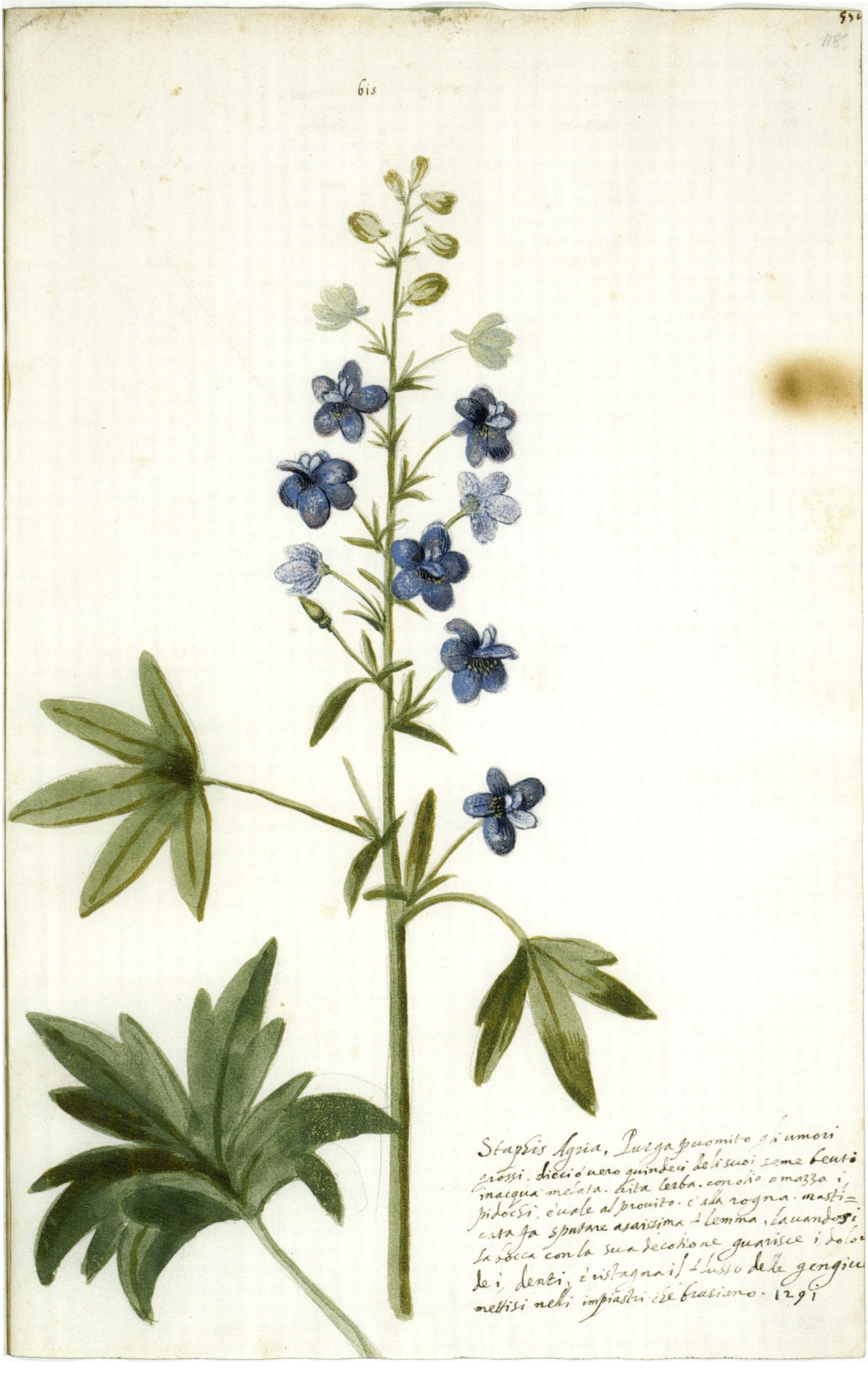
bis
Staphis Agria, Purga p uomito gli umori
grossi. dieci ò uero quindeci de li suoi seme beuti
in acqua melata. trita lerba. con olio amazza i
pidocchi; è uale al pruito. e alla rogna. masti=
cata fa sputare asaissima flemma, lauandosi
la bocca con la sua decottione guarisce i dolo
de i denti, è ristagna il flusso delle gengiu
mettisi nelli impiastri che brusiano. 1291

119. Spanish broom, *Spartium junceum* L.

Erbario Miniato, fol. 119 (RL 27809)

NUMBERING: *616*

ANNOTATION: *Genestra. Mesue la pose tra i semplici solutivi, il fiore / sostieno poca decotione, ma il seme asai piu, solve questo p*[*er*] *ł / vomito. e' p*[*er*] *disotto volerosamente la flema, e' le materie. che sonno / nelle gionture, e' mondifica le reni da tutte le superfluta: provoca / gagliargdamente l'orina, e' rompe le pietre delle reni, e della vesica, / e' no*[*n*] *vi lascia condensare dentro materia alcuna in pietra, i fiori beuti / con mele rosato. overo nelle uova, risolvano le scruofole: conferisce / alle sciatiche. alle podagre, e' al dolore delle reni, 1295.* ('Broom. Mesue placed it among the purgative simples. The flower takes little decocting, but the seed much more; this is an effective remedy for phlegm by vomiting and discharge from below, and for substances in the joints; it clears kidneys of all superfluities. It induces urination very effectively and breaks stones in the kidneys and bladder, letting no substance solidify into stone within them. The flowers, drunk with rose honey or with eggs, cure scrofulas. It is beneficial for sciatica, gout and kidney pains. 1295.'). [From Mattioli 1568, pp. 1295–6]

VERSO: offset of 121

LITERATURE: Freedberg 2002, pp. 210 (fig. 8.10), 212–13

Spanish broom is a shrub of the family Fabaceae. It is common around the Mediterranean, forming thickets in sunny, exposed areas, particularly along the coast, from sea level to an altitude of 700m. The generic name *Spartium* derives from the Greek σπάρτον (*sparton*), 'rope', as the flexible branches could be used in place of cord, and rope and cloth could be made from the fibres of the branches, as both Theophrastus and Pliny noted.

On the left is an erect, smooth, branching stem ending in a loose raceme of bright yellow flowers. The lower ones are in full bloom, and we can see the characteristic formation of the petals – a well-developed upright petal with divergent wings and a narrow carina (two fused petals enclosing the stamens and pistil). The pistils and stamens are hidden by the petals. The peduncles may be reflexed or erect depending on the maturity of the blossom. The smooth, slender branch on the right bears two long brown seed pods on erect axes with persisting calyxes.

Mattioli describes at length the uses of the 'Genestra' and notes that it may be confused with the 'Spartio' of Dioscorides. The inscription here, however, copies out those passages that Mattioli drew from the work of 'Mesue', that is, the *Opera medicinalia* of the great Islamic authority on the pharmacological properties of plants, Abu Zakariya Yuhanna ibn Masawayh (777–857). His texts were translated into Latin, Italian and many other languages and were still in use during the sixteenth century.

119.

616

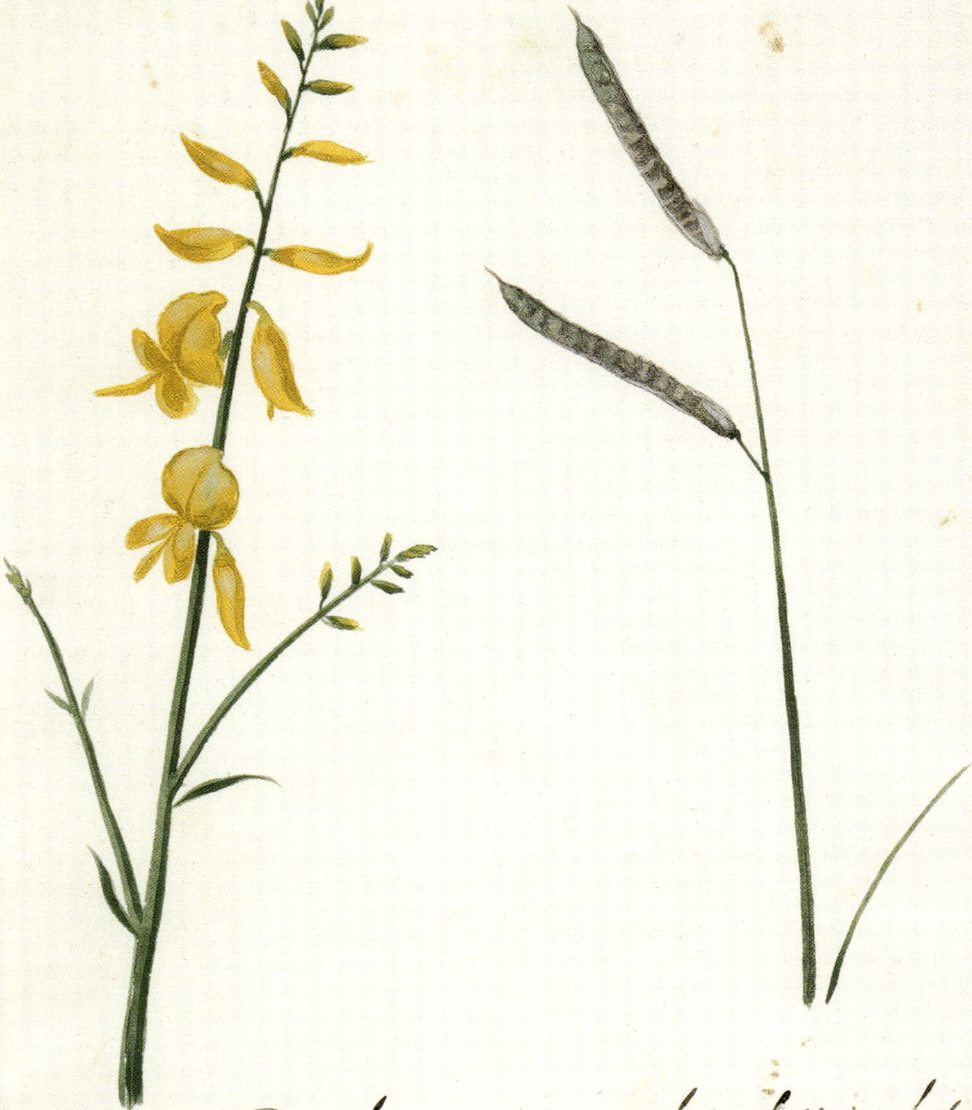

Genestra. Mesue la pose tra i semplici solutivi, il fiore
sostiene poca decottione, ma il seme assai più, solue questo per
uomito, è per disotto uolerosamente la flema, è le materie. che sonno
nelle gionture, è mondifica le reni, è tutte le superfluità; prouoca
gagliardamente l'orina, è rompe le pietre delle reni, è della uesica,
è nõ vi lascia condensare dentro materia alcuna in pietra. i fiori beuti
con mele rosato, ouero nelle uoua, risoluono le scrofole. conferisce
alle sciatiche. alle podagre, è al dolore delle reni; 1295.

120. Poet's cassia, *Osyris alba* L.

Erbario Miniato, fol. 120 (RL 27810)

NUMBERING: *617*

ANNOTATION: *Spetie de Ginestra: no*[*n*] *scritta dal Matiolo.* ('Species of broom: not mentioned by Mattioli.')

VERSO: offset of **195**

The poet's cassia is a shrub of the family Santalaceae, which grows in the Mediterranean scrub at altitudes from sea level to 800m. The stem is erect, smooth and densely branched with sparse, narrow leaves. Many of the twigs carry at their extremity a round, bright red stone-fruit. To the left is a detail of a small branch with several tiny yellow flowers at its apex; one is fully opened, showing the corolla's four rounded petals. Lower down are three twigs bearing several narrow, sessile leaves.

Poet's cassia has no known medicinal uses. The generic name *Osyris* was used by Dioscorides; though it is not known for what plant exactly, it must have been one with a sour taste since the Greek οξύς (*oxys*) means 'acid'. Nor is it known exactly what Virgil and other Latin writers meant by *cassia*, beyond the fact that it was a fragrant shrub. *Osyris alba* has been suggested, but Daubeny's suggestion of a daphne is now widely accepted (Daubeny 1865, p. 123); he proposed *Daphne gnidium*, but *Daphne laureola* and other species have their advocates (e.g. Abbe 1965, pp. 142–4).

120.

617

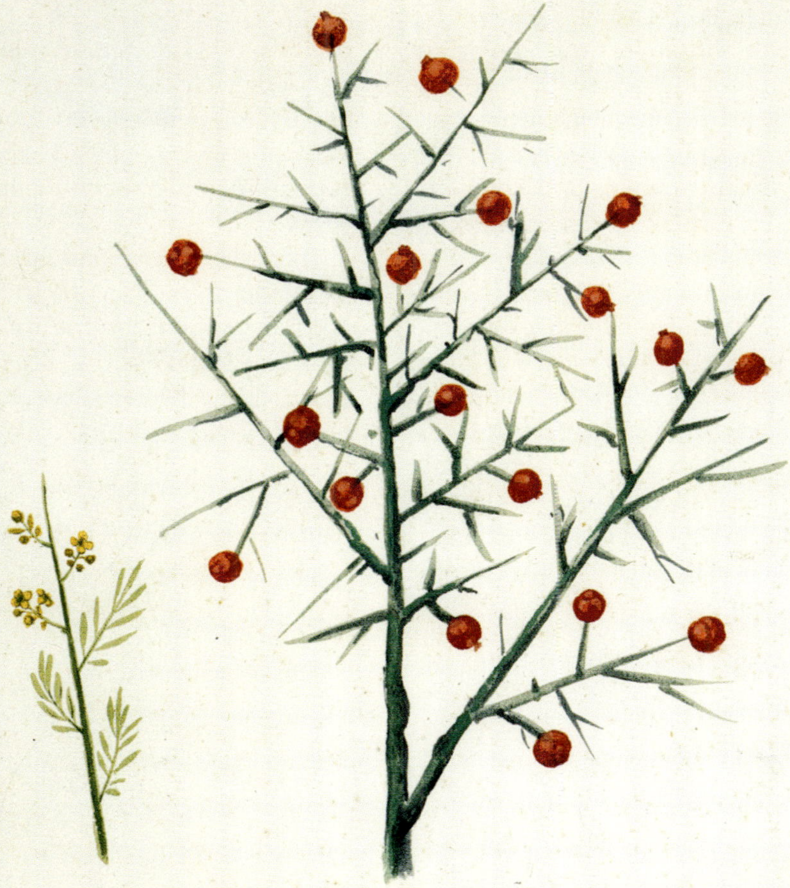

Spetie de Ginestra: nō scritta dal Matiolo.

121. Lilac, *Syringa vulgaris* L.

Erbario Miniato, fol. 121 (RL 27811)

Watermark: Figure 56

NUMBERING: *618*

ANNOTATION: ~~*istrece orientale*~~*.; Lilach, overo Seringa dal fiore torchino,* ~~*il mio*~~ */* ~~*libro no*~~[~~*n*~~] ~~*ne scrive niente*~~ *nel mio matiolo grande.* *1297*. ['~~oriental istrece~~. Lilac, or turquoise-flowered syrinx, ~~my book does not mention it~~ in my large Mattioli, 1297.']. [From Mattioli 1568, p. 1297]

The lilac is a shrub of the family Oleaceae, indigenous to Turkey and the Balkans. It has been cultivated in western Europe since at least the sixteenth century, and many varieties exist with single or double blooms ranging in colour from purple to white. It seems to have been described for the first time by Pierre Belon (1517–64) in 1553, and blue- and white-flowered varieties were discussed in Dodoens's *Pemptades* (1583, pp. 777–8). The fresh leaves of the lilac have tonic and astringent properties and were considered a useful specific against malaria. The fruit and bark have tonic and antipyretic properties, while the flowers may be steeped in oil to produce a liniment for the relief of rheumatic ailments.

This specimen has a smooth, woody, slightly contorted stem bearing pairs of heart-shaped leaves with smooth margins and a prominent central vein. The stem terminates in a panicle of light purple flowers shaped like elongated tubes and ending in four lobes. The flowers' pistil and stamens cannot be seen. To the right the drawing is unfinished, the leaves merely outlined in black chalk.

The note at the foot of the drawing refers the reader to the lilac depicted on p. 1297 of the *Discorsi*. Mattioli introduced this plant as a possible match for the 'Ghianda unguentaria' described by Dioscorides, about whose identity he was uncertain (it was probably *Moringa oleifera*: see Mariotti 1997, p. 212). He also suggests that his lilac corresponded to the plant called 'Ostrys' by Theophrastus, commonly known in Italian as *seringa dal fior porporeo* ('purple-flowered syrinx').

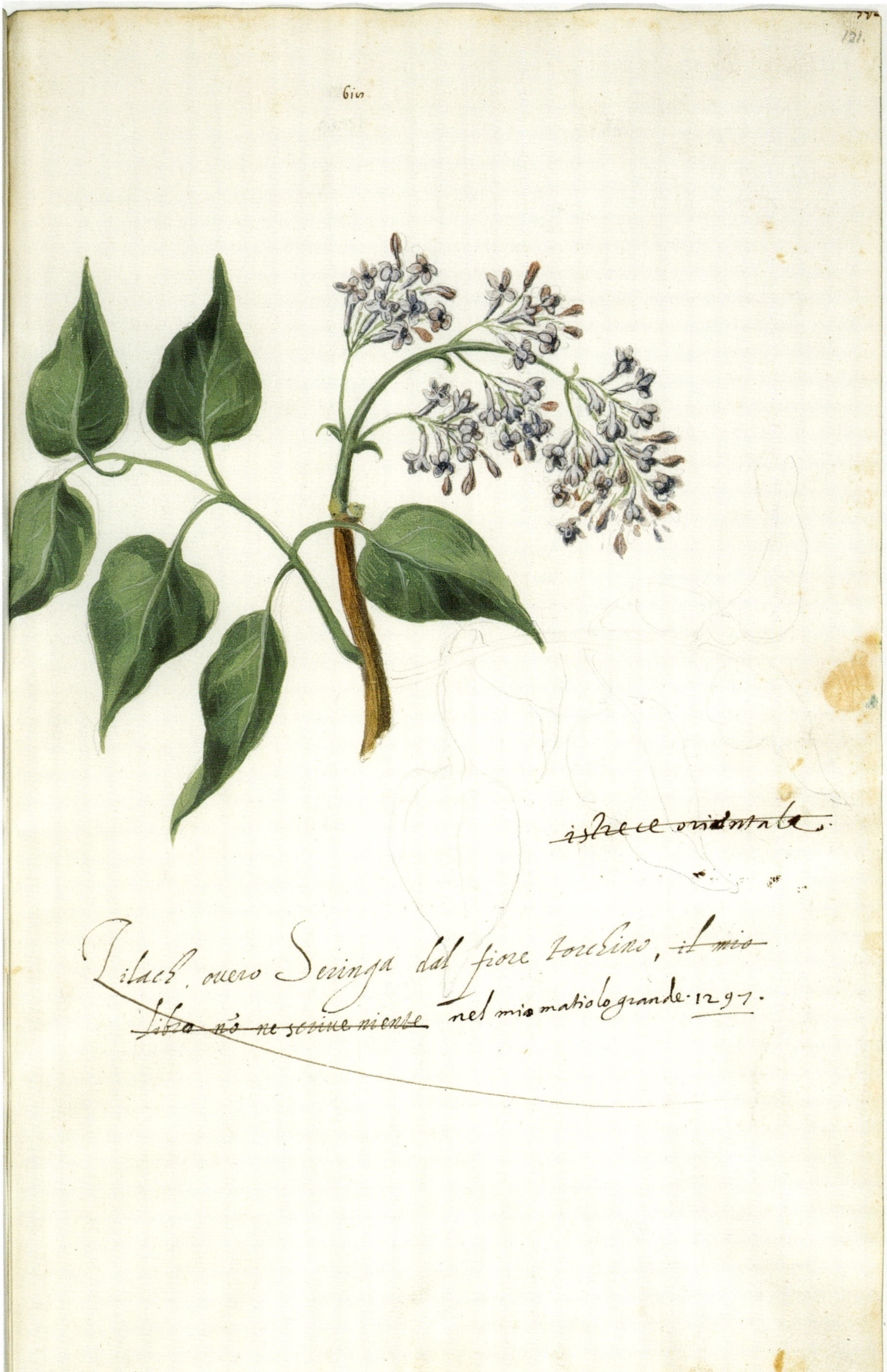
121.
Lilach, overo Seringa dal fiore torchino, ~~il mio libro nõ ne scrive niente~~ nel mio matiolo grande · 1297 ·

122. Mock orange, *Philadelphus coronarius* L.

Erbario Miniato, fol. 122 (RL 27812)

Watermark: Eagle 15

NUMBERING: *619*

ANNOTATION: [cut] *Lilac overo siring*[–] */dal* [–] [*fiore bianco*] ('Lilac or [white-flowered] syrinx')

The mock orange is a perennial shrub of the family Saxifragaceae, native to the Caucasus and now naturalized across the northern hemisphere (see also **123**). In southern Europe it grows in forests at altitudes from sea level to 800m. Cultivated as an ornamental plant, the mock orange exists in many varieties with single or double blooms, and sometimes a band of white or yellow along the margins of the leaves. The English name refers to the fragrance of its flower, which is reminiscent of the orange blossom. Some authors trace the origin of the genus name *Philadelphus* to the Greek words for 'friend', φίλος (*philos*) and 'brother', αδελφός (*adelphos*), perhaps an allusion to the large number of stamens in its flower.

A flower, cut short at the level of the peduncle, is here shown in two views. The white corolla consists of four wide lobes that are rounded and notched at their apices, and a large number of stamens with yellow anthers can be seen emerging from the centre of the corolla. In the drawing on the right the artist shows the calyx with its long narrow teeth and a slight swelling indicating the presence of the ovary. The leaf is oval in shape with acute apices and slightly toothed margins, a short peduncle and faintly visible veins.

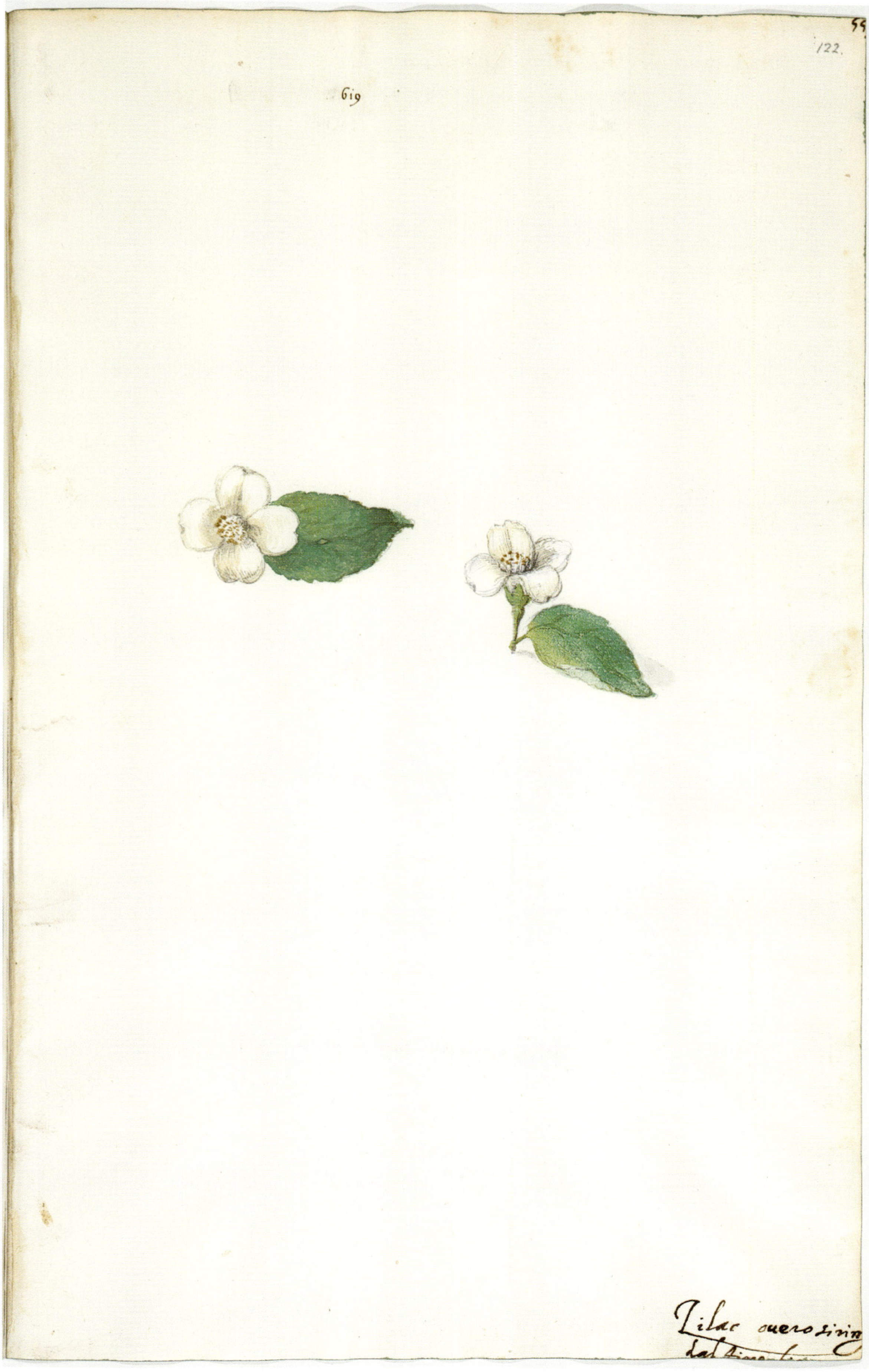
122.
619
Lilac overo sirin

123. Mock orange, *Philadelphus coronarius* L.

Erbario Miniato, fol. 123 (RL 27813)

NUMBERING: *620*

ANNOTATION: *UNALTRO LILAC* ('Another lilac')

This drawing shows a sprig of mock orange (see **122**) with three flowers. The slender, woody branch bears opposite leaves that are broadly lanceolate with acute apices and slightly toothed margins. The flowers have short peduncles, deeply toothed calyxes and white corollas divided into four broad petals with rounded lobes. At their centres numerous stamens with yellow anthers can be seen, though the pistil is not visible.

A sketch for this drawing is found on the verso of **4**.

VNALTRO LILAC

620

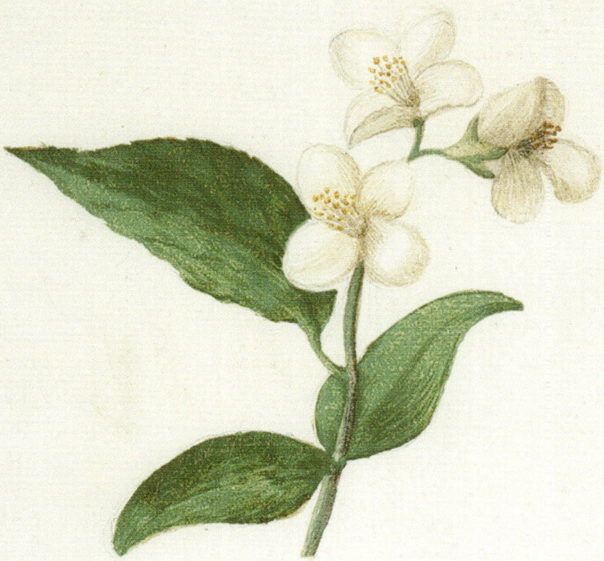

124. Bladder campion, *Silene vulgaris* (Moench) Garcke

Erbario Miniato, fol. 124 (RL 27814)

Watermark: Eagle 18

NUMBERING: *621*

ANNOTATION: *Stridula, / Ben bianco.* ('*Stridula*; white Ben.')

The bladder campion is a perennial of the family Caryophyllaceae. It abounds in the Mediterranean and temperate and tropical regions of Asia, growing in meadows with gravelly soil at altitudes from sea level to 2,800m. The specimen illustrated here has a long, straight, slender stem. Its leaves are narrow and lanceolate with a prominent central vein. Seven flowers grow from long, narrow stems with paired lanceolate bracts. Although not evident in this drawing, their white corollas are composed of five petals, each deeply incised into two lobes. The stamens and pistil are not visible, but one of the flowers on the right has three fine filaments which (if they are interpreted as stigmas) could indicate that it is a female flower, for the bladder campion is dioecious. A swollen calyx contains the flower's ovary.

The bladder campion has no medicinal properties, but is sometimes used as forage. The name *Silene*, probably derived from Silenus, was originally used for the plant now known as *Vesicaria*. It may also be linked to the Greek for saliva, σίαλον (*sialon*), referring to the white substance secreted by the stem and roots of many species of this genus. The common Italian name, *stridula*, refers to the squeak made by the stem when plucked. According to Mattioli (p. 1300) 'Ben' or 'Been' and its variations 'Ben bianco' and 'Ben rosso' were the Arabic names for Dioscorides' 'Ghianda unguentaria' (see **121**), a plant from which oil was extracted. The name 'behen' is still used for *Silene vulgaris* and for species from which 'ben oil' is extracted (including *Moringa oleifera*, the ben-oil or horseradish tree).

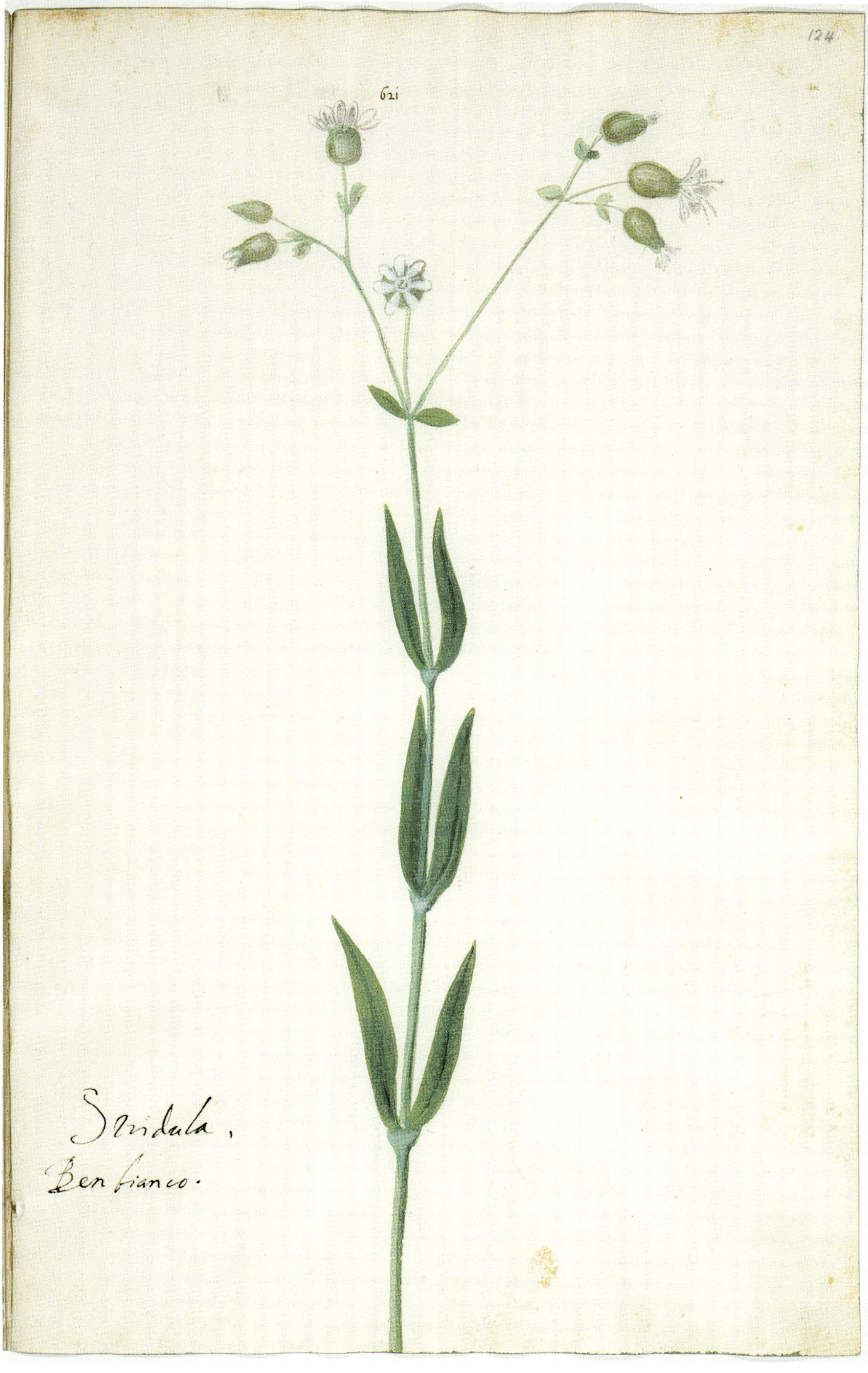
124.
621
Scridula.
Ben bianco.

125. Bunch-flowering daffodil, *Narcissus tazetta* L.; golden bunch-flowering daffodil, *Narcissus aureus* Loisel.; common sternbergia, *Sternbergia lutea* (L.) Ker-Gawl. ex Sprengel

Erbario Miniato, fol. 125 (RL 27815)

Watermark: Eagle 18

NUMBERING: *622*

ANNOTATION: *Narciso, la radice cotta tanto mangiata / quanto beuta. fa vomitare: giova alle / cotture del fuoco: aplicatavi posta* [M: *pesta*] */ con un poco di mele, messa i, su i, nervi / tagliati, gli consolida. 1303*; *N:º 32* ('Narcissus. The cooked root either eaten or drunk induces vomiting. It is beneficial for burns. Ground and applied with a little honey on cut nerves, it strengthens them. 1303. No. 32'). [From Mattioli 1568, p. 1302]

On this sheet three different flowering bulbous plants are depicted, two of which are shown with their bulbs. The drawing at centre left illustrates a flowering stem of *Narcissus aureus*. The floral axis is erect, with long, flexible pedicels emerging from a sheath-like bract. The flower consists of a yellow perianth divided into six acute segments. The yellowish-orange corona is shaped like a small cup and hides the stamens and pistil. The swelling of a long section of the pedicel just below the corolla indicates the presence of the ovary.

The large drawing at upper centre depicts *Narcissus tazetta*. An erect, tapering floral axis ends in five flowers borne on reflexed pedicels. Three long, narrow leaves envelop the scape for one-third of its length. The flower consists of a white perianth divided into six rounded segments with a bright yellow paracorolla. The ovary is contained in the pedicel; the pistil and stamens are not shown. The bulb is smooth with a short brown tunic.

The narcissus (see also **126**) has been admired since antiquity because of its unusual form and delicate scent. According to Plutarch, the name derived from the Greek νάρκη (*narke*), 'numbness' (hence also 'narcotic'), because it was believed that one could be drugged by its perfume. Greek mythology relates the story of the youth Narcissus, who fell in love with his own image reflected in a pool of water. He eventually pined away and died, and in his place a flower grew that, according to Ovid, was 'yellow in the centre with white petals all around'. The bulb is toxic (as suggested in the annotation), and contact with the plant may cause skin rashes. The flower is an important ingredient of cosmetics and is cultivated in vast quantities in southern France (150,000kg per year), Palestine, Syria and China.

At lower right is a common sternbergia (see **53**). The scape of the plant is short and slender. The leaves are small, yellowish-brown and linear in form with rounded apices and light-coloured veins. The yellow perianth is made up of six oval segments; at its centre one can glimpse four of the flower's six anthers. The bulb is pear-shaped with a whitish tunic that covers the scape for two-thirds of its length.

Mattioli illustrates various types of 'Narcisso', including a tulip ('Narcisso V', p. 1305), and *Narcissus tazetta* ('Narcisso' and 'Narcisso II', pp. 1301–2). While the inscription is drawn from a passage by Dioscorides on p. 1302, the reader is referred to the illustration of a 'Narcisso Constantinopolitano' on p. 1303, which is actually a sea daffodil, *Pancratium maritimum*. The other two plants depicted here do not appear in Mattioli's work.

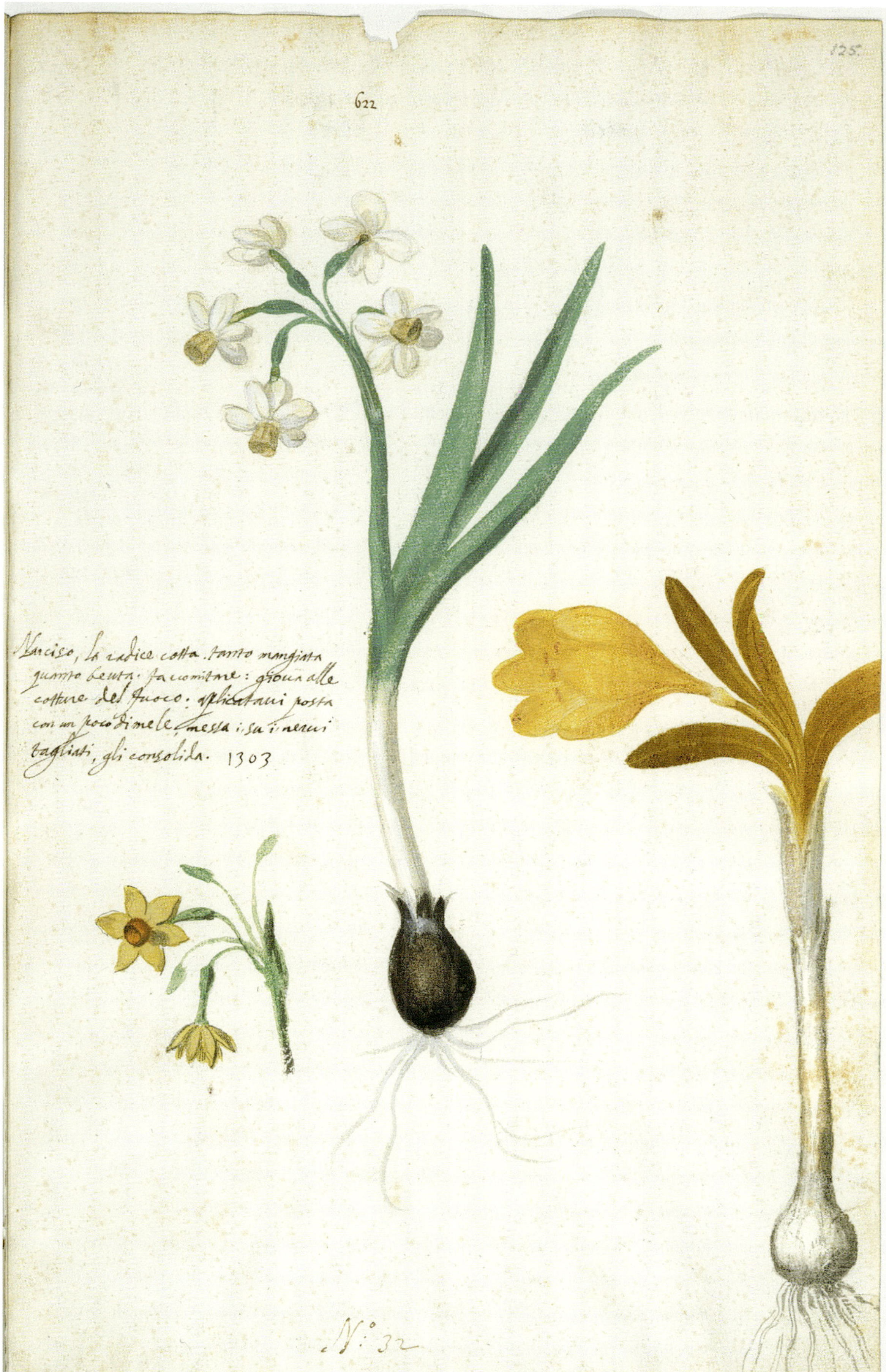
125.
622
Narciso, la radice cotta. tanto mangiata
quanto beuta. fa uomitare: giouà alle
cotture del fuoco: aplicataui posta
con un poco di mele, messa i su i nerui
tagliati, gli consolida. 1303
N.o 32

126. Snowdrop, *Galanthus nivalis* L.; bunch-flowering daffodil, *Narcissus tazetta* L. cv.

Erbario Miniato, fol. 126 (RL 27816)

Lower figure cut from another sheet and pasted on to the folio. *Watermark*: Lamb 6

NUMBERING: *623*

ANNOTATION: [cut] *Narciso sesto. nel mattiol[o]* ('Sixth Narcissus in Mattioli'). [From Mattioli 1568, p. 1306]

The folio shows two snowdrops and, cut out and pasted to the sheet, the flowering scape of what appears to be a cultivar of *Narcissus tazetta* (see **125**).

The snowdrop is a bulbous plant of the family Amaryllidaceae, found in damp forests from Europe to the Caucasus at altitudes from sea level to 1,200m. The scape is slender and enveloped in a white bract with a broad green band along each margin. A slender, reflexed peduncle carries the plant's single flower. The perianth is white and composed of six segments; the three oval outer segments are well developed, while the three internal ones are smaller (with a green spot at their distal extremity) and surround the stamens and the pistil, which are just discernible in the drawing on the right. The name *Galanthus* is derived from the Greek γάλα (*gala*), 'milk', and ἄνθος (*anthos*), 'blossom', referring to the white colour of the flower.

The bunch-flowering daffodil has an erect stem that terminates in a whorl of four flowers whose peduncles are long, slender and reflexed. The base of the whorl of flowers is enveloped in a short white bract. The flowers consist of double corollas divided into numerous segments. The internal corona is not very clearly drawn but appears to be yellowish and deeply lobed; the stamens and pistils are not shown. The colour of the stem suggests that it had been cut some time before the drawing was made.

The two drawings in the upper part of the sheet correspond to the illustration of *Galanthus nivalis*, called by Mattioli 'Narcisso VI', on p. 1306 of the *Discorsi*. The third flower could be the same as the 'Narcisso' on p. 1301, which illustrates *Narcissus tazetta*, the first of a series of cultivated varieties shown in flower.

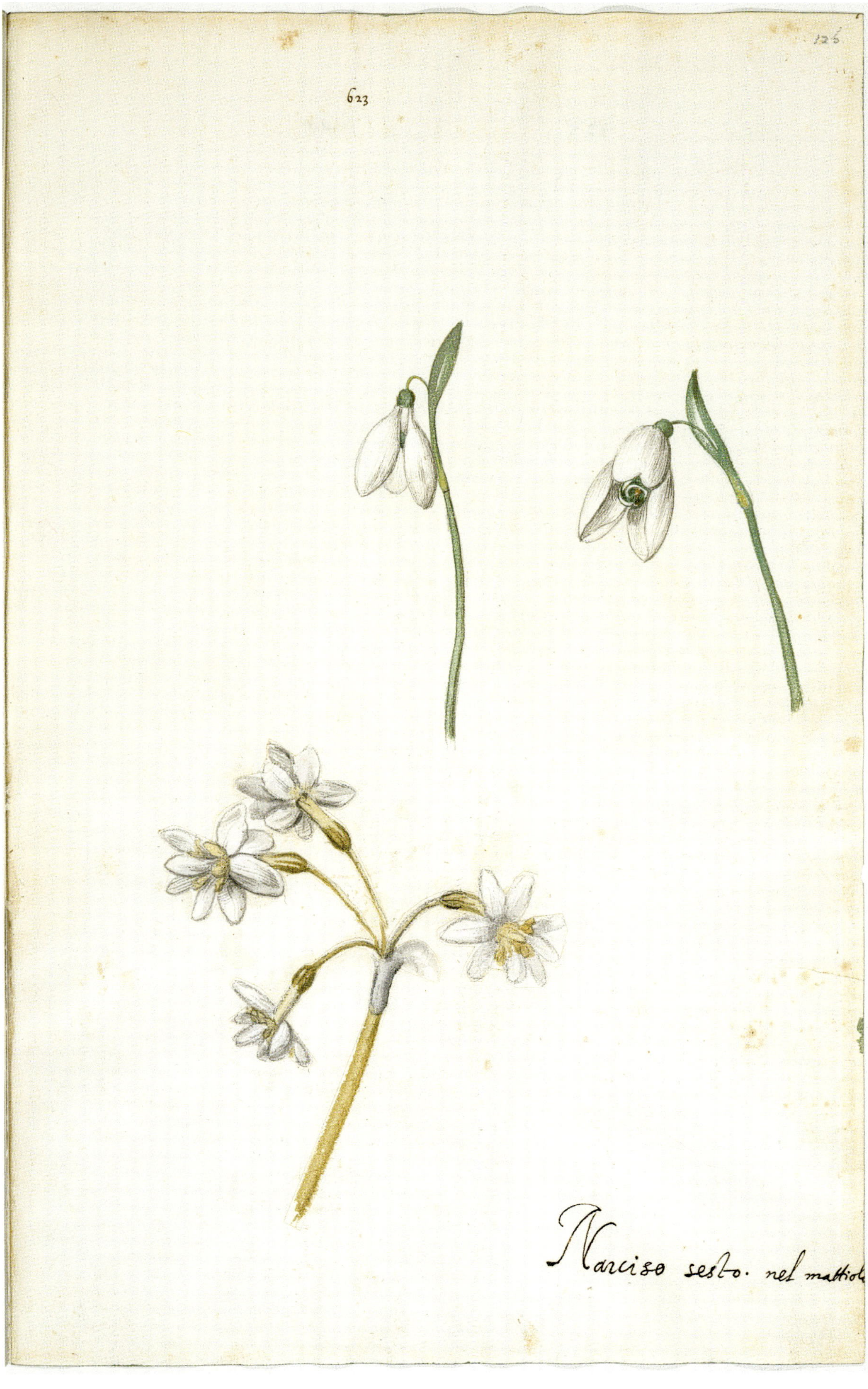
126
623
Narciso sesto. nel mattioli

127. Poet's narcissus, *Narcissus poeticus* L.

Erbario Miniato, fol. 127 (RL 27817)

Watermark: Eagle 22

NUMBERING: *624*

ANNOTATION: *UNALTRO NARCISSO* ('Another narcissus')

The poet's narcissus is a bulbous plant of the family Amaryllidaceae. It grows in the mountains and forests of south-western Europe at altitudes from 600m to 1,600m. The scape is long, erect and flattened on two sides, with a characteristic elliptical cross-section. The three leaves are linear and almost as long as the scape. The floral peduncle is enveloped in a yellowish, membranous spathe. The corolla is pure white and divided into ovate segments. The corona is yellow with a red border, hence the alternative common name 'pheasant's eye'. The anthers and the pistil are not clearly visible and the bulb is not shown.

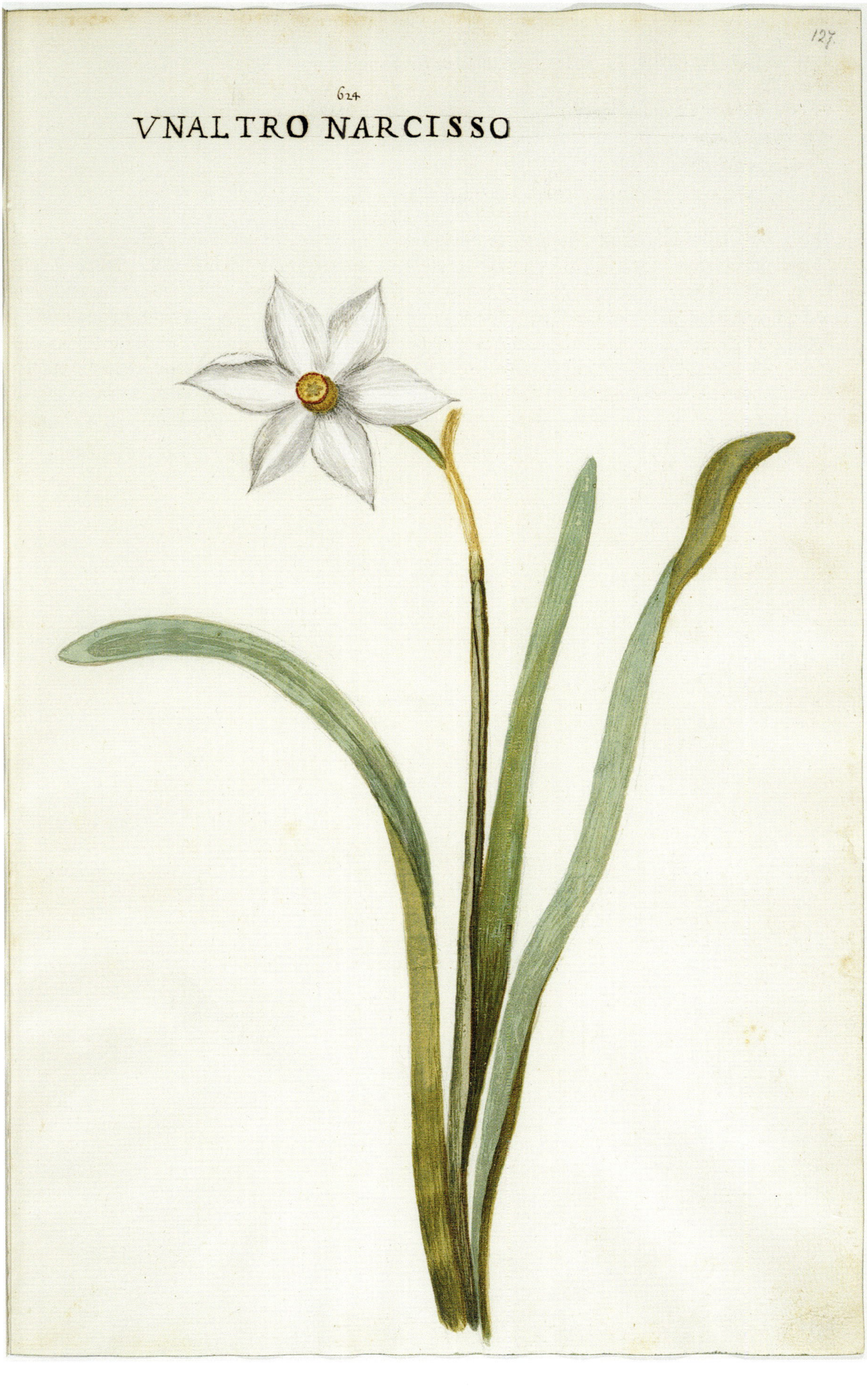
127
624
VNALTRO NARCISSO

128. Wild daffodil, *Narcissus pseudonarcissus* L.

Erbario Miniato, fol. 128 (RL 27818)

Watermark: Lamb 5

NUMBERING: *625*

ANNOTATION: *PSEUDONARCISSO LUTEO* ('Yellow false narcissus')

The wild daffodil is a perennial bulbous plant of the family Amaryllidaceae. It grows wild in Europe, northern Africa and the temperate regions of Asia, at altitudes from sea level to 800m, and is cultivated as an ornamental. Like other members of the Amaryllidaceae, the bulb of the daffodil is poisonous, and contact with the plant can cause skin rashes (see also **125**).

The plant is shown with its long scape and distinctive flower in profile; at lower left is an almost frontal detail of the flower. At the base of the peduncle are a pair of small membranous spathes. The flower is made up of a corolla divided into six lanceolate segments and a long, trombone-shaped corona with an irregularly toothed border. In a detail the artist has sketched the pistil and anthers within the corona.

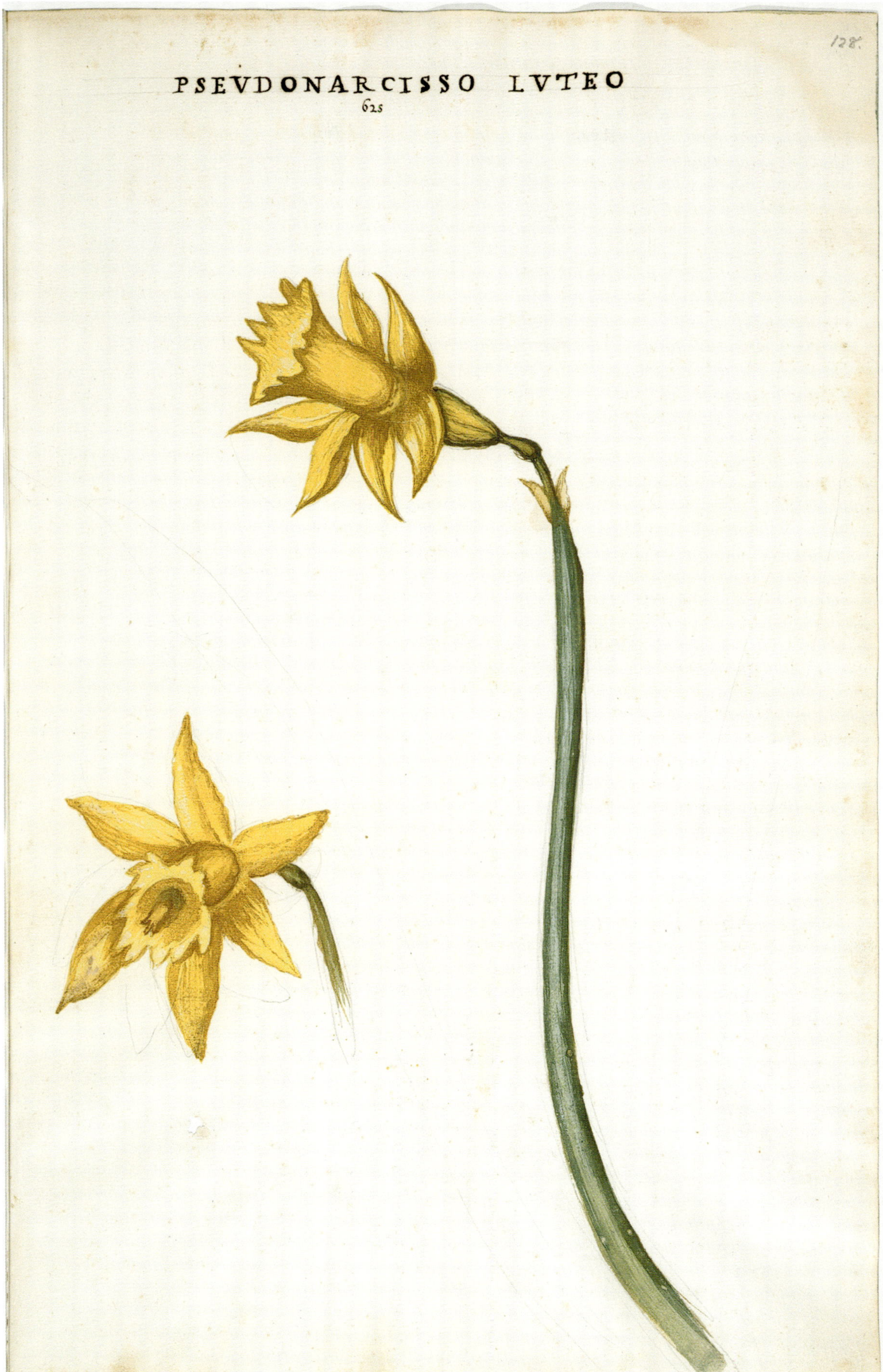
128.
PSEVDONARCISSO LVTEO
625

129. Castor-bean, *Ricinus communis* L.

Erbario Miniato, fol. 129 (RL 27819)

NUMBERING: *626*

ANNOTATION: *fiore; seme; frutto; Ricino. . 1310.* ('flower; seed; fruit; *Ricino*. 1310'). [From Mattioli 1568, p. 1310]

This drawing shows the leaf, flower, seed and fruit of the castor-bean plant, a perennial of the family Euphorbiaceae. Probably native to Africa, it has become naturalized in all the tropical and subtropical regions of the world and grows wild at altitudes from sea level to 800m. In temperate climates the plant is raised as an annual and many cultivars exist.

The leaf is dark green and divided into seven long, pointed lobes with finely toothed margins. The petiole is attached to the centre of the leaf, from which radiate its prominent light-coloured veins. At lower left is a detail of the male flower, a spherical, yellowish mass consisting of numerous stamens enclosed in a calyx. The corolla is absent. Below is the fruit, a dark green spherical capsule divided into three chambers and covered with spines. Above is the tricoccous, the internal portion of the pericarp with three cavities each containing a seed. Next to this is the seed itself, ovoid and dark with a marbled pattern.

The castor-bean plant was known to the ancient Egyptians, and the Greek κρότων (*kroton*) by which Dioscorides referred to the plant apparently derives from the Egyptian word for tick, the parasite that attaches itself to the skin of warm-blooded animals including humans, and that resembles the castor bean in both form and colour. The genus name *Ricinus* comes from the Latin word for the same insect.

Ricinus communis is widely cultivated for its oil which can be used, either alone or in combination with oils from other plants such as the poppy and *Croton tilium*, in various pharmaceutical and industrial applications. In Europe it has been cultivated as a medicinal plant since the fifteenth century. The seeds contain a highly poisonous alkaloid (ricinine), from which the powerful cytotoxin ricin can be manufactured.

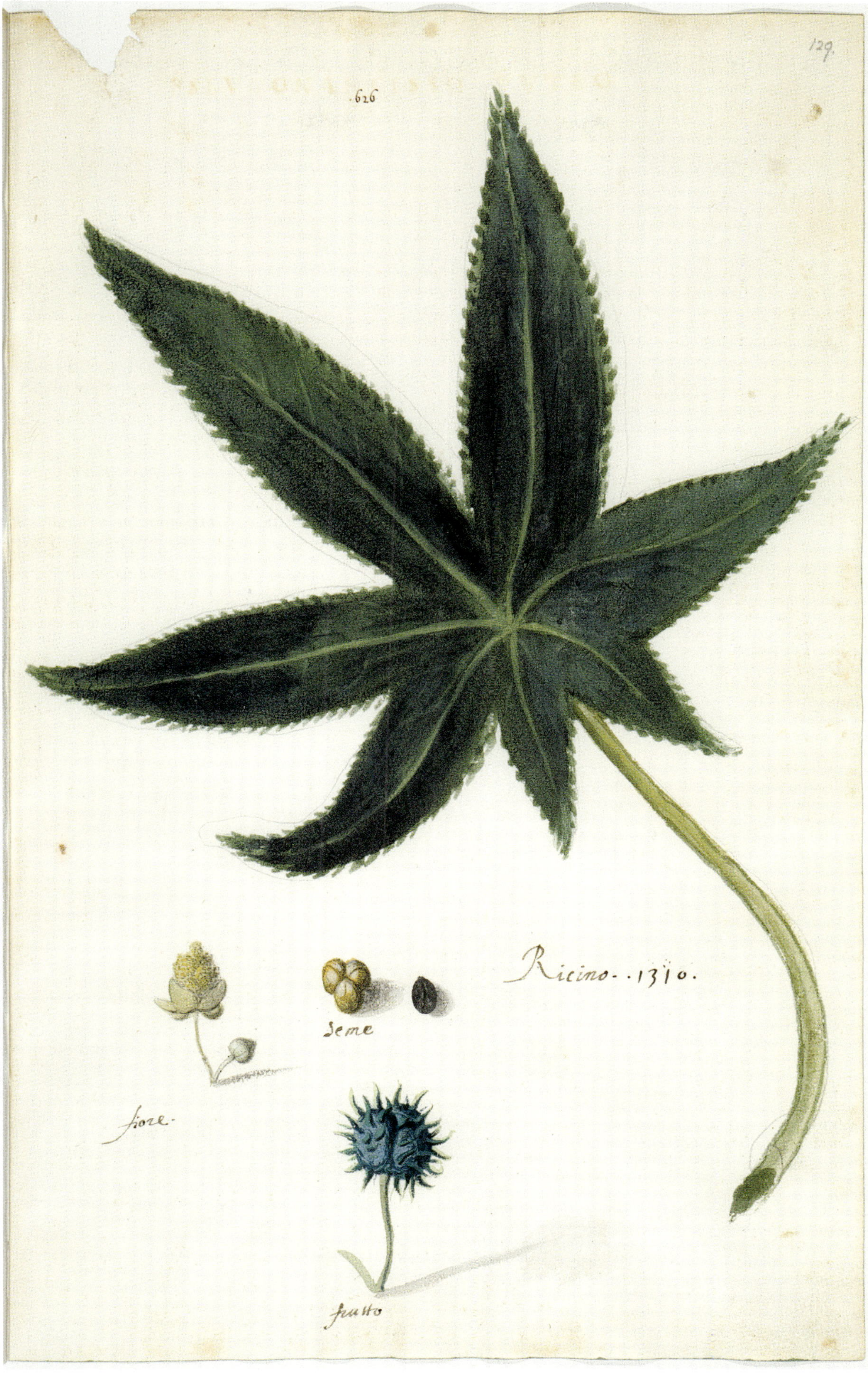
129.
.626
Ricino. .1310.
seme
fiore.
frutto

130. Solar spurge, *Euphorbia helioscopia* L.; cypress spurge, *Euphorbia cyparissias* L.; large Mediterranean spurge, *Euphorbia characias* L.

Erbario Miniato, fol. 130 (RL 27820)

Watermark: Eagle 18

NUMBERING: *627*

ANNOTATION: *Tithimalo ~~Characia~~ helioscopio; Tithimalo Characia; Tithimalo ciparissio; i Tithimali, sonno di 7. spetie, il maschio ha nome characia, chiamano pero' / ancora da alcuni amigdaloide: la femina chiamano mirtite, e' altrimente / cariite, e' mirsinite: il terzo. ha nome paralio, il quale chiamano ancora / tithimalide: l'altro helioscopio: il quinto ciparissio: il sesto dendroide: / il settimo platiphillo: il loro succo purga il corpo. solve la colera, e' / la flema, beuto con acqua melata. fa vomitare, il latte che si ritrova nelle / suoi frondi e' fusti, messo nei, denti li leva il dolore, sana unto le volatice. /e' le formiche. e' leva via le ~~xxx~~ verruche, i porri ~~e' i Thimi~~. Valle a' pterigii / delle dita. e' a i, carboncelli, al ulcere corosive, alle cancrene, e' alle fistole. /la radice beuta con acqua melata. purga p[er] disotto: lavesi la bocca con la decotio[ne] / fatta con aceto. quando doglino i, denti. 1311* ('*Tithimalo ~~Characia~~ Helioscopio. Tithimalo Characia; Tithimalo ciparissio*; there are seven types of *Tithimali*: the male has the name *characia*, but is still called by some *amigdaloide*; the female they call *mirtite*, or otherwise *cariite*, and *mirsinite*; the third has the name *paralio*, and is still called *tithimalide*; the other *helioscopio*; the fifth *ciparissio*; the sixth *dendroide*; the seventh *platiphillo*. Their juice purges the body, eliminates choler and phlegm. Drunk with honey water, it induces vomiting. When placed on the teeth the latex found in its leaves and stems relieves pain. Rubbed in it cures irritations and pricklings of the skin, and lifts away verrucas, warts ~~and *Thimi*~~. Good for pterygium of the fingers, and carbuncles, corrosive ulcers, gangrene and fistulas. The root, drunk with honey water, purges from below. When the teeth hurt the mouth can be rinsed with a decoction made with vinegar. 1311'). [From Mattioli 1568, pp. 1310–12]

This folio shows three species of euphorbia or spurge, of the family Euphorbiaceae. The solar spurge, to the left, grows throughout the world in uncultivated fields from sea level to 1,200m. The stem of this specimen is erect and smooth, and bears four alternate, lanceolate leaves with rounded tips and smooth margins. At its apex is a whorl of rounded, leaf-like bracts and a cluster of flowers on long, erect peduncles. The details have been sketched in with tiny strokes of yellowish paint.

The cypress spurge, at centre, is native to central Europe, growing in dry meadows at altitudes from sea level to 1,500m. Its stem is erect and slender, with a large number of alternate, linear leaves near its apex. The stem is crowned by a verticil of tiny yellow flowers on long, slender peduncles. Each flower is supported by a large pair of united yellow bracts.

The large Mediterranean spurge, to the right, grows in the dry forests and shrubland of the Mediterranean. The thick, erect, light green stem has long, tapering leaves growing along its entire length. At the apex of the stem is a whorl of five light green, oval bracts bearing a cluster of five slender peduncles. Each of the inflorescences is supported by a pair of united bracts forming a cup from which spring two peduncles that carry the maturing capsules. At the base of each capsule the red glands of the flower can be seen.

According to Pliny, the name *Euphorbia* derived from the name of the physician and king of Mauritania, Euphorbius. It has been suggested that the name simply means 'good fodder', from the Greek ευφορβία (*euphorbia*), but since almost all the plants in this genus produce a poisonous caustic white latex, this seems unlikely. The ancient Greeks also called the euphorbias τιθύμαλος (*tithymalos*), 'plant which sends forth buds'; this was rendered in Italian as *titimaglio* or *titimalo*. The solar spurge was also called *svegliarino* (from the verb 'to awaken') in Italian, because if a gardener inadvertently rubbed some of its juice into his eyes they would sting for days, preventing him from sleeping.

The extensive notes at the foot of the sheet are drawn from Dioscorides' chapter on 'Tithimali' (pp. 1310–12 in the *Discorsi*). Mattioli illustrated seven species of 'Tithimali', of which the three shown here correspond to the 'Tithimalo helioscopio' on p. 1314, the 'Tithimalo ciparissio' on p. 1315 and the 'Tithimalo characia' on p. 1311.

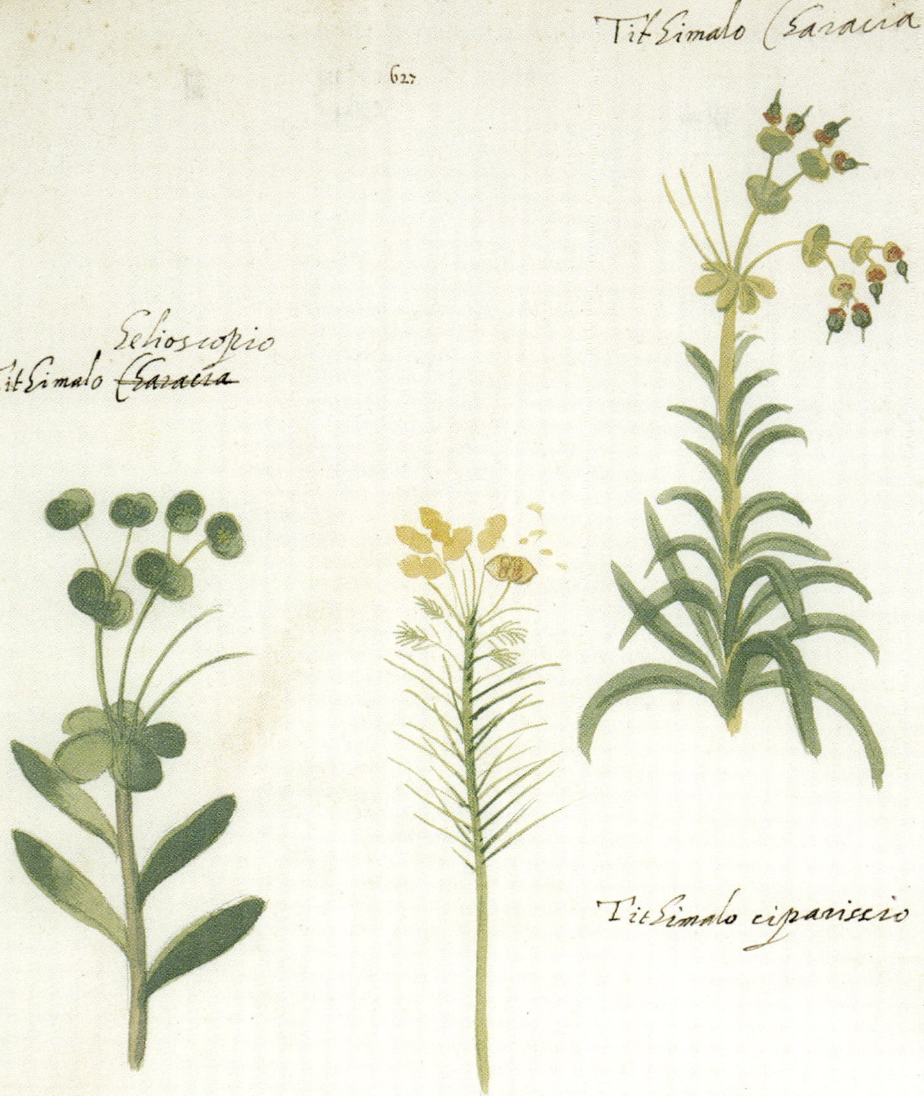

i Titimali, sonno di 7. spetie, il maschio ha nome characia, chiamano però ancora da alcuni amigdaloide: la femina chiamano mirtite, ò altrimente cariite, è mirsinite: il terzo ha nome paralio, il quale chiamano ancora titimalide: l'altro helioscopio: il quinto ciparissio: il sesto dendroide: il settimo platiphillo: il loro succo purga il corpo. solue la colera, è la flema, beuto con acqua melata. fa uomitare, il latte che si ritroua nelle suoi frondi è fusti, messo nei denti li leua il dolore. sana unto. le uolatiche. è le formiche. è leua uia le ~~[illegible]~~ uerruche, i porri, ~~[illegible]~~. Valle à i pterigii delle dita. è a i carboncelli, al ulcere corosiue, alle cancrene, è alle fistole. la radice beuta con acqua melata. purga per disotto: lauesi la bocca con la decottione fatta con aceto. quando doglino i denti, 1311

131. Cantabrian bindweed, *Convolvulus cantabrica* L.

Erbario Miniato, fol. 131 (RL 27821)

NUMBERING: *628*

ANNOTATION: [cut] *Scammonium mi*[–] / *plinii. nel* [*D*... erased]*Ei*[–] / *878* ('*Scammonium* [–] of Pliny; in *Eicones* 878'). [From Tabernaemontanus 1590, p. 878]

The Cantabrian bindweed is a perennial of the family Convolvulaceae, which grows in the Mediterranean region on limestone cliffs and in dry meadows and uncultivated land at altitudes to 1,300m. The stem of this specimen is erect and slender, and bears narrow, sessile, lanceolate leaves with acute apices, slightly toothed edges and light green undersides. Bright pink, trumpet-shaped flowers with bell-shaped calyxes grow on long, straight stems from the axils of the leaves. Two buds are also shown.

The specific epithet *cantabrica* derives from Cantabria in northern Spain. Clusius, in his *Rariorum plantarum historia* (1601), called the plant 'Cantabrica quorundarum' and Linnaeus adopted Clusius's term when he named this species. The name in the annotation has been partly cut off, but is probably the one used by Tabernaemontanus on the cited page of his *Eicones plantarum seu stirpium* (p. 878), 'Scammonium minus Plinij'. On p. 1325 of the *Discorsi* is an illustration of a plant that Mattioli calls 'Scammonea', which is actually scammony, *Convolvulus scammonia*.

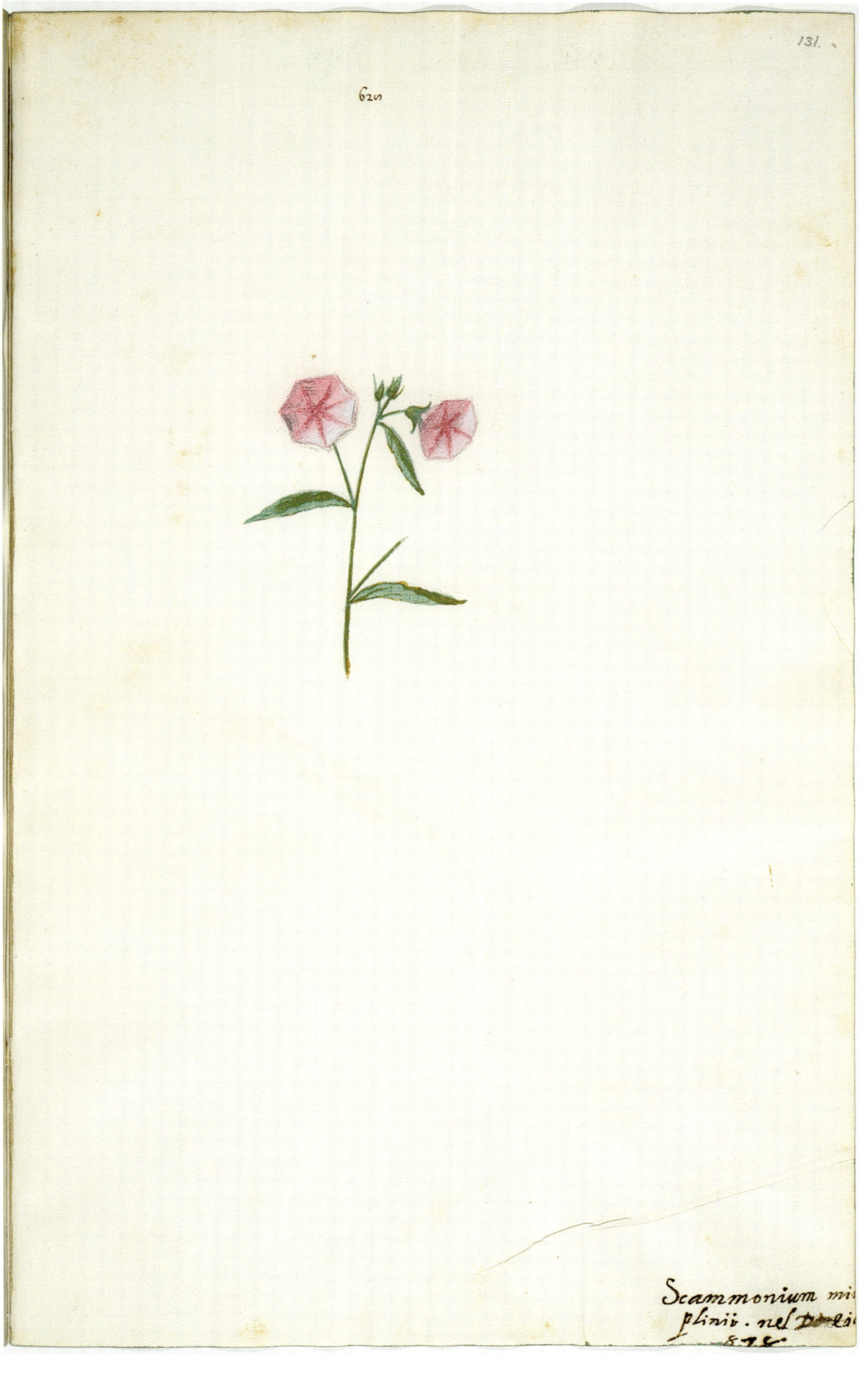
131.
620
Scammonium mi
plinii . nel

132. Spurge laurel, *Daphne laureola* L.

Erbario Miniato, fol. 132 (RL 27822)

Watermark: Fleur de lys 51

NUMBERING: *629*

ANNOTATION: *Mezereon' o Ulivella, è simile al veleno, perche nuoce a tutte / li membra principali, ove sonno le miniere de tutte le virtù del / corpo, pero si coregge quando si vol dare p[er] alcuna medecina / e' calda, le sue pilole o' acini, sonno inuso apresso li moderni / medici, p[er] li hidropici, ma no[n] si danno se no[n] a i, corpi robusti, / loda Galeno, p[er] mondificare lulcere corosive, al VIII libro de / la faculta de i, semplice, 1327 – 10.* (*Mezereon* or *Ulivella* is similar to poison because it harms all the principal members wherein lie the sources of all the virtues of the body. However, this may be counteracted when one wishes to administer it for some medication. It is warm. Its berries or pips are used by modern physicians for dropsy patients, but must be given only to those of robust constitution. Galen praises it for clearing corrosive ulcers in his eighth book on the properties of simples. 1327 – 10.'). [From Mattioli 1568, pp. 1327–9]

VERSO: offset of **130**

The spurge laurel is a perennial of the family Thymelaeaceae, found in the broadleaved forests of the Mediterranean. The stem of this specimen is erect, robust, smooth and tapering, lined with alternate, lanceolate leaves that have short petioles, smooth margins and a dark, central vein which stands out against the lighter green of the leaf blade. From the axils of the lower leaves numerous glossy black stone-fruit hang from reflexed peduncles. The unfinished detail of the flower at lower right shows a long peduncle growing from the axil of a leaf (indicated only by a black chalk outline), bearing a small cluster made up of three to four yellowish-green flowers whose corollas are divided into four lobes.

The genus name *Daphne* comes from the Greek myth of the nymph who, seeking to escape Apollo, called upon the gods to save her and was transformed into a laurel tree. The Greeks linked the bay laurel and the spurge laurel because of similarities in their leaves and fruit. The spurge laurel was used as a purgative, sparingly because it was known to be toxic. According to Mattioli (*I Discorsi*, p. 1326), *Mezereon* was the Arabic name for two plants called by Dioscorides 'Thimelea' and 'Chamelea' (probably *Daphne* spp.). He cites the Arabic authority Mesue (see **119**) on the toxicity of the *Mezereon*, and it is this passage of the *Discorsi* that the *Erbario* mostly draws upon. The annotation cites p. 1327, where a 'Chamelea' is illustrated, but the identity of the plant represented in that figure is uncertain.

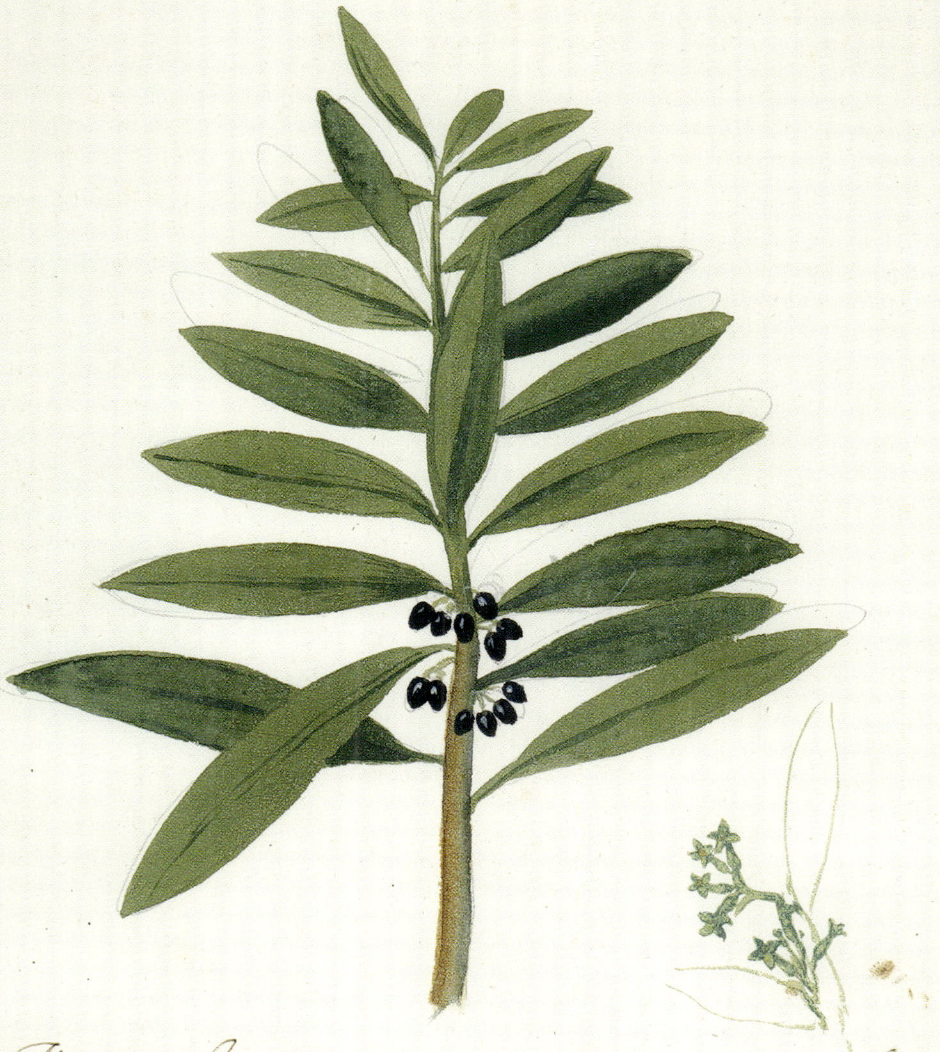

Mezereon o Olivella, è simile al veleno, perche nuoce a tutte
li membra principali; oue sonno le miniere de tutte le virtù del
corpo, pero si coregge quando si vol dare per alcuna medecina
è calda, le suo pilole ò acini, sonno in uso apresso li moderni
medici, per li Hidropici, ma nõ si danno se nõ a i corpi robusti
loda Galeno per mondificare lulcere corosive, al VIII libro de
la facultà de i semplice, 1327 - 10.

133. Guelder rose, *Viburnum opulus* L. cv.

Erbario Miniato, fol. 133 (RL 27823)

NUMBERING: *630*

ANNOTATION: *SAMBUCO AQUATICO PULIANTO* ('Aquatic many-flowered elder')

The guelder rose is a large shrub (up to 5m in height) of the family Caprifoliaceae. It flourishes in the temperate, forested zones of Europe and Asia Minor at altitudes from sea level to 1,100m. The plant has a smooth, slender, flexible stem with olive-green, trilobed leaves growing from short petioles with small, fringed stipules. The globe-like inflorescence is made up of numerous white flowers whose tubular corollas are divided into five broad, oval lobes. In its natural state the inflorescence takes the form of a loose corymb of large, sterile flowers surrounding a cluster of smaller, fertile flowers. The artist has depicted here a showy cultivated variety known as *palla di neve* ('snowball'), which may be seen in many of the floral still-life paintings of the period.

The origin of the name *Viburnum*, used in ancient Rome for one species of the genus, is not known but may be linked to the Latin *viere*, 'to plait or weave', since the flexible branches were used to fashion garlands, baskets and other woven objects. Although mainly cultivated as an ornamental, the guelder rose also has medicinal properties. The bark, gathered in the autumn, can be used to treat muscle spasms, particularly in women during childbirth or menopause. An infusion of the plant may serve as a mouthwash and disinfectant in cases of throat infection.

As in **131**, the annotation does not cite Mattioli (who illustrates a 'Sambuco aquatico' on p. 1332 of the *Discorsi*), but the sheet is nonetheless placed in Mattioli sequence within the *Erbario*.

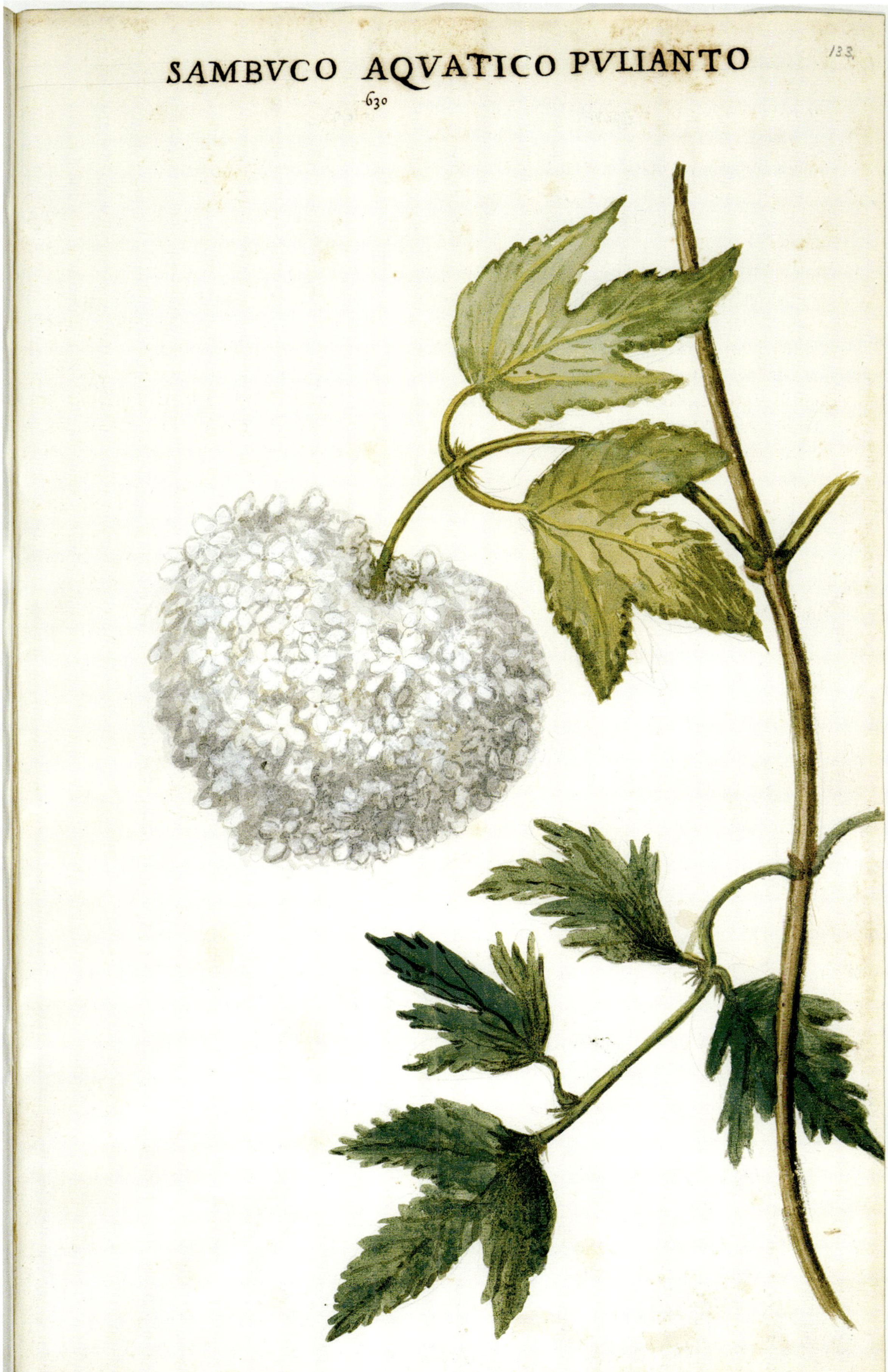
SAMBVCO AQVATICO PVLIANTO
630
133

134. Dodder, *Cuscuta* sp.

Erbario Miniato, fol. 134 (RL 27824)

Watermark: Eagle (range 14–20)

NUMBERING: *631*

ANNOTATION: *Epithimo solve gli humori malinconici piu d' ogni altra medecina, il che / fa egli con agevolezza, e senza molestia. vale nelle infirmita del capo, come / melanconia, mal caduco, vertigine, dolori antichi, e simili, causati da humori malinconici, vale al tremore del cuore, alle sincope, et alle infirmita malincolice, / alle opilatione. e' altri difetti di milza, matricali e' delle reni, e' solenne. medecina / p[er] il cancoro, p[er] la lepra, disecca. scalda nel terzo grado, 1340* ('*Epithimo* cures melancholic humours better than any other medicine. It does this with great ease and no harm. It is good for infirmities of the head such as melancholy, epilepsy, vertigo, chronic pains and the like caused by melancholic humours. It is good for heart palpitations, syncope and melancholy infirmities; for obstructions and other problems of the spleen, the uterus and the kidneys. It is an exceptional medicine for cancer, for leprosy. It dries, warms in the third degree. 1340'). [From Mattioli 1568, p. 1340]

This drawing depicts a bundle of some species of dodder, a common parasitic weed of the family Convolvulaceae which envelops its host and draws off nutrients by means of suckers (see also **135**). The artist has rapidly sketched its tangled mass of slender, brownish-red stems dotted with small, white, five-petalled flowers.

There was some confusion among the classical authorities as to the nature of this plant, as related by Mattioli (pp. 1339–42). Dioscorides thought it was related to thyme, while others, including Mesue (see **119**) described it instead as a parasite of thyme (hence the name *epithimo*, '[growing] on thyme'). The medicinal properties of the plant listed by Cesi are mostly drawn from Mattioli's commentaries on Mesue and Galen on p. 1340 of the *Discorsi*. The 'Epithimo' illustrated on p. 1341 is *Cuscuta epithymum*.

631

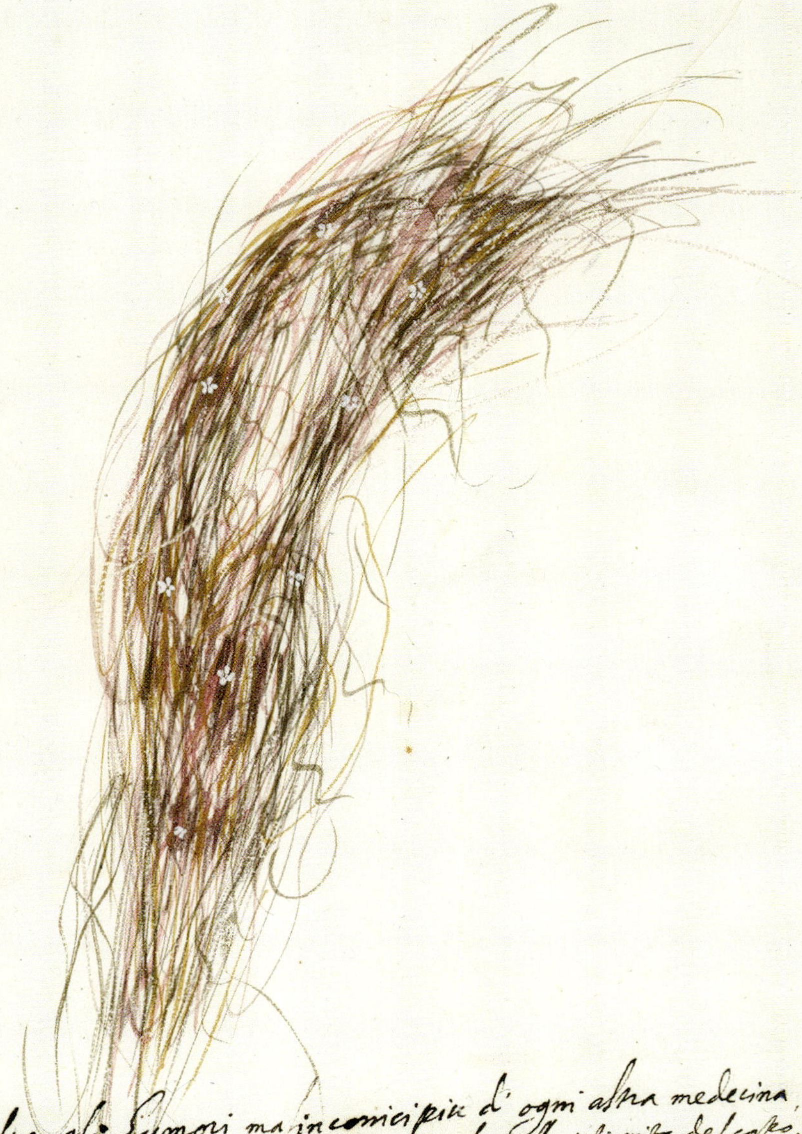

Epitimo solue gli humori malincolici piu d'ogni altra medecina, il che
fa egli con agevolezza, e senza molestia, uale nelle infirmita del capo, come
malanconia, mal caduco, vertigine, dolori antichi, e simili, causati da humori
malinconici, uale al tremore del cuore, alle sincope, et alle infirmita malincolice,
alle opilatione, e altri difetti di milza, matricali e delle veni, e solenne medecina
per il cancero, per la Lepra, disecca, scalda nel terzo grado, 1340

135. Dodder, *Cuscuta* sp.

Erbario Miniato, fol. 135 (RL 27825)

NUMBERING: *632*

ANNOTATION: *Cuscuta, ha virtu' astersiva, e' confortativa, con una certa sua stitticita', / che ella contiene, apre le oppilationi del fegato, e' parimente della milza, / mondifica le vene, e' l sangue da gli humori tanto colerici, quanto flematici, / provoca el orina,: cura il trabocco del fiele causato da opilatione de fe= / gato, giova alle febre de i fanciulli, purga p*[*er*] *disotto la ~~cole~~ chole= / ra rossa, 1342* ('*Cuscuta* has cleansing and soothing properties, with a certain constipating quality. It opens occlusions of the liver and likewise of the spleen, cleanses veins and blood of both choleric and phlegmatic humours. It stimulates urination, cures excess bile caused by obstruction of the liver, is beneficial for fever in children, and purges red bile from down below. 1342'). [From Mattioli 1568, pp. 1341–2]

This is another specimen of dodder (see **134**), identified by Cesi as the 'Cuscuta' (now a generic name) illustrated on p. 1342 of the *Discorsi* (*Cuscuta* sp.). The annotations are taken from Mattioli's description of the 'Cuscuta', a plant which he introduced to his commentary on Dioscorides' 'Epithimo' (the 'Cuscuta' had not been mentioned by Dioscorides).

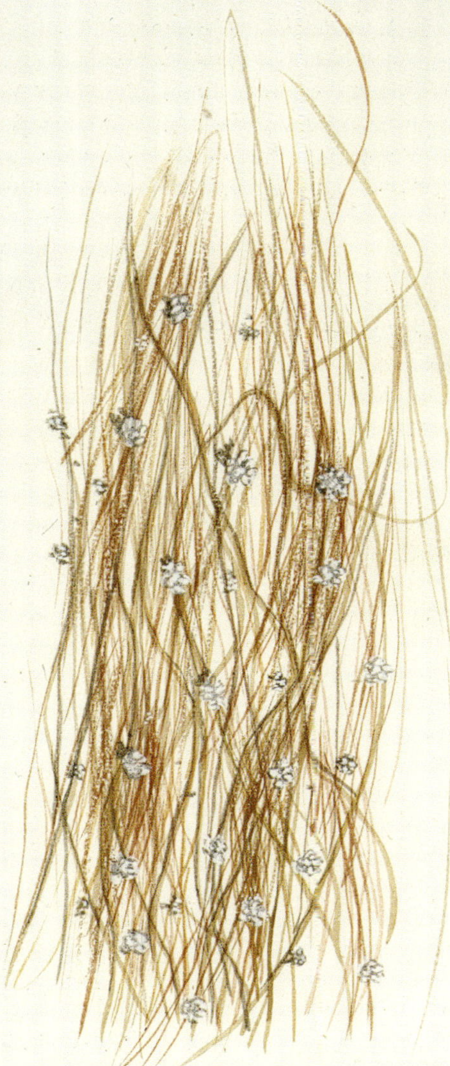

Cuscuta, La virtù abstersiva, e confortativa, con una certa sua stitticità, che ella contiene, apre le oppilationi del fegato, e parimente della milza, mondifica le vene, e'l sangue da gli humori tanto colerici, quanto flematici; provoca el orina;: cura il trabocco del fiele ~~cau~~sato da opilatione de fegato, giova alle febre de i, fanciulli; purga per di sotto la ~~colo~~ colera rossa, 1342

136. Bittersweet, *Solanum dulcamara* L.

Erbario Miniato, fol. 136 (RL 27826)

Watermark: Eagle 14

NUMBERING: *633*

ANNOTATION: *Vite salvatica. La radice bollita nel acqua, e' beuta in doi / ciathi di vino inaquato con acqua marina, purga / l'humidita del corpo. e pero si dà ella à gli hi= / dropici, spegne la sua ~~uva~~ uva i difetti, è le macole della / pelle della faccia, e' de ogni altro luogo,* 1345 ('Wild vine. The root, boiled in water and drunk in two cups of wine diluted with sea water, purges the body of humidity. And for this reason it is also given to dropsy patients. Its grape eliminates blemishes and spots from the skin of the face and from every other place. 1345'). [From Mattioli 1568, pp. 1344–5]

The bittersweet is a perennial shrub of the family Solanaceae which grows throughout the temperate zones of the northern hemisphere, in damp forests and shady uncultivated fields at altitudes from sea level to 1,100m. Like many species of Solanaceae (see **14–23**) it is poisonous, and it was known as the *vite di Giuda* ('the vine of Judas') in Tuscany and as the *pomodoro del serpente* ('viper's tomato') or the *bacca del diavolo, del lupo* or *del rospo* ('devil's', 'wolf's' or 'toad's berry') in other parts of Italy. A concoction of couch grass, mallow, burdock and bittersweet was used to cleanse the blood.

The stem here is erect and knobbly. The leaves are lanceolate with smooth margins; usually they have two smaller lobes at their base, as is suggested by the black chalk outlines beneath the two leaves on the right. A twig bears eight red oval berries on long pedicels. At lower right is a detail of a flowering twig; the long-stemmed flowers, arranged in a loose cluster, have lilac corollas divided into five acute lobes. The united anthers can be seen protruding in a yellow cone from the centre of each flower.

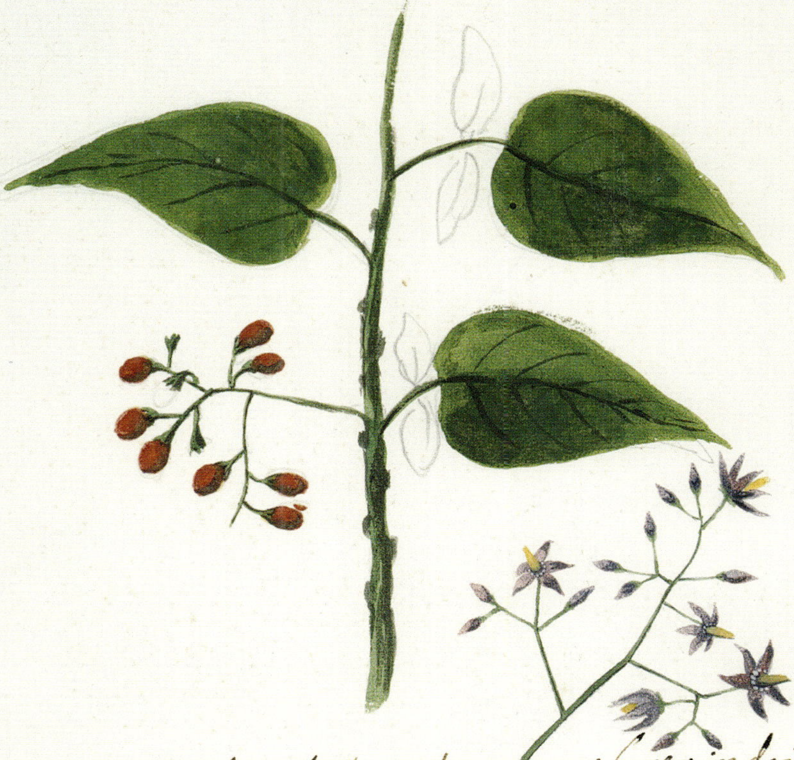

Vite saluatica, la radice bollita nel acqua, e' beuta in doi ciathi di vino inaquato con acqua marina, purga l'humidità del corpo. e pero si dà ella à gli hi= dropici, spegne la suauua i difetti, e' le macole della pelle della faccia, e' de ogni altro luogo, 1345

137. Black bryony, *Tamus communis* L.

Erbario Miniato, fol. 137 (RL 27827)

Watermark: Eagle 18

NUMBERING: *634*

ANNOTATION: *frutti acerbi de la vite nera. 1348* ('Unripe fruit of the black vine. 1348'). [From Mattioli 1568, p. 1348]

Black bryony is a perennial of the family Dioscoreaceae (see also **139**). Common throughout the Mediterranean, it grows along hedges and in clearings and forests at altitudes from sea level to 800m, and is cultivated as an ornamental. This specimen has a light green, slender, twining stem and heart-shaped leaves with smooth margins and dark veins. A small number of green fruit grow on short pedicels from the axil of each leaf; when fully mature the berries become bright red. Three tiny female flowers can be seen attached to the uppermost node.

Pliny and Columella used the term *Tamus* to refer to a type of wild vine, and Linnaeus adopted the name for this genus even though it does not include any true vines. Many of the common names for the plant – *uva del diavolo, radice vergine, sigillo della Madonna* ('devil's grape', 'Virgin's root', 'Madonna's seal') in Italy, and *raisin du diable* ('devil's berry') in France – reflect its opposing properties: it was used as both an emetic and a purgative, and compresses prepared with the juice would speed the healing of bruises, but could also raise them.

634

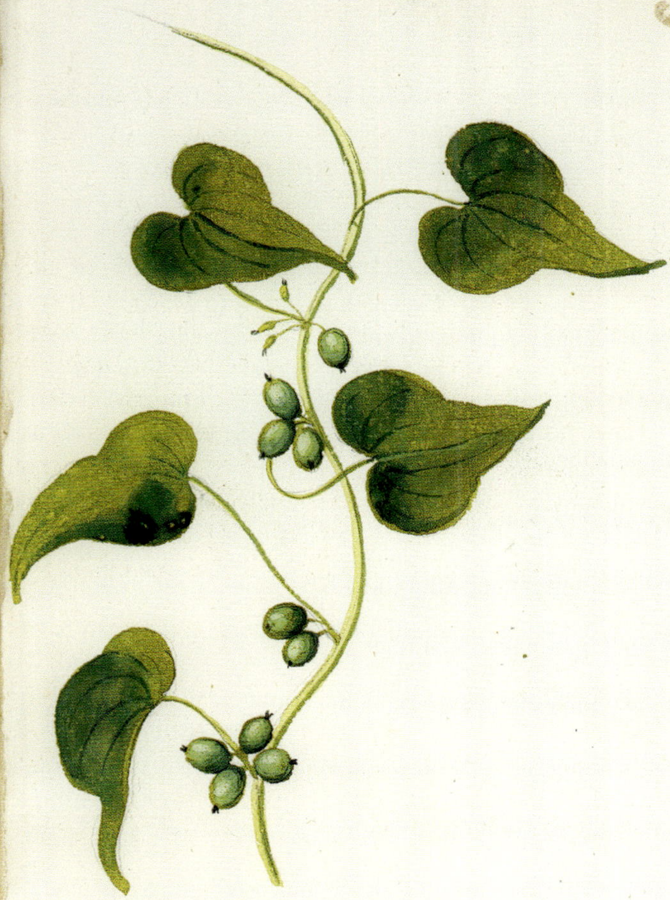

frutti acerbi de la uite nera. 1348

138. White bryony, *Bryonia dioica* Jacq. 1774

Erbario Miniato, fol. 138 (RL 27828)

Watermark: Fleur de lys 49

NUMBERING: *635*

ANNOTATION: *La Vite bianca. alcuni la chiamano / Brionia. i' fusti piu teneri cotti ne i, cibi / solvano il corpo. e' provocano l'orina, si mettano ne li impiastri / p[er] li cancari, spegne le macule della faccia. i, cuosi, le lentigine, / e' le cicatrici, nere, impiastrata con vino, risolve le infiamagioni, e' / rompe le posteme, si mette nelle medicine corosive, vale al mal caduco, dassi nelle / medesimo modo, a' i, ~~tigisi~~, vertiginosi, giova beuta a' i, morsi delle vipere. provoca / le secondine, delle donne, e' similmente il parto, beuta ~~l orina~~ provoca el'orina, / p[er] la tosse, p[er] li spasemati, p[er] li Rotti, p[er] li dolori del corpo, consuma la milza, / purga la ~~mal~~ madrice, il seme. si unge p[er] la rogna, p[er] la scabbia, 1347* ('The white vine. Some call it bryony. The tenderest stems cooked in food are laxative and induce urination; they are used in poultices for cancers. It eliminates facial blemishes, pustules, freckles and dark scars. Applied with wine it cures inflammations and bursts abscesses. It is added to corrosive medicines, is good for epilepsy and is administered in the same way to those suffering from vertigo. When drunk it is effective against snake bites. It facilitates elimination of the placenta in women, and similarly childbirth. It induces urination when drunk. For coughs, spasms, ruptures, pains in the body. It reduces the spleen, purges the uterus. The seed is rubbed on for psoriasis and scabies. 1347'). [From Mattioli 1568, pp. 1346–7]

The white bryony is a perennial of the family Cucurbitaceae (and thus unrelated to the black bryony, **137**, which belongs to the Dioscoreaceae). It grows in damp, shady areas around the Mediterranean, and is cultivated as an ornamental. Here two branches are shown with slender stems, coiled tendrils and large, irregularly shaped leaves. There are several clusters of male flowers, with greenish-white corollas divided into five lobes and barely visible yellow anthers.

The name bryony derives from the Greek βρυόεις (*bryoeis*), 'weedy' or 'flourishing', probably a reference to the rapidity with which the plant spreads. It was once used as a purgative and diuretic, but its roots contain a toxic substance that is highly irritating to the skin.

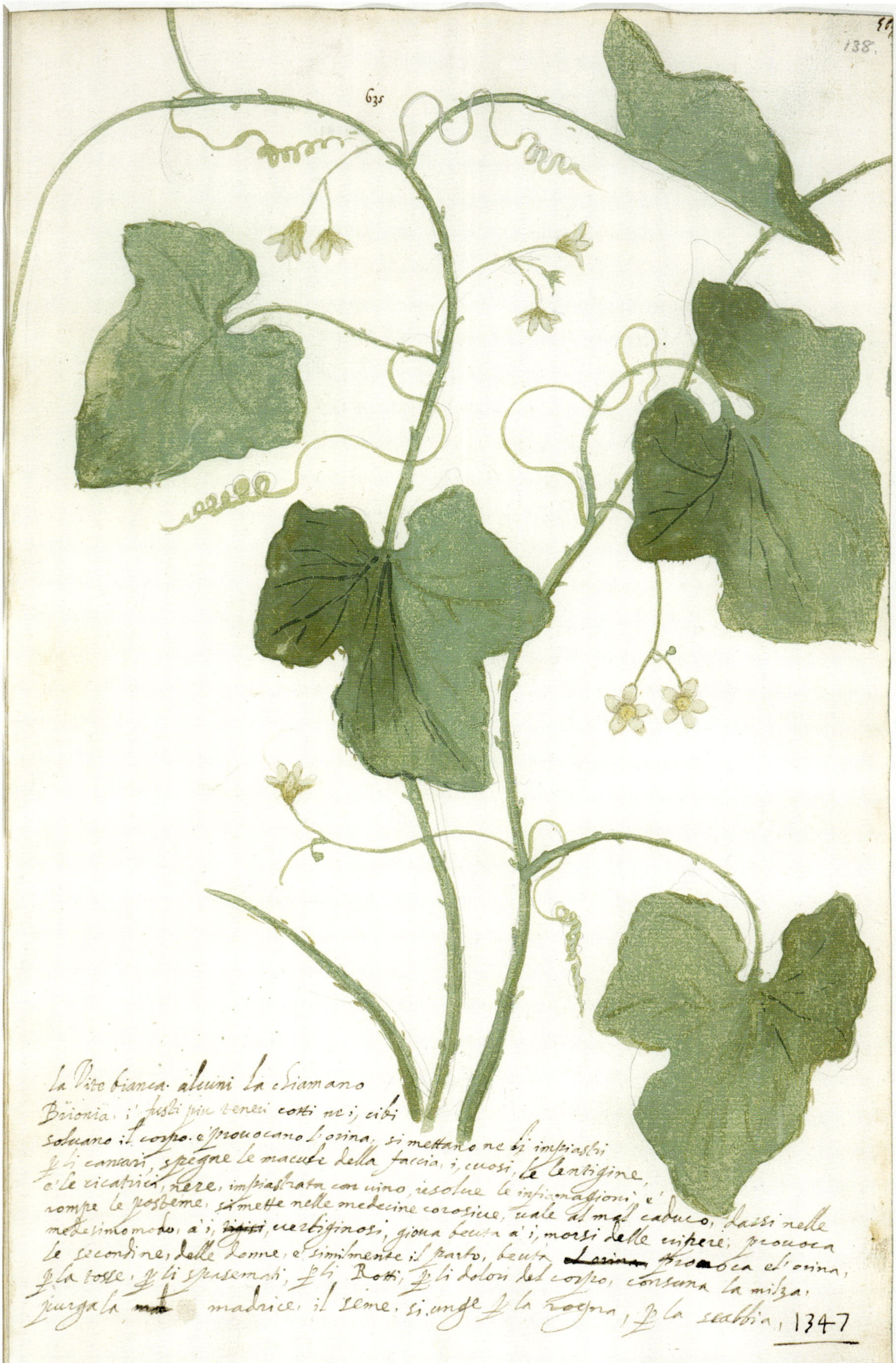
51
138.
635
la Vite bianca alcuni la chiamano
Brionia, i fusti piu teneri cotti ne i cibi
soluano il corpo e prouocano l'orina, si mettano ne li impiastri
p li cancari, spegne le macule della faccia, i, cuosi, le lentigine
e le cicatrici, nere, impiastrata con uino, risolue le infiamagioni, e
rompe le posteme, si mette nelle medecine corosiue, uale al mal caduco, dassi nelle
medesimo modo, a i, vertiginosi, gioua beuta a i, morsi delle uipere, prouoca
le secondine, delle donne, e similmente il parto, beuta prouoca el'orina,
p la tosse, p li spasimati, p li Rotti, p li dolori del corpo, consuma la milza,
purga la madrice, il seme, si unge p la rogna, p la scabbia, 1347

139. Black bryony, *Tamus communis* L.

Erbario Miniato, fol. 139 (RL 27829)

Watermark: Fleur de lys 51

NUMBERING: *636*

ANNOTATION: *fiori de la vite nera ò Brionia; Vite Nera, laquale chiamano alcuni Brionia, nera, provoca / i mestui, fanno orinare, sminuisce la milza, giova a' i, vertigi= / nosi, al mal caduco, e' a' i paralitici la radice ha la medesima / natura de le vite bianche, ma no[n] e' cosi aficacie, impiastrisi le / fronde con vino, al lulcere del collo de li animali, che vanno / sotto al giogo, 1348.* ('Flowers of the black vine or bryony. The black vine, which some call black bryony, induces menstruation and urination, reduces the spleen, is effective against vertigo, epilepsy, and is good for paralysis. The root has the same quality as the white vine, but is not as effective. The leaves are applied with wine to the neck ulcers of animals that work under the yoke. 1348.'). [From Mattioli 1568, p. 1348]

This is a second drawing of the black bryony (see **137**). Here the artist shows the plant in flower. From each node of the slender, greenish-brown stem grow two or three heart-shaped leaves and several racemes of yellowish-green, male flowers.

Fronde la uite nera ó Brionia
636

139.

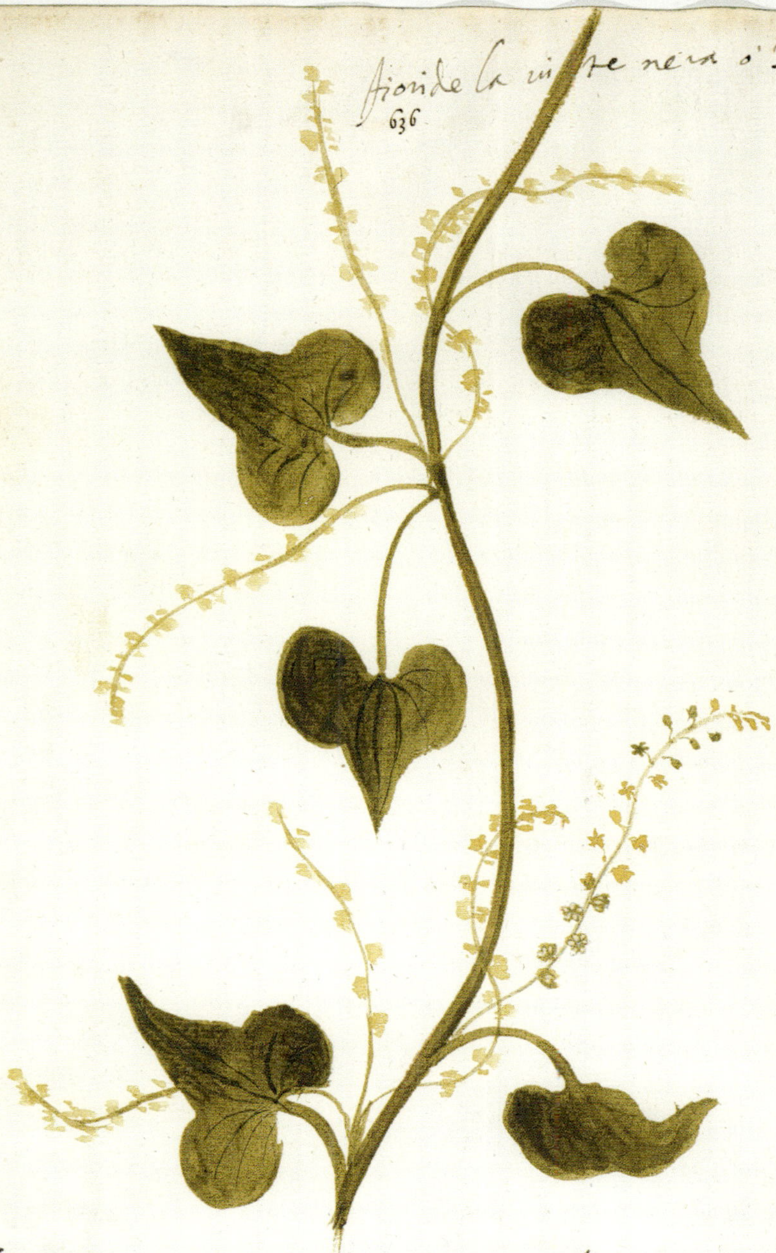

Vite Nera, laquale chiamano alcuni Brionia, nera, prouoca
i mestrui, fanno orinare, sminuisce la milza, gioua a' i uertigi=
nosi, al mal caduco, e' a' i paralitici la radice ha la medesima
natura de le uite bianche, ma nō e' cosi eficacie, impiastrisi le
fronde con uino, al lulcere del collo de li animali che uanno
sotto al giogo, 1348.

140. Balsam apple, *Momordica balsamina* L.

Erbario Miniato, fol. 140 (RL 27830)

NUMBERING: *637*

ANNOTATION: *La Balsamina, hanno le sue frondi virtu / di consolidare tutte le ferite. E' masime de / nervi. el olio, che per infusione si fa del suo frutto. conferisce a' tutte le fe= / rite, alle posteme. e ulcere delle mammelle, levandone il dolore: ~~e' parimente~~ / ~~all'ulcere, posteme e' dolori della madrice.~~ quando vi si getta dentro con la siringa. / vale ai dolori del parto. e a' quelli dell' HEMORRHOIDI mirabilmente. il perche / si fa egli particolarmente. infondendo i suoi frutti nell'olio di mandorle dolci, e / mettendo per ogni libra de olio una oncia di vernice liquida, spegne il fervore / delle cotture del fuoco. e di tutte le calide posteme. vale alle ponture de i, /~~nel~~ nervi, e' asotiglia le cicatrice. Referiscono alcuni de i, moderni, che se le / donne sterili entrano prima in un bagno fatto con herbe matricali, e' poscia / si ungano la bocca della madrice con questo olio, e' si congiungano poscia / con il marito. facilmente si ingravidano: e' salutiferissima per l'ulcere del / la madrice: Giova benissimo alle crepature INTESTINALI, ungendone spesso / il luoco con esso caldo. La polvere dell' herba data alla quantita d' un' cucchiaro / con acqua di piantagine. consolida le ferite de li interiora. ancora che la / ferita pasasse da una banda e' laltra. e' altri dicano che la medesima polvere / vale a' i dolori colici, e' delli budella. del che opera con mirabile prestezza, / 1349* ('*Balsamina.* Its leaves have the quality of healing all wounds, especially of the nerves. The oil made from its fruit by infusion is beneficial for all wounds, abscesses, and ulcers of the breast, taking their pain away; ~~and likewise for ulcers, abscesses, and pains in the uterus~~ when injected with a syringe. It is wonderfully effective against labour pains and those caused by haemorrhoids, for which in particular its fruit is soaked in sweet almond oil and for every pound of oil one ounce of liquid resin is added. It extinguishes the throbbing of burns and of all hot abscesses, is effective against pains of the nerves and reduces scars. Some modern authors say that if barren women first take a bath prepared with fertility herbs and rub the opening of the uterus with this oil, and then lie with their husbands, they will easily conceive. It is very beneficial for ulcers of the uterus. It is most effective against intestinal lesions, applying warm oil to the site frequently. The powder of the herb administered in the quantity of one spoonful together with the juice of the plantain heals internal wounds before they can spread. And others say that the same powder is effective against colic and intestinal pains, in which it works with admirable rapidity. 1349'). [From Mattioli 1568, pp. 1349, 1351]

LITERATURE: Freedberg 2002, pp. 206–7 (fig. 8.3), 209

The balsam apple, a member of the family Cucurbitaceae, is native to tropical Asia and Australia and has become naturalized in Africa and the Mediterranean, where it grows in citrus orchards and vineyards (see also **141**). Fuchs (1542, p. 188) recorded that it had recently been introduced into Germany, and was being grown in German gardens; it had reached England by 1568, when William Turner noted that 'it groweth much in Italy, and in some places of England in gardines' (Turner 1568, p. 16). This is one of the finest and most complete drawings in the *Erbario Miniato*, with unusually extensive notes transcribing almost all the passages in the *Discorsi* relating to the properties of the plant.

The stem of the plant is slender, smooth and straight between widely spaced nodes. From each node grows a leaf, a flower and a tendril. The leaves are divided into five lobes with indented margins. The flowers have long peduncles, acute sepals and five broad overlapping petals that are either white or light yellow. The fruit, shown immature at centre left and mature at upper right, is oval in shape and covered with pointed tubercles arranged in longitudinal rows. There are three seeds of different colours – brown, yellow and orange-red – which correspond to the stages of maturation of the fruit. At centre right is a detail of the finely branching root.

637

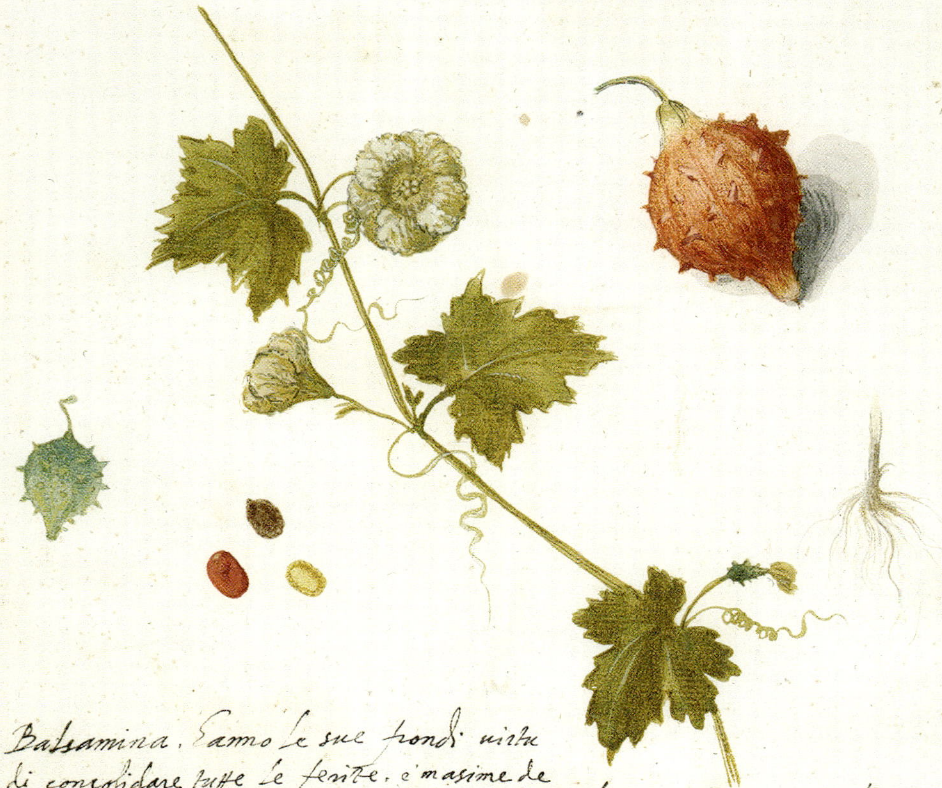

La Balsamina. hanno le sue frondi virtù di consolidare tutte le ferite. e masime de nervi. el olio, che per infusione si fa del suo frutto. conferisce à tutte le ferite, alle posteme. e ulcere delle mammelle, levandone il dolore: ~~è parimente all'ulcere, posteme e dolori della madrice.~~ quando vi si getta dentro con la siringa. vale ai dolori del parto. e á quelli dell' HEMORRHOIDI mirabilmente. il perche si fa egli particolarmente. infondendo i suoi frutti nell' olio di mandorle dolci; e mettendo per ogni libra de olio una oncia di vernice liquida, spegne il fervore delle cotture del fuoco. e di tutte le calide posteme. vale alle ponture de i, ~~ne~~ nervi, é asotiglia le cicatrice. Referiscono alcuni de i, moderni, che se le donne sterili entrano prima in un bagno fatto con herbe matricali, é poscia si ungano la bocca della madrice con questo olio, é si congiungano poscia con il marito. facilmente si ingravidano: é salutiferissima per l'ulcere della madrice: Giova benissimo alle crepature INTESTINALI, ungendone spesso il luoco con esso callo. La polvere dell' herba data alla quantità d' un cucchiaro con acqua di piantagine. consolida le ferite de li interiora. ancora che la ferita passasse da una banda é l'altra. é altri dicano che la medesima polvere vale á i dolori colici, é delli budella. del che opera con mirabile prestezza.

1349

141. Balsam apple, *Momordica balsamina* L.

Erbario Miniato, fol. 141 (RL 27831)

Watermark: Lamb 7

NUMBERING: *638*

ANNOTATION: *BALSAMINA*

This is another specimen of the balsam apple (see **140**), with a flower and two fruits. The stem is smooth, slender and sinuous. The three leaves are palmate-lobate in form with deeply toothed margins and tendrils growing from their axils. The pale yellow flower, carried on a long, sinuous peduncle, is made up of five petals with rounded apices. Below is an enlarged detail of an opened fruit, showing the dull orange pulp and six red seeds.

142. Garden balsam, *Impatiens balsamina* L.

Erbario Miniato, fol. 142 (RL 27832)

NUMBERING: *639*

ANNOTATION: *Un altra Balsamina. 1350 Matthioli.* ('Another *Balsamina*. 1350 [in] Mattioli.'). [From Mattioli 1568, p. 1350]

The garden balsam, of the family Balsaminaceae, is native to south-east Asia at altitudes from sea level to 1,000m, and has been cultivated as an ornamental in Europe since the Middle Ages. The branch is thick, smooth and light in colour, becoming almost white at its extremity. The lanceolate leaves have short stems, acute apices and finely toothed margins. Dark veins can be seen against the glossy, deep-green leaf blades. The pink flowers have short peduncles and bilabial corollas; the lower lip is divided into two deep lobes. One of the sepals protrudes in a long curved spur. Several fruits are shown growing at the base of the branch; they take the form of rounded capsules containing a number of tiny brown oval seeds, shown below.

143. Wall fern, *Polypodium vulgare* L.

Erbario Miniato, fol. 143 (RL 27833)

NUMBERING: *640*

ANNOTATION: *Polipodio. 1355; Della Filicola, overo Polipodio, a' virtu di purgare, cuocesi p[er] solvere / il corpo. La farina de la seccha. beuta con acqua melata. solve / la cholera, e la flemma. vale impiastrata valerosamente, alle / giunture smosse, e' alle setole che nascono tra le dita.* ('Polypodium. 1355. On the *Filicola* or Polypodium. It has a purgative quality. Cook it to purge the body. The flour of the dried plant drunk in honey water eliminates choler and phlegm. Applied externally it is most effective for dislocated joints and for the cracks that develop between the fingers.'). [From Mattioli 1568, pp. 1354–5]

LITERATURE: Freedberg 2002, pp. 226–8 (fig. 8.26)

The wall fern is a perennial of the family Polypodiaceae, common throughout the temperate zones of the world. It grows on walls and the trunks of fallen trees at altitudes from sea level to 2,400m.

The frond with its slender, sinuous axis is divided into light green pinnas (leaflets) with smooth margins and blunt apices. The creeping rhizome bears numerous small branching roots. Dried and ground, the rhizome was used to prepare diuretics, laxatives and a remedy for liver disorders.

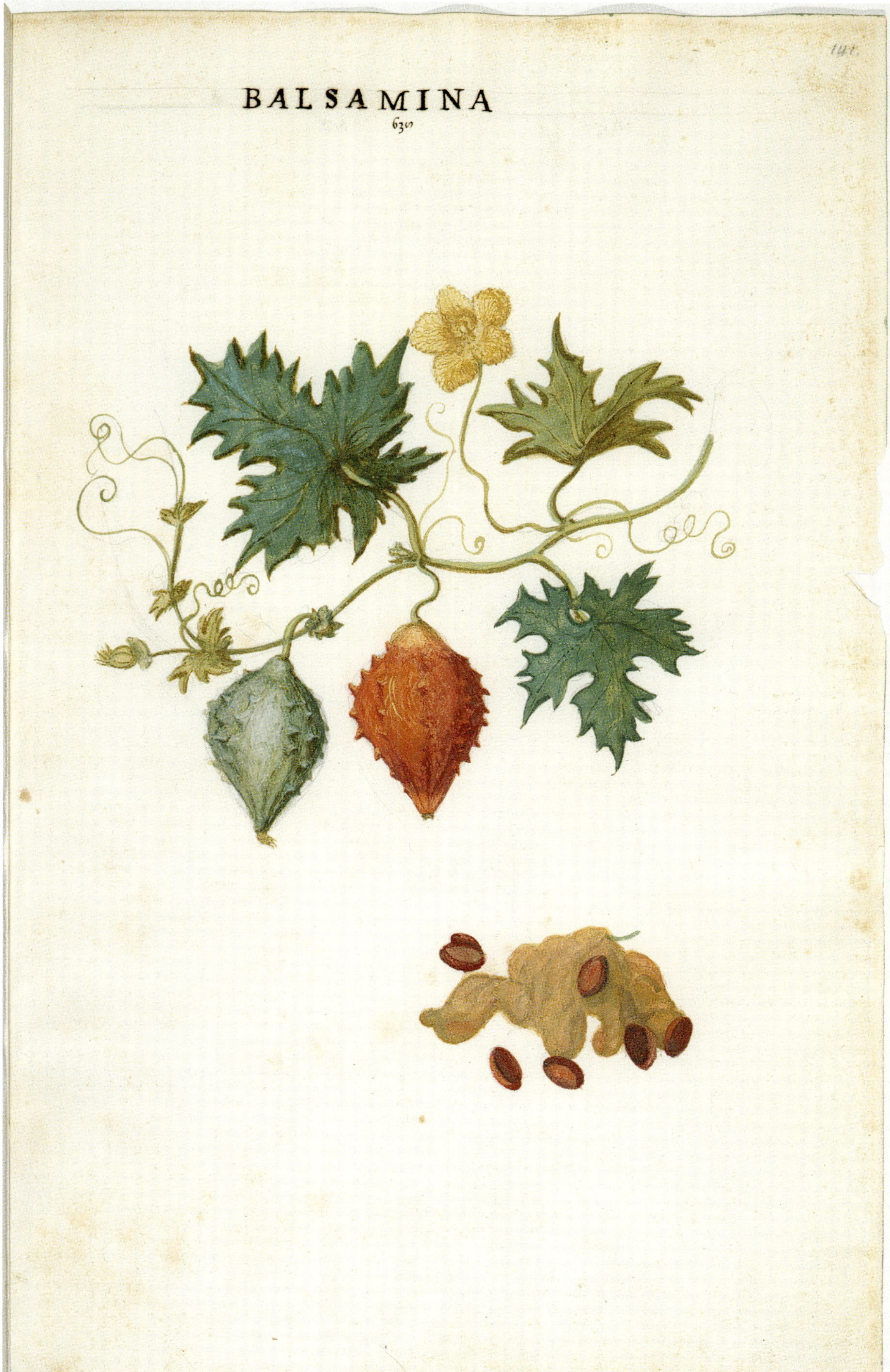
BALSAMINA

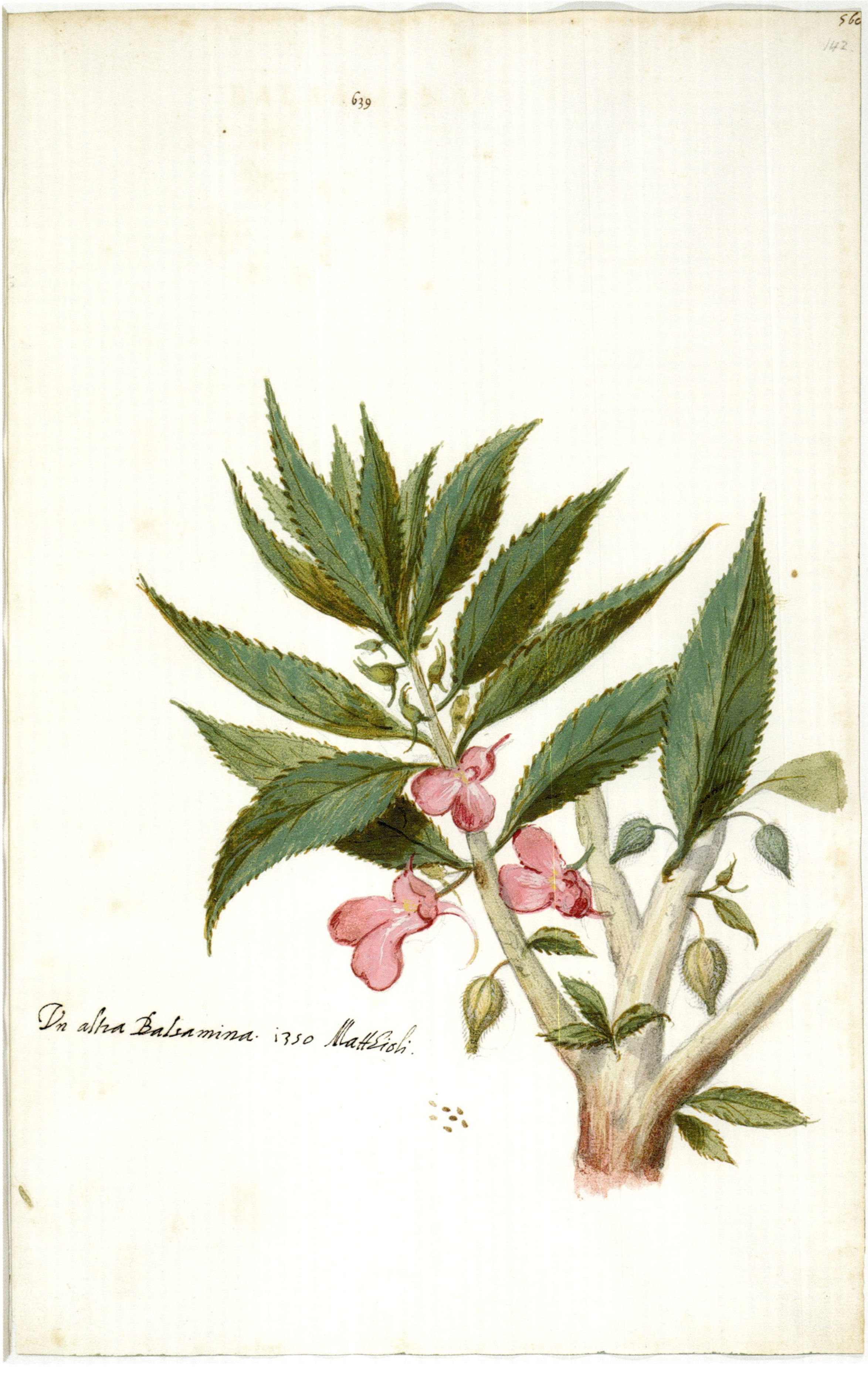
56c
142
639
Vn altra Balsamina. 1350 Matthioli.

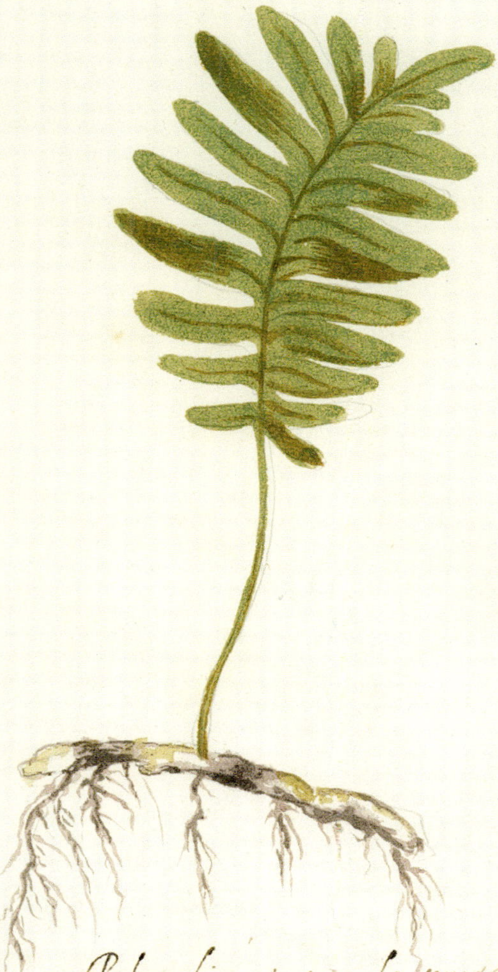

Polipodio · 1355

Della Filicola, ouero Polipodio, a' uirtu di purgare, cuocesi p̃ soluere il corpo. la farina de la secca. beuta con acqua melata. solue la colera, e la flemma. uale impiastrata ualerosamente, alle giunture smosse. e' alle setole che nascono tra le dita,

144. Ass's spleenwort, *Asplenium onopteris* L.

Erbario Miniato, fol. 144 (RL 27834)

Watermark: Eagle 18

NUMBERING: *641*

ANNOTATION: *Driopteri, questa trita e' / unti. fa cadere i, peli. 1357* ('*Driopteri*. Ground and anointed, this makes hair fall out. 1357'). [From Mattioli 1568, pp. 1356–7]

Ass's spleenwort is a perennial fern of the family Aspleniaceae. It is common in the southern Mediterranean, growing in oak forests at altitudes from sea level to 1,500m. The long slender axis is dark brown near the base, becoming light green near its end. It is lined with delicate leaflets that gradually decrease in size towards the apex. The name of the genus is derived from the Greek σπλήν (*splen*), 'spleen', as many species of the genus were considered remedies for disorders of the spleen. Like the maidenhair spleenwort (**104**), the ass's spleenwort was also used to treat throat infections.

Cesi mistakenly identifies the plant as the 'Driopteri' illustrated on p. 1357 of the *Discorsi*, which is actually the brittle bladder fern, *Cystopteris fragilis*.

144.

641

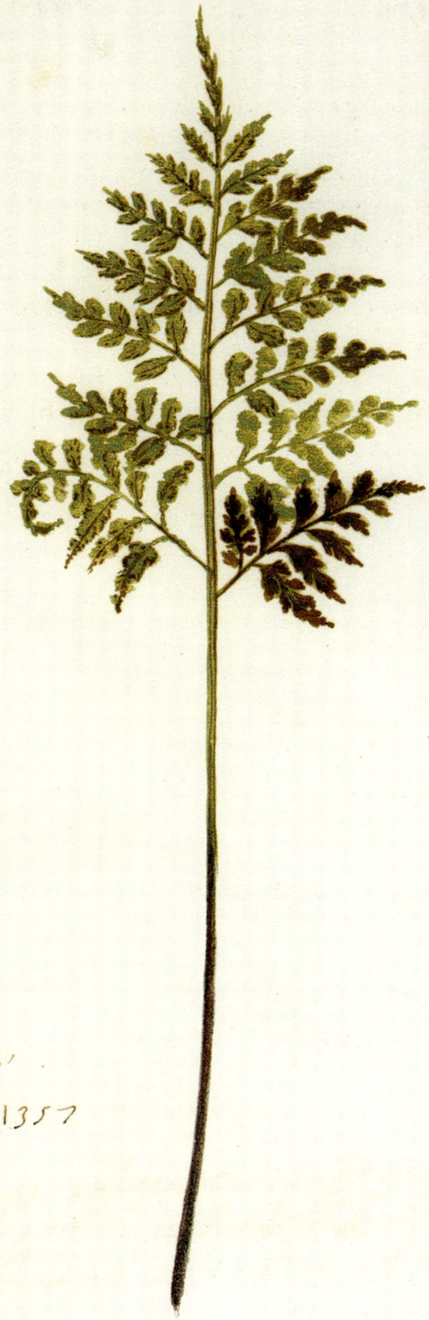

Driopteri, questa trita e'
unt. fa cadere i peli. 1357

145. Safflower, *Carthamus tinctorius* L.

Erbario Miniato, fol. 145 (RL 27835)

Watermark: Fleur de lys 50

NUMBERING: *642*

ANNOTATION: *Cnico. chiamasi volgarmente zaffarano Saracinesco / quantunque gli spitiali, imitando gli Arabi lo chiamano Carthamo / e' di natura calida nel terzo ordine. nel Mattiolo, 1358* ('*Cnico*. Commonly called Saracen saffron despite the fact that apothecaries, in imitation of the Arabs, call it cardamon. It is warm by nature, of the third order. In Mattioli, 1358'). [From Mattioli 1568, pp. 1358–9]

LITERATURE: Solinas 1989, pp. 59 (fig. 40), 63

The safflower is an annual of the family Asteraceae. Probably native to Asia, it was cultivated by the Egyptians and Babylonians, who used the seeds as a source of cooking oil and the dried flowers to dye cloth. The Romans seem to have been interested only in its medicinal properties, but the plant's applications began to multiply and its cultivation spread again during the Middle Ages. The stigmas were used to adulterate saffron; the safflower contains two colorants, a yellow dye that is soluble in water and a red dye that is soluble in alcohol, the latter once known in the textile trade as *rosso vegetale*. Today it is cultivated as an ornamental and for forage.

The specimen has a slender, smooth and sinuous stem and alternate, sessile, lanceolate leaves with smooth margins and acute apices. The flower heads are subtended by numerous small leaves; the enveloping scales and bright orange flowers are not shown in detail.

642

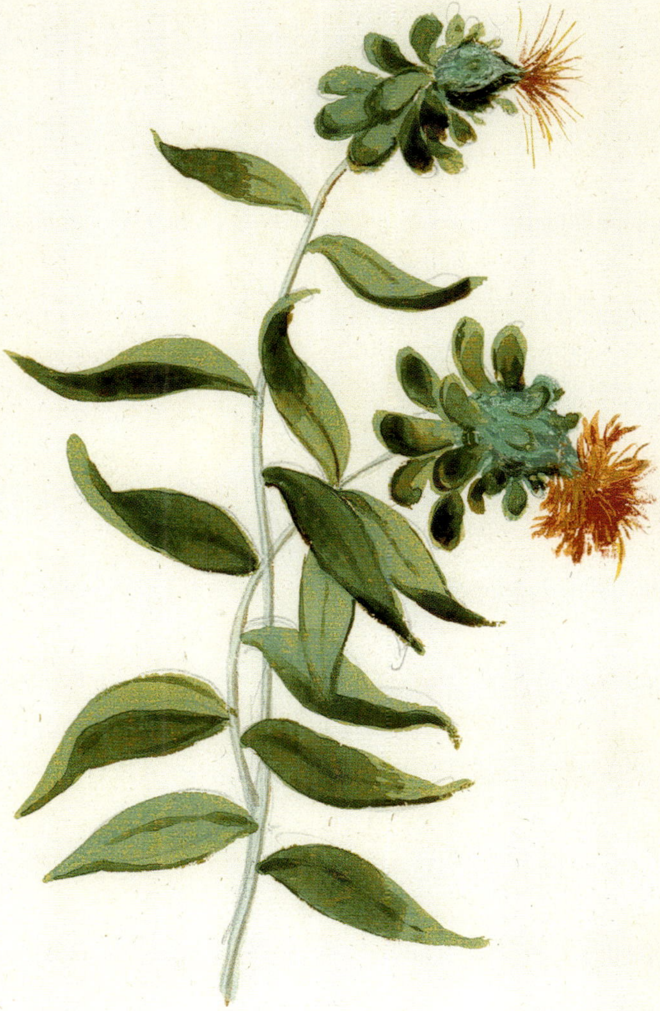

Cnïco. chiamasi volgarmente zaffarano Saracinesco
quantunque gli spitiali, imitando gli Arabi · lo chiamano Carthame
è di natura calida nel terzo ordine · nel Mattiolo, 1358.

146. Annual mercury, *Mercurialis annua* L.

Erbario Miniato, fol. 146 (RL 27836)

NUMBERING: *643*

ANNOTATION: *Mercorella femina.* 1361; *Mercorella* ~~*femi*~~ *Maschio; La Mercorella si ritruova maschio e' femina, Mangisi / luna e' laltra p[er] solvere il corpo. La sua decotione / fatta nel aqua solve la colera, e' gli umori acquosi, / credesi che le frondi de la femina beute, overo messe / nella natura dapoi le purgatione del mestruo, faccino / ingravidare di femina, e' quelle dle maschio, il maschio.* ('Female *Mercorella*. 1361; Male *Mercorella*; *Mercorella* can be found male and female. One and the other are eaten to purge the body. A decoction made with water eliminates bile and watery humours. It is believed that the leaves of the female plant, drunk or applied to the vulva after menstruation, induce the conception of females, and those of the male plant induce the conception of males.'). [From Mattioli 1568, pp. 1359–61]

Annual mercury is an annual of the family Euphorbiaceae. It is a common weed native to the Mediterranean and central Europe, and naturalized in the rest of the world, at altitudes from sea level to 1,300m. The name comes from the ancient *herba mercurialis*, as the Greeks believed that the god Hermes (i.e. Mercury) discovered the medicinal properties of the plant. The annual mercury was widely used in traditional medicine (in Piedmont it was known as 'the witch's herb'), though since the end of the eighteenth century it has been recognized as poisonous.

This illustration shows two sprigs of the plant. On the left is the base of a plant with male flowers, and on the right the upper part of a branch bearing female flowers. The plant has a smooth, erect stem, a long white taproot and opposite branches that begin at the base and continue along the length of the stem, as is suggested by the unfinished upper portion of the drawing on the left. The leaves are ovate with toothed margins and dark veins. Slender spikes growing from their axils bear tiny yellow male flowers. The branch on the right is shown in the early fruiting stage, and immature rounded green capsules can be seen at the base of the leaves.

Mattioli illustrated the 'Mercorella maschio' on p. 1360 and the 'Mercorella femina' on p. 1361 of the *Discorsi*, but he confused the male plant with the female (as do the inscriptions on this drawing). Mattioli was here following Dioscorides, who described the female plant as endowed with 'abundant clustered seed' and the male with 'small, round seed, disposed in pairs like testicles close to the leaves' (p. 1359). This error was repeated in the works of Dodoens, Lobelius and Daléchamps among others, as well as in the herbals of Gherardo Cibo (Rome, BA, *Erbario B*, vol. 3, fols 69–71, nos 763–765; see Penzig 1905, p. 114) and Ulisse Aldrovandi (Bologna, BU, MS Aldrovandi, *Tavole* vol. 3, *Piante fiori frutta*, fols 126 and 129).

643

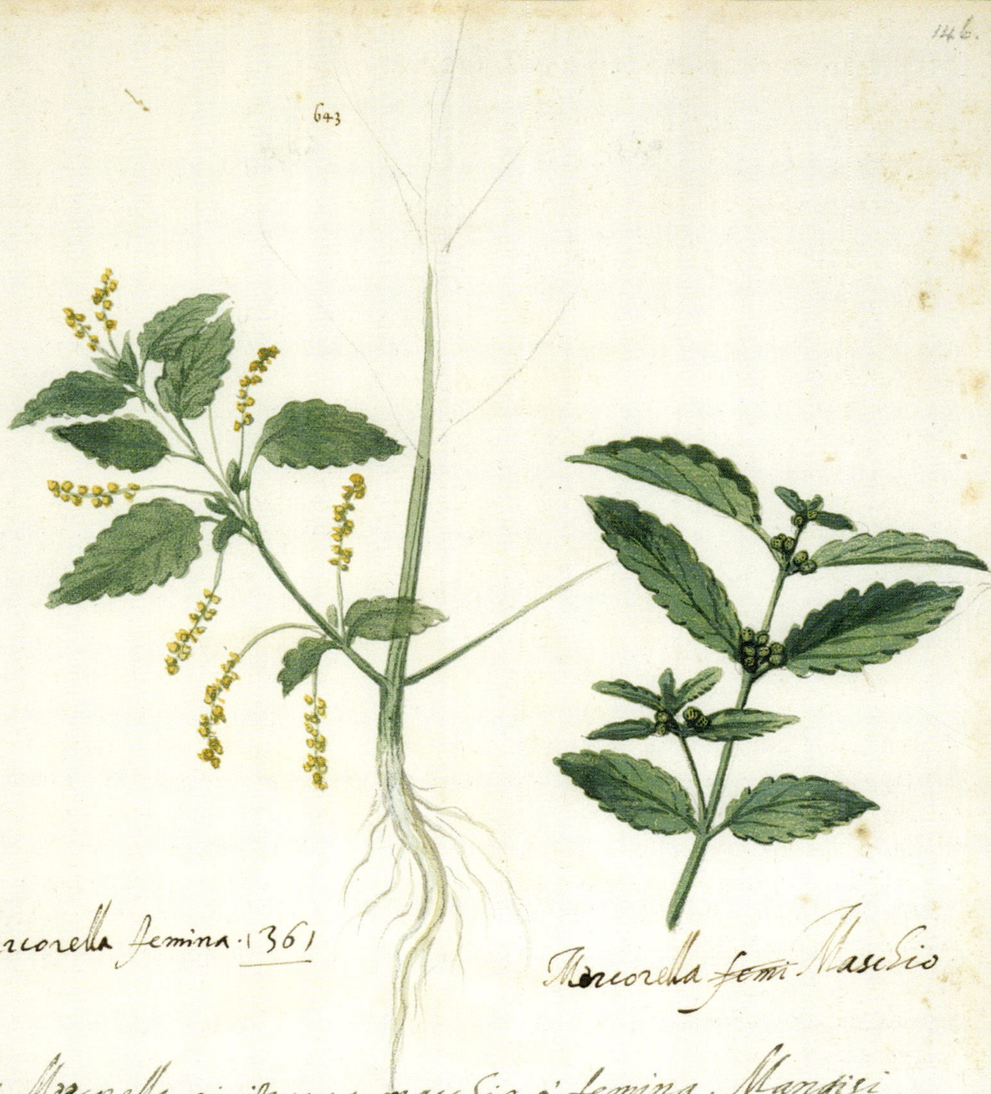

Mercorella femina 1361

Mercorella ~~femi~~ Maschio

La Mercorella si ritruoua maschio, e femina, Mangisi
l'una e l'altra ꝑ soluere il corpo, La sua decotione
fatta nel acqua solue la colera, e gli umori acquosi,
credesi che le frondi de la femina beute, ouero messe
nella natura dapoi le purgatione del mestruo, faccino
ingrauidare di femina, e quelle di maschio, il maschio,

147. Heliotrope, *Heliotropium europaeum* L.

Erbario Miniato, fol. 147 (RL 27837)

Watermark: Eagle 18

NUMBERING: *644*

ANNOTATION: [cut] *Heliotropio Magiore, da alcuni Scorpiuro. La decotione de unmanipolo / de lerba fatta nel acqua, beuta purga p*[*er*] *il corpo la collera, e' la / flemma, vale tanto beuta con vino, quanto impiastrata, alle pontu= / re degli scorpione. il suo seme beuto con vino guarisce la febre quart*[*a*] */ na. e' la terzana, il seme impiastrato, disecca le formiche verruca*[–] */ e' pendenti, i thimi. e similmente l'epinittidi, impiastrinsi utilmente le / frondi a' gli ardori del capo de i, fanciulli, alle podagre, e' alli dislogag*[*i*] */ oni delle giunture, provocano i, mestui, e' aplicate trite di sotto. Fann*[*o*] */ partorire. 1363* ('Greater heliotrope, called by some *Scorpiuro*. The decoction of a bunch of the herb, made in water and drunk, purges the body of choler and phlegm. For scorpion stings it is effective both drunk with wine or applied externally. Its seed drunk with wine cures quartan and tertian fevers. The seed applied as a poultice dries domed and pendant verrucas, fleshy excrescences and also nocturnal rashes. The leaves in a poultice are beneficial for head fevers in children, for gout, and for dislocated joints. They stimulate menstruation, and are applied minced to the lower parts to induce labour. 1363'). [From Mattioli 1568, p. 1363]

The heliotrope is an annual of the family Boraginaceae, common throughout southern Europe, the Mediterranean and the Middle East. It flourishes in cultivated and uncultivated terrain at altitudes from sea level to 600m. The plant has an erect, smooth, branching stem that tapers markedly at its apex. The alternate leaves are ovate in form with smooth margins and short petioles. Tiny white flowers grow at the ends of paired cymes. The slightly swollen calyxes contain the fruit of the plant. On the right is a detail of the long taproot.

In antiquity it was thought that the heliotrope's flower followed the rotation of the sun, hence its Latin name *heliotropium*, from the Greek ἥλιος (*helios*), 'sun', and τροπή (*trope*), 'turn'. The flower was identified with the nymph Clytie who (as recounted in Ovid's *Metamorphoses*) fell in love with the sun god Apollo, was transformed into a flower and followed his progress across the sky each day; that flower, however, was violet rather than white. Giovanni Battista della Porta's *Phytognomonica* (1588, p. 185) illustrated and described a 'Heliotropium maior' as an antidote for scorpion bites, in accordance with the doctrine of signatures (following the shape of the cymes; see also **154** and **155**).

644

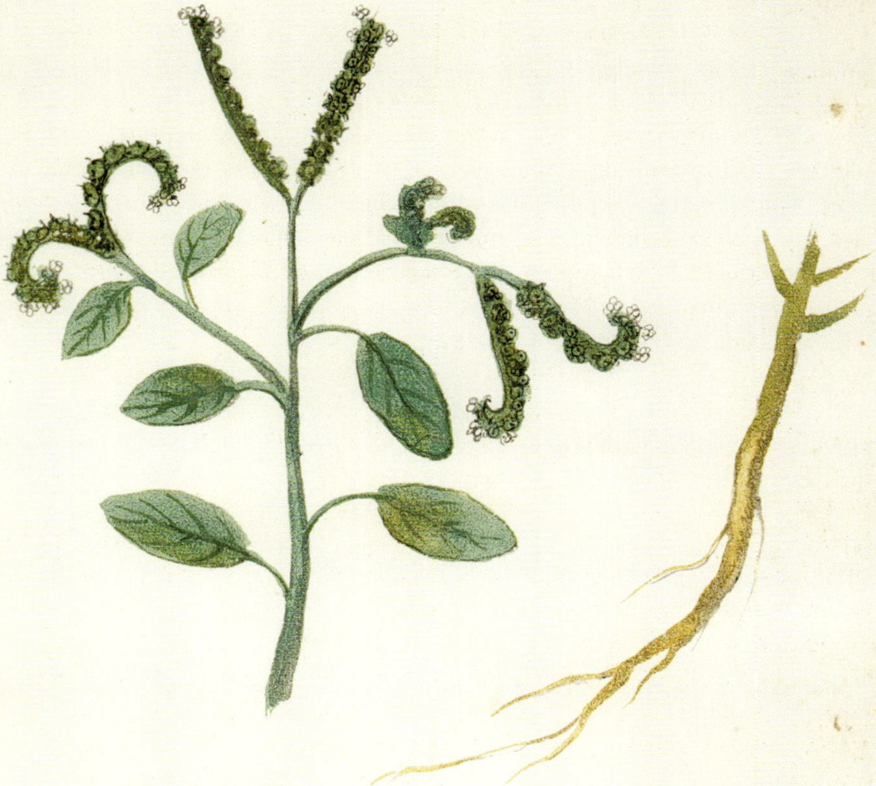

Heliotropio Magiore, da alcuni Scorpiuro. la decottione de un manipolo
de l'erba fatta nel acqua, beuta purga p il corpo la collora, é la
flemma, uale tanto beuta con uino, quanto impiastrata, alle pontu=
re degli scorpione. il suo seme beuto con uino. guarisce la febre quart
na. é la terzana. il seme impiastrato, disecca le formice e uerruca
é pendenti, i timi. e similmente l'epinittidi, impiastinsi utilmente le
frondi á gli ardori del capo de i, fanciulli; alle podagre, é alli dislogag
oni delle giunture. prouocano i, mestrui, é aplicate trite disotto. fann
partorire. 1363

148. Turnsole, *Chrozophora tinctoria* (L.) A. Juss.

Erbario Miniato, fol. 148 (RL 27838)

NUMBERING: *645*

ANNOTATION: *Unaltro Heliotropio 1363* ('Another heliotrope, 1363')

VERSO: offset of **155**

The turnsole is a herbaceous annual of the family Euphorbiaceae, found in dry, calcareous soil and under cultivation along the coast in the Mediterranean and Near East. The stem of the plant is erect, smooth and light green. The broad ovate leaves have long petioles, pointed apices and slightly undulating margins. The plant is shown in the fruiting stage; its dark, bristly pods are arranged in groups of three on long, slightly reflexed peduncles. On the left is a detail of the long, yellow, slightly branching taproot.

The turnsole has been known since antiquity as the source of a dark blue dye contained in the top part of the plant and its fruit. In Provence, cloth was soaked in the dye, sprinkled with urine and allowed to dry, after which it was placed between two layers of straw above a pile of fermenting manure. The cloth would take on a fine cobalt blue; if this process was repeated a deep purple was achieved. This cloth was exported to Holland where it was used to wrap cheeses during the ageing process, giving the rind its characteristic red colour.

Cesi has supplied the same reference to Mattioli as for the previous sheet, but the turnsole is actually illustrated on p. 1364 of the *Discorsi* as a 'Heliotropio minore'.

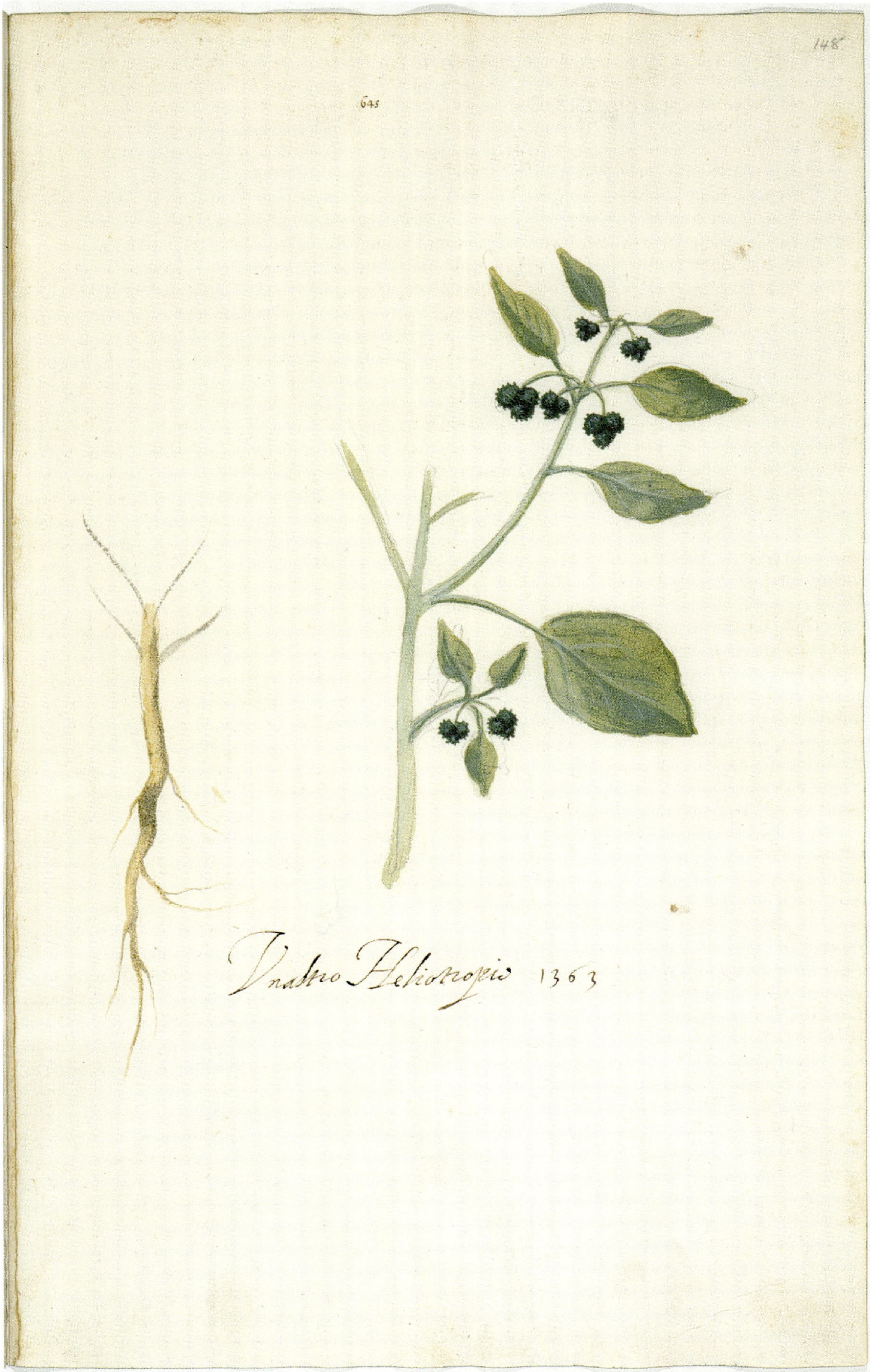
148
645
Vnaltro Heliotropio 1363

149. Pot marigold, *Calendula officinalis* L.

Erbario Miniato, fol. 149 (RL 27839)

NUMBERING: *646*

ANNOTATION: *Seme; Caltha, e' di natura stitica e' costrettiva. provoca i, mestrui, / la polvere de la seccha, messa ~~pe~~ sopra i, denti, che doglino, / vi conferisce assai. 1365; N:º 59* ('Seed; *Caltha*. It is constipating and constrictive in nature. It induces menstruation. The powder of the dried plant, applied to teeth that hurt, is very effective. 1365; No. 59'). [From Mattioli 1568, pp. 1365–7]

The pot marigold is a herbaceous annual of the family Asteraceae. Its original habitat is unknown; it is naturalized all over the world at altitudes from sea level to 600m, and is cultivated as a garden plant (see also **150–151**, **193**). The artist shows a stem of the plant with the flower head in profile, a detail of the head in a frontal view, and another detail of the spiny fruits packed in their receptacle. The plant has a slender, flexible stem and long, lanceolate leaves. The flower head, which grows from a scaly sheath, consists of an outer ring of bright orange, ligulate flowers and a central bundle of dark brown, tubular flowers.

The genus name *Calendula* derives from the fact that during the summer the marigold blossoms regularly once a month. The plant was associated with the moon because of the crescent shape of its seed, and (like many other flowers) with the goddess Venus; according to one legend, the flower sprang up where her tears fell to earth after the death of Adonis. Mattioli rejected the claims of those who identified the 'calendula' ('commonly called *Fior rancio* in Tuscany') with the 'greater heliotrope' (**147**); he was uncertain, however, as to whether the 'calendula' corresponded to the plant called 'caltha' by Virgil and Pliny (*I Discorsi*, pp. 1364–6), which name was derived from the Greek κάλαθος (*kalathos*), a vase-shaped basket, probably a reference to the form of the inflorescence.

646

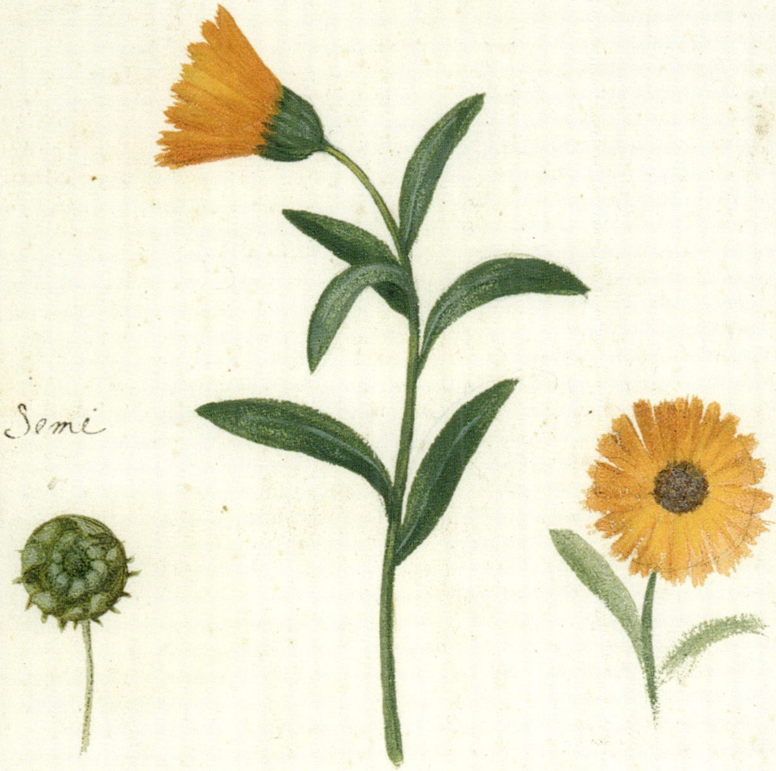

Caltha, è di natura stitica e costrettiva. provoca i mestrui, la polvere de la secca, messa ~~so~~ sopra i denti, che dogliono, vi conferisce assai. 1365.

N.° 59

150. Pot marigold, *Calendula officinalis* L. cv.

Erbario Miniato, fol. 150 (RL 27840)

Watermark: Eagle 19

NUMBERING: *647*

ANNOTATION: *CALTHA*

The artist shows here the flowering stem of a cultivated variety of the pot marigold (see **149**), and on the left the flower head of another, more heavily petalled cultivar.

151. Pot marigold, *Calendula officinalis* L. cv.

Erbario Miniato, fol. 151 (RL 27841)

NUMBERING: *648*

ANNOTATION: *Calta pulianta* ('Many-flowered *Calta*')

This folio shows another cultivar of the pot marigold (see **149**). The flower head is made up of two concentric rings of bright orange ligulate flowers surrounding a bundle of brick-red tubular flowers. Growing on long stalks in a circle around this flower head are seven smaller capitulums, each composed of orange ligulate flowers (cf. **193**). A branch with a flower bud springs from the axil of the lower pair of leaves.

Such 'monstrosities' were enthusiastically cultivated and frequently depicted in sixteenth- and seventeenth-century florilegia. This taste is better documented in northern Europe and in England than in Italy, since Gerard's *Herball* (1597), while ostensibly devoted to medicinal plants, also provides a great deal of information about garden varieties. Gerard frequently details not only double flowers but 'hose-in-hose' varieties, with additional corollas springing from the main corolla.

152. Marigold, *Tagetes* sp., probably African marigold, *Tagetes erecta* L.

Erbario Miniato, fol. 152 (RL 27842)

Two sheets joined horizontally at centre: upper sheet 193 x 275 mm, lower sheet 231 x 275 mm

NUMBERING: *649*

ANNOTATION: [cut] [*Garofani*] *Indiani Magiori* ('Greater Indian carnations')

The genus *Tagetes*, garden annuals of the family Asteraceae, originally came from Central and South America and have been cultivated in Europe since the beginning of the sixteenth century; a specimen appears in the dried herbarium begun by Gherardo Cibo in 1532. Two species came to be favoured for the ornamental garden, the African marigold, *Tagetes erecta*, and the French marigold, *Tagetes patula*. Each derives its common name from the route by which it arrived in Europe. The species illustrated here cannot be identified with certainty but is probably the former (see also **153**).

Four variant specimens are shown on two joined pieces of paper, two above with finely fringed, alternate leaves and two below with pinnate leaves. The stems are erect and smooth, broadening to form the flower's receptacle. In three the capitulum is made up entirely of ligulate florets, while the specimen at upper right has seven ligulate florets with, at their centre, what appear to be tubular flowers.

CALTHA

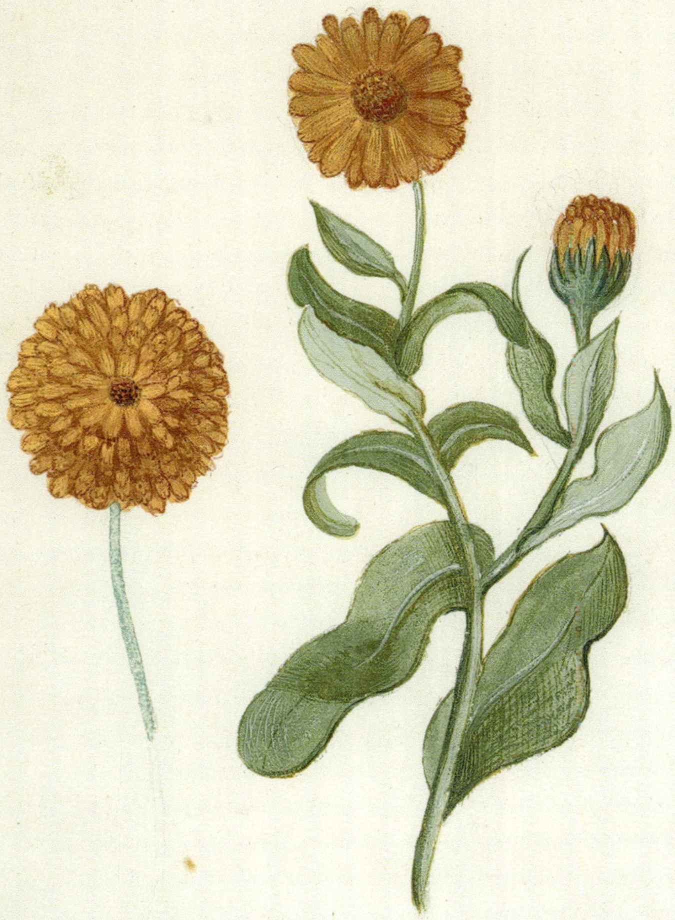

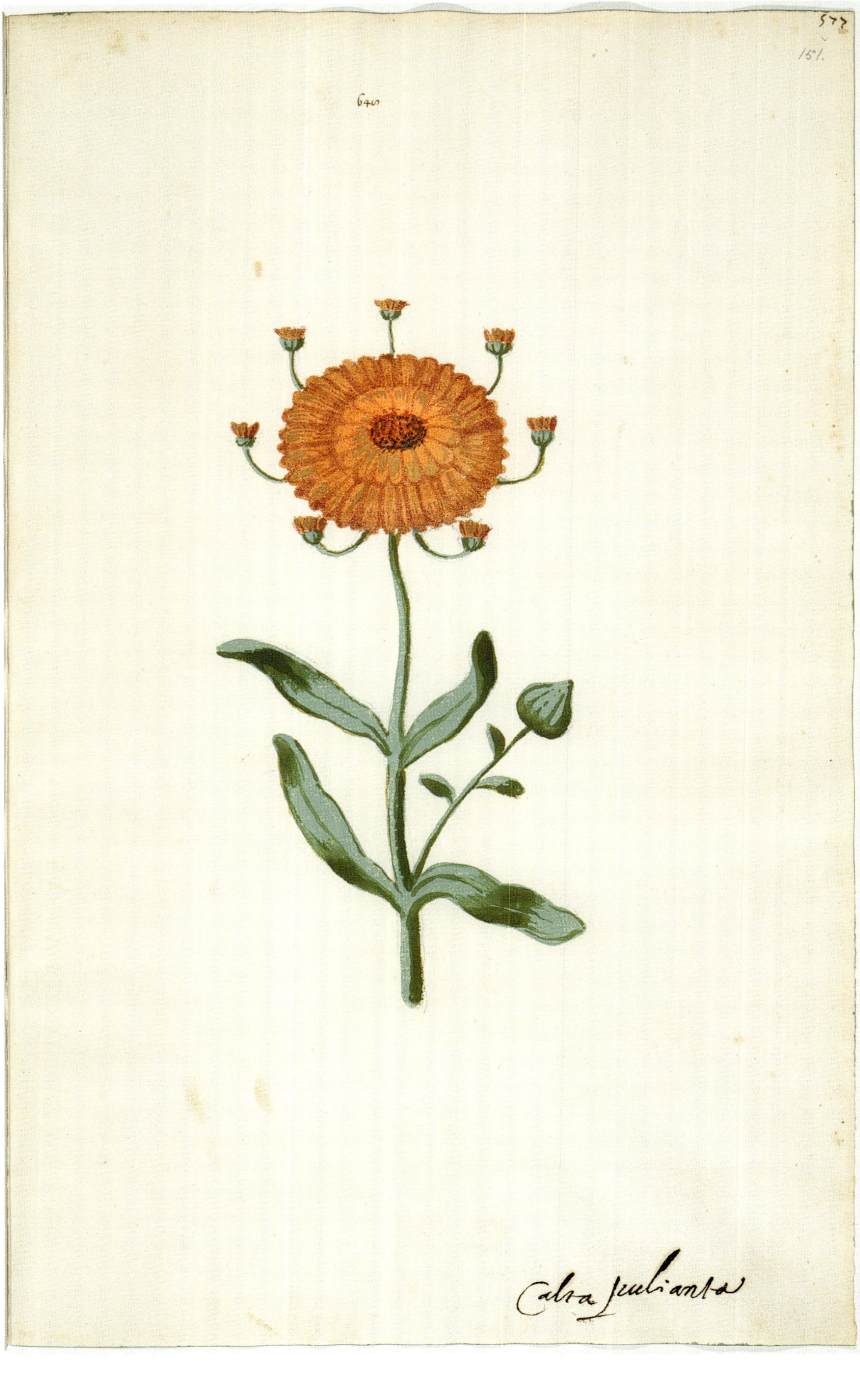
577
151.
640
Calta

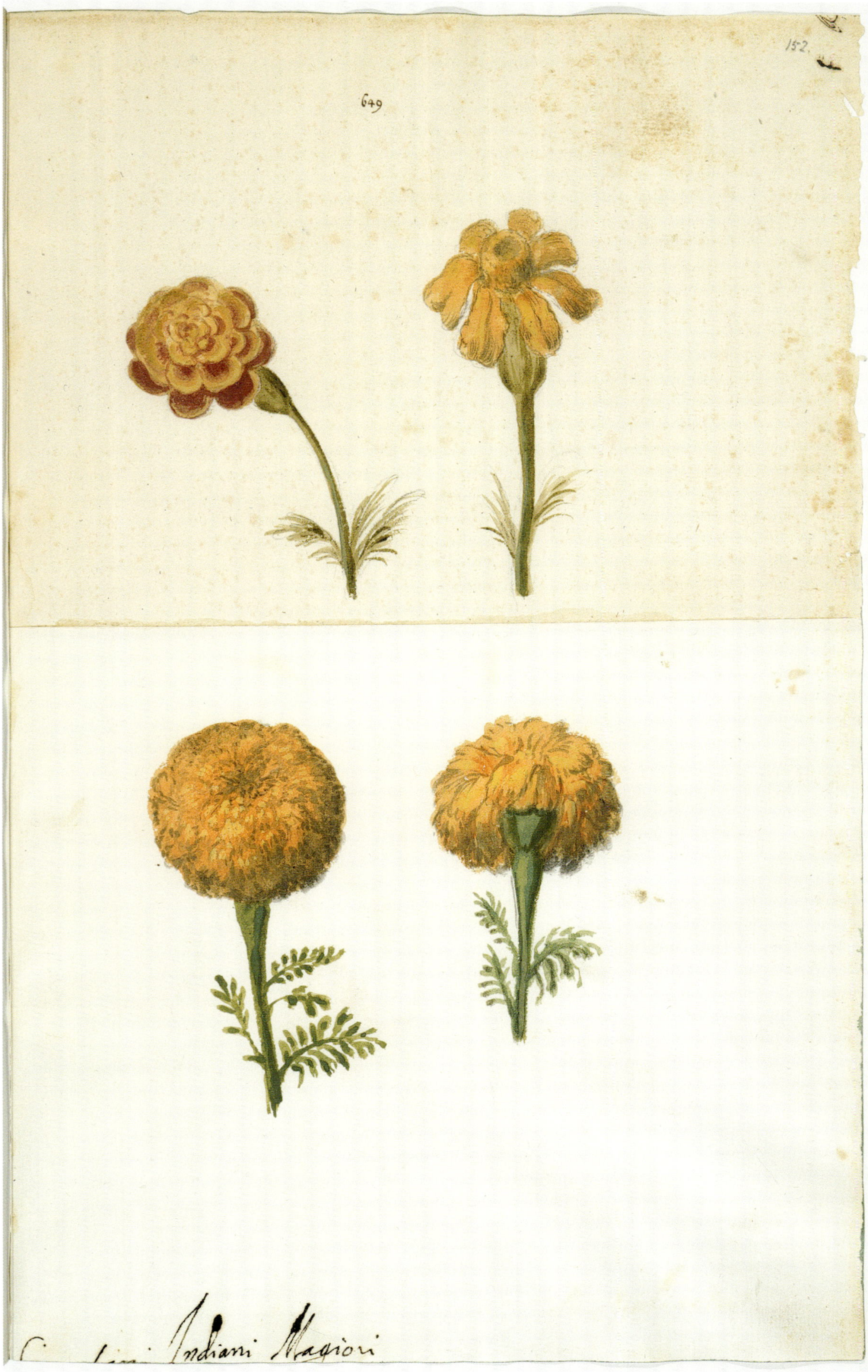
152.
649
Indiani Magiori

153. Marigolds, *Tagetes* spp.; one possibly muster-John-Henry, *Tagetes minuta* L.

Erbario Miniato, fol. 153 (RL 27843)

Watermark: Fleur de lys 49

NUMBERING: *650*

ANNOTATION: *Garofani indiani magiori. 1367; minori; Flos aphricanus, dal Dodoneo.* ('Greater Indian carnations. 1367; lesser; called African flower by Dodoens.'). [From Mattioli 1568, pp. 1366–7]

The main illustration shows the flowering stem of a marigold (see **152**). The stem of the plant is erect, smooth and branching. Each of the leaves is divided into eleven segments which are lanceolate with acute apices and finely toothed margins. The flower heads are borne on long, erect scapes that broaden at the level of the receptacle. The flowers of both specimens are ligulate and reddish-orange. To the right is a single flower head of what may be another species of the same genus, perhaps the muster-John-Henry, *Tagetes minuta*.

The 'Garofano indiano minore' illustrated by Mattioli on p. 1367 is identifiable as muster-John-Henry, and therefore correctly identified in the inscription as the right-hand specimen here. Mattioli's 'Garofano indiano maggiore', as the left-hand specimen on this sheet and those on **152** are named, is illustrated on p. 1366 of the *Discorsi*, and is an African marigold (*Tagetes erecta*).

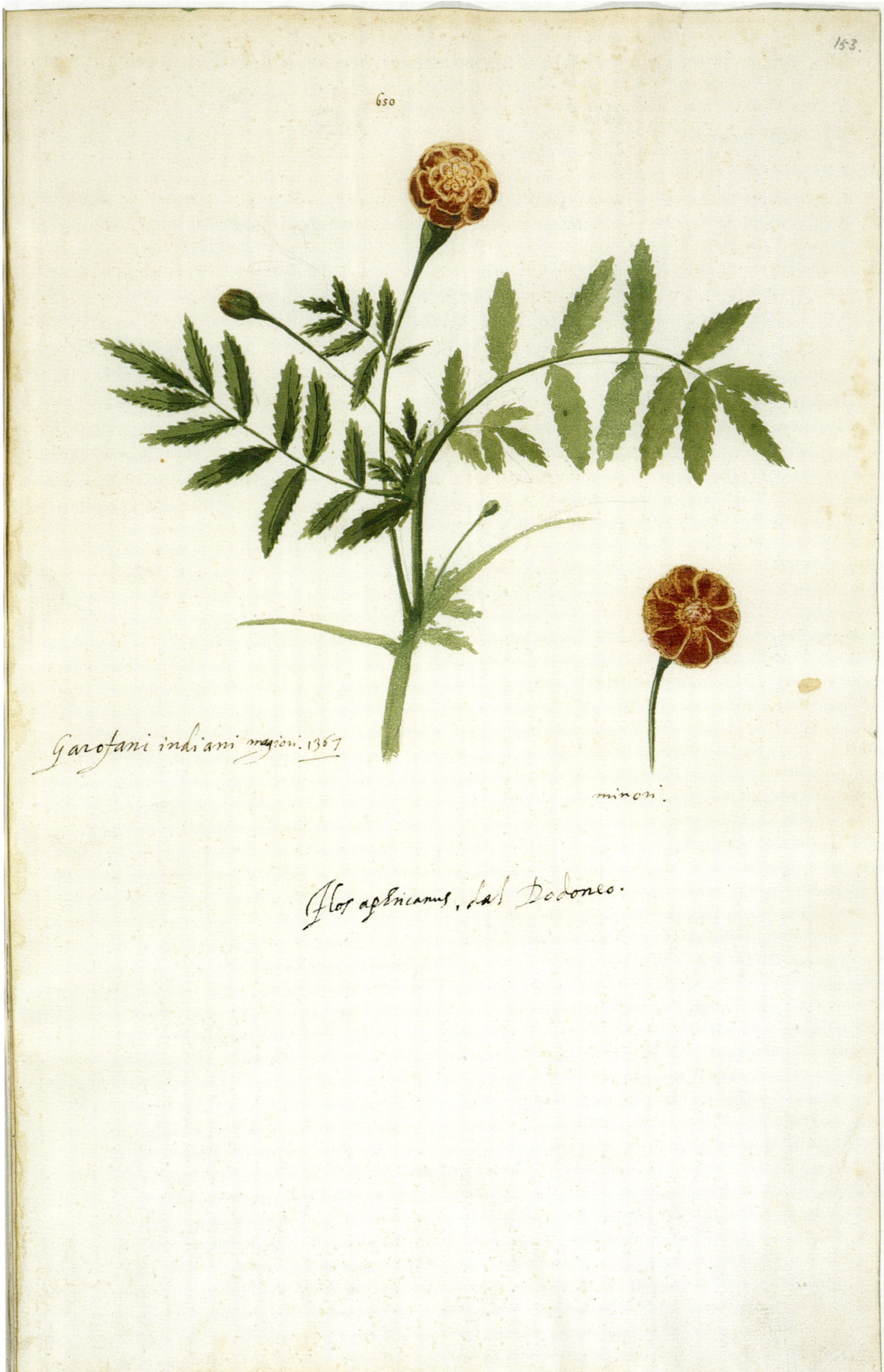
153.
650
Garofani indiani magiori. 1367
minori.
Flos aphricanus, dal Dodoneo.

154. Annual scorpion vetch, *Coronilla scorpioides* (L.) W.D.J. Koch

Erbario Miniato, fol. 154 (RL 27844)

Watermark: Eagle 18

NUMBERING: 651

ANNOTATION: *Scorpiode, questa impiastrata su le ponture de gli / Scorpione. e' veramente rimedio presentaneo, 1368* ('*Scorpiode*. Spread over scorpion stings this is truly an almost instantaneous remedy, 1368').
[From Mattioli 1568, pp. 1367–8]

The scorpion vetch is a herbaceous annual of the family Fabaceae. It is widespread in the Mediterranean and temperate regions of Asia, growing on arid soil and as a weed near inhabited areas, at altitudes from sea level to 800m. The arrangement of the flowers in the form of a small crown gave rise to the Latin name for this plant, *Coronilla*. Like the heliotrope (**147**) and caterpillar plant (**155**), the plant was considered to be an antidote to scorpion bites because of the shape of its pods.

The entire plant is shown here, including its root, flowers and fruit. The green stem is erect and smooth; the sessile, oval leaves have smooth margins and a pair of rounded segments at their base. Two tiny yellow flowers borne on slender reflexed peduncles can be seen at the apex of the stem. The fruit takes the form of long slender pods arranged in pairs on long peduncles. The taproot is short and slender with little branching.

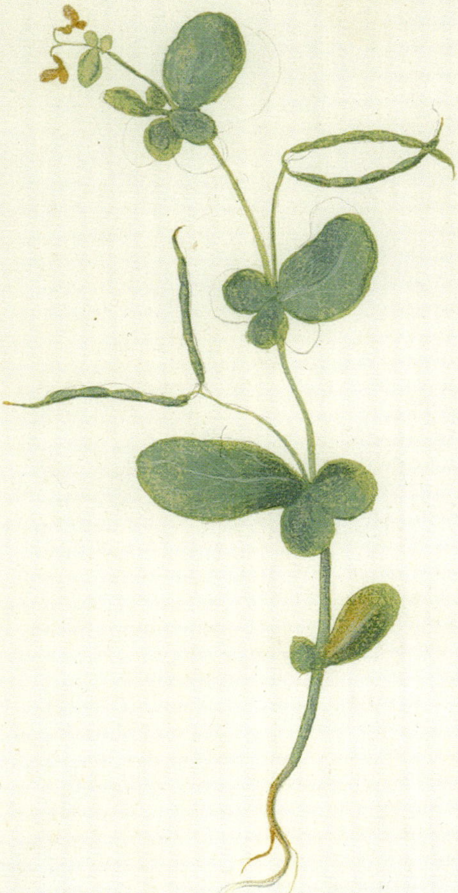

Scorpiode, questa impiastrata su le ponture de gli Scorpione. e' ueramente rimedio presentaneo, 1368